A PORTRAIT OF THE ARTIST AS A YOUNG MAN

青年艺术家的肖像

James Joyce

顾 问	方 平
主 编	孔庆华
副主编	陈 艳
	张德玉
注 释	徐 平

青岛出版社

图书在版编目(CIP)数据

青年艺术家的肖像/(爱尔兰)乔伊斯(Joyce,J.)著;
徐平注释.—青岛:青岛出版社,2003
(大学生必读英语经典名著)
ISBN 7-5436-2860-0

Ⅰ.青... Ⅱ.①乔...②徐... Ⅲ.英语—语言读
物,小说 Ⅳ.H319.4:I

中国版本图书馆 CIP 数据核字(2003)第 028660 号

书　　名	**青年艺术家的肖像**
作　　者	James Joyce
注　　释	徐　平
出版发行	青岛出版社
社　　址	青岛市徐州路 77 号(266071)
邮购电话	(0532)5814750　5840228
责任编辑	曹永毅
装帧设计	张小玉
出版时间	2003 年 6 月第 1 版　2003 年 6 月第 1 次印刷
印　　刷	青岛星球印刷有限公司
开　　本	32 开(787×960mm)
印　　张	9.75
字　　数	238 千
ISBN	7-5436-2860-0
定　　价	12.70 元

(青岛版图书售出后发现缺页、散页、错装、倒装、字迹模糊等,
请寄回承印公司调换。电话:0532-8183519　邮编:266400)

序 言

一个民族由于文学的产生,语言的色彩因而更丰富,语言的表现力更生动了。在文学的民族宝库中蕴藏着民族语言的精华。在不同的人生场合,我们有所感悟、有所感慨时,往往会感激古人,把我们想倾吐而又不知该怎么说的,表达得那么贴切、精辟,如同自己的肺腑之言。例如:"同是天涯沦落人,相逢何必曾相识。""不识庐山真面目,只缘身在此山中。"

我们甚至不曾意识到我们的日常谈吐中已融入了代代相传、都有来历的语言,而且多不胜举,像"割鸡焉用牛刀"(《论语·阳货》),"人言可畏"(《诗·郑风·将仲子》),"战战兢兢"(《诗·小雅·小旻》),"勾心斗角"(《阿房宫赋》),"三思而行"(《论语·公冶长》)等等。孔子自述"三十而立,四十而不惑,五十而知天命"(《论语·为政》);我们借以表达人已进入某一阶段时,就说"而立之年"、"不惑之年"、"知命之年"。

英美文学中的佳句、警句,同样显示出进入日常语言的亲和力。例如:美国期刊《时代》(*Time*,2002,12,23)发表专文推荐可能为奥斯卡年度最佳外语片的《对她说》(*Talk to Her*),文章标题脱胎于《第十二夜》开头第一句"If music be the food of love, play on",作者巧妙地把它改为"If Conversation Be the Food of Love, Talk On"("如果谈话是爱情的食粮,谈下去吧")。

第二次世界大战期间,英国首相邱吉尔访美,呼吁大力援助战争物资,引用了狄更斯笔下的孤儿奥列佛·退斯特,在儿童收容所中饥饿难忍,端起一只空碗,向掌勺的人发出的那一声迫切的呼吁:"Give me more!"(再添一些吧!)借助于这文学背景,在座的议员们为之动容,演讲收到了非常好的效果。

明白了一个民族的语言精华蕴藏在他们优秀的文学作品中,也就可以理解我们编写这套"英美文学经典丛书"的宗旨所在了。因为对于广大英语学习者来说,掌握了基本词汇量,攻克了语法等难点,具备了一定的阅读能力,又有志于进一步提高自己的英语修养,从而对于英语能有更深入、更亲切的认知,那么广泛阅读,尤其是有选择地精读优秀的英美文学,可说是不二法门了。

导　读

在 20 世纪的英国文坛，詹姆斯·乔伊斯(James Joyce,
1882－1941)以其空前绝后的胆识，在小说的语言、形式、
内容等方面都对传统的英国文学提出了挑战，勇于探索，
大胆创新，在英国文学史上写下了辉煌的一页。他的旷
世之作《尤利西斯》把意识流文学推向巅峰，奠定了他作
为意识流小说大师的地位，使其成为 20 世纪最卓越的英
语作家。

詹姆斯·乔伊斯一生命运多舛，在他的生活和事业的
道路上布满荆棘，但他凭着对文学艺术的挚爱和追求，直
面人生，以自己独特的艺术风格，开辟了一片崭新的文学
天地。乔伊斯于 1882 年出生于爱尔兰首都都柏林的一
个中产阶级家庭，父亲是个税务员，母亲是个虔诚的天主
教徒。乔伊斯从小在耶稣会学校接受天主教教育，先后
在两所学校读书，学习成绩总是名列前茅。在中学毕业
前，乔伊斯开始对宗教信仰产生怀疑，对都柏林庸俗无聊
的社会生活感到厌恶，并立志献身文学。1898 年，乔伊斯
入都柏林大学攻读现代语言课程。大学时代的乔伊斯对
文学、哲学、美学产生了浓厚的兴趣，并以其充满真知灼
见的文学评论显露出杰出的写作才华。1902 年大学毕业
后，乔伊斯赴法国学医。同鲁迅、郭沫若一样，忧国忧民

的乔伊斯最终还是弃医从文,希望用他手中的那支笔,塑造爱尔兰人的灵魂。1904 年,乔伊斯与爱尔兰西部的农家少女诺拉坠入爱河,并双双出走,开始了他那长达 37 年之久的流亡生活,实践着他的"流亡是我的美学"的艺术主张。他先后在罗马、的里雅斯特、苏黎世等地以教授英语为生,同时进行文学创作。1920 年定居巴黎,专事写作。1941 年病逝于苏黎世。

乔伊斯不是一个多产作家,在他近 40 年的创作生涯中,总共写下了 7 部作品。一部短篇小说集:《都柏林人》(*Dubliners*, 1914);两本诗集:《室内乐》(*Chamber Music*, 1907)、《一首一便士的诗》(*Pomes Penyeach*, 1927);一个剧本《流亡者》(*Exiles*, 1918);三部长篇小说:《青年艺术家的肖像》(*A Portrait of the Artist as a Young Man*, 1916, 以下简称《肖像》)、《尤利西斯》(*Ulysses*, 1922)、《芬尼根的守灵夜》(*Finnegans Wake*, 1939, 以下简称《守灵夜》)。但在这不多的几部作品里,乔伊斯倾注了自己的全部心血,以高度严肃认真的态度,履行着一个艺术家的历史使命。《尤利西斯》和《守灵夜》是他苦心孤诣的杰作,历来被评论界认为是他的两部伟大作品,《尤利西斯》被公认为是他的代表作。在这两部作品中,乔伊斯以"前不见古人,后不见来者"的勇气和胆量,对小说的形式和结构进行了彻底的革新,对小说的语言和文体进行了大胆的实验,创造了意识流小说的辉煌,同时也把它推到了发展的极致。他的小说对欧美文学乃至世界文学都产生了重大影响,他的小说创作激励了一代又一代作家。我国的现当代文学,特别是新时期文学也明显地留下了乔伊斯小说的影响的印痕。乔伊斯是个旷世奇才,又是一个执著的艺术追求者和探索者,他在文学园地里的辛勤耕耘,终于得到了丰厚的回报,他呕心沥血写下的当时被视为天书的作品,已被今人所理解和接受。1998年,在美国兰登书屋(Random House)"现代文库"编审委员会评选的"20世纪百部最佳英语小说"中,《尤利西斯》名列第一,《肖像》名列第三。1999年,英国著名的"水石书店"邀请47位专家评选"对21世纪最有影响的小说",《尤利西斯》又是名列第一。这两个第一已足以说明:乔伊斯小说的价值已得到世人的承认,他在世界文学史上的大师地位已得到今人的公认。诚如乔伊斯研究专家艾尔曼所说:"他以自己的智慧写出了他的作品,同样,又以他的智慧使世人去阅读他的作品"。①

　阅读乔伊斯的小说,我们发现,乔伊斯的小说创作是沿着这样一条轨迹变化和发展的:现实主义——现实主义与现代主义相结合——现代主义——后现代主义。其小说创作的主要表现手法是:从"精神顿悟"(epiphany)到"意识流"(stream of consciousness)。其小说创作的内容及其特色是:从小我到大我,从个体到群体,从微观到宏观,从内部到外部,主要探索人类社会现实的另一面——人类的心灵世界。应当说,探索和展现人的心灵是乔伊斯小说的核心内容。毋庸置疑,在乔伊斯的所有小说中,我们都读出了20世纪上半叶都柏林的社会现实,更读出了那个时代的都柏林人的心理现实。换句话说,乔伊斯把二者融为一体,用最恰当的艺术形式和表现手法,在他

---

① Richard Ellmann, *James Joyce*, New York: Oxford University Press, 1983, P.744.

的每一部(篇)小说中再现和表现出来。贝克特说乔伊斯的小说是"形式即内容,内容即形式",①这话切中肯綮。的的确确,在乔伊斯的小说中,形式与内容得到了较为完美的统一。

在乔伊斯的小说创作道路上,《肖像》是他的第一部长篇小说。这部自传体小说情节非常简单,描写了主人公斯蒂芬·迪德勒斯冲破罩在他身上的"家庭、国家、宗教"的三张大网、走向艺术的心路历程,塑造了一个从幼稚的童年到较为成熟的青年艺术家的人的形象,表达了一个"飞离"的主题。在乔伊斯的三部长篇小说中,《肖像》是读者最多的一部。它虽不是他的代表作,但它在乔伊斯的小说创作中却占有着举足轻重的地位。这是因为《肖像》不仅基本包含了他的所有小说创作的主题,而且几乎囊括了他的所有的艺术表现手法。这部小说的重大思想价值和艺术上的开拓创新给乔伊斯带来了文学声誉,从而奠定了乔伊斯在英国小说史上的重要地位。

《肖像》兼容了现实主义和现代主义,既具有写实性,又富有现代性。在《肖像》中,乔伊斯继承了传统的现实主义精华,用写实的手法为读者留下了一份20世纪初爱尔兰政治、经济、文化的社会备忘录。《肖像》虽没有细致的大篇幅的对社会大事件的重笔涂抹,但却有真实的点睛之笔。比如第一章中"圣诞晚宴"那个场景就是最好的现实主义的画龙点睛式的描写,当时爱尔兰社会的政治、宗教、文化以及爱尔兰人的精神面貌和生存环境全在"圣

---

① Samuel Beckett, et al. *Our Exagmination Round His Factification For Incamination of Work In Progress*, Northampyon: John Dickens & Conner Ltd., 1962, p.14.

诞餐桌"上的家庭辩论中再现了出来。小说中,乔伊斯用印象主义、表现主义、象征主义、意识流、"精神顿悟"的表现手法和非个性化的内聚焦叙述来描写斯蒂芬的心灵和意识,这都是乔伊斯对现代主义表现技巧的实验,而且实验非常成功,收到极佳的艺术效果。《肖像》的现代性不仅仅体现在现代主义表现手法上,还体现在现代意识上。小说摒弃了传统的描写集体而改为描写个人,抛弃了传统的描写英雄而改为描写普通人,从传统的写个人与社会的矛盾冲突进而转到写人的精神、灵魂和自我。简言之,《肖像》是现实主义和现代主义的结合体,它既有传统的基因,又有现代的新质。它是乔伊斯的小说创作中从现实主义向现代主义的过渡——上承《都柏林人》中的现实主义,下启《尤利西斯》和《守灵夜》中的现代主义。

《肖像》对于我们认识20世纪初的爱尔兰社会有着重要的参考价值。这部小说通过主人公斯蒂芬由童年到青年的成长经历和他的性格发展史,深刻地揭露了其家庭的平庸和守旧,鞭挞了宗教的虚伪和阴险,批判了社会的黑暗和险恶,向读者展示了一幅活生生的20世纪初爱尔兰特别是都柏林社会的现实图画。斯蒂芬所生活的爱尔兰,在大英帝国的政治压迫、经济掠夺、文化侵略下,社会一片黑暗荒凉,天主教的影响无处不在,无孔不入,弥漫在爱尔兰的角角落落,麻痹着人的灵魂,使众多的爱尔兰人成为活着的死人,精神瘫痪,无力反抗,也不思反抗。小说的主人公就是在这样的社会环境中成长的,在与家庭、社会、宗教的一系列的矛盾和冲突中,斯蒂芬形成了他的叛逆性格,最后冲出樊笼,远走高飞到属于他自己的自由的艺术王国。《肖像》是艺术家青年时期的真实写照,也是爱尔兰社会的真实写照。小说的"飞离"主题和斯蒂芬的意义就在这里,小说的思想认识价值和社会价值也在这里。

《肖像》具有很高的审美价值,富有永久性的艺术魅力。阅读《肖像》,我们不难得出这样的结论:《肖像》是一个内容与形式得到完美结合的艺术品。在《肖像》中,"形式即内容,内容即形式",它那与内容相契合的文体的多元和多元的叙述开拓了英国小说的语体、文体、叙述的疆域。乔伊斯用儿童语体、少年语体、成年语体描写着斯蒂芬不同的人生阶段的经历,用对话体、独白体、教义体和日记体表达着不同的内容,用内聚焦叙述、外聚焦叙述、内外聚焦结合叙述、精神顿悟、意识流手法展示着斯蒂芬的内心情感和思想意识。这是《肖像》在艺术上的一大特色,也就是这一特色把它与英国文学史上的其他自传体小说区别开来。小说语言的对应性、通感性、音乐性、隐喻性、象征性使《肖像》的语言富有魔力和张力,鲜活迷人,准确恰当,又意蕴无穷。小说的独特的象征艺术总让读者流连忘返,总让读者展开想象的翅膀。它的独特就在于小说中的所有象征意象都与小说的主题紧密相联,乔伊斯把主题寓于意象之中,用意象来揭示主题、反映意识,不管这些意象有无生命,在乔伊斯的笔下,它们都成了富有灵性和具有意识的生命实体。在这些生命实体中,蕴涵着丰富的思想和意义。

《肖像》是青年艺术家斯蒂芬的心灵发展史,也是所有艺术家的心灵发展史。乔伊斯在小说的题目里用 A Portrait of the Artist 取代 A Portrait of an Artist 的时候,就已把双重的含义融在了里面。在斯蒂芬的心路历程中,伴随着斯蒂芬的性格成长和发展的是一系列的矛盾和冲突以及这些矛盾和冲突的解决。斯蒂芬从小深受天主教的熏染和压迫,不断地被家庭、国家、教会催促着,耳畔常常回响着父亲、神父的聒噪声:要"道歉",要"忏悔",要"顺从",要"服务",可他胸中跳动的是一颗不安分的艺术家的心灵,他要自由,要独立,要创造。这是艺术家与社会的矛盾和冲突,这些矛盾和冲突在小说中是这样解决的:斯蒂芬先是到校长那里去状告多兰神父,表面上似乎是投入到"正义"的怀抱;后又投入到都柏林妓女的怀抱;继之又投入到上帝的怀抱;再继之在"涉水鸽女"的感召下,投入到大地的怀抱;最后远走高飞,投入到艺术的怀抱。这就是小说《肖像》各章的最后展示给我们的五个画面,这五个画面组接起来就是斯蒂芬的生命的轨迹,这条轨迹留给我们的"不是一份身份表,而是一条情感曲线"。①在这条情感曲线上,我们看到了一个痛苦挣扎着的灵魂,同时,也看到了《肖像》结构艺术的精湛。实际上,青年艺术家斯蒂芬的痛苦也是天下所有艺术家的痛苦,因为他们全都思想丰富,都在追求自由、独立、都在寻找自我、发现自我,并在追求自由、独立和寻找自我、发现自我的过程中进行创造、表现自我,进而实现自我和自己的生命价值。他们都痛苦着,挣扎着,追求着,创造着,实现着。斯蒂芬这个个案,概括了艺术家的全部,斯蒂芬与社会与生活的关系,也是艺术家与社会与生活的关系。

在《肖像》中,乔伊斯通过斯蒂芬之口,表达了他的美

① Morris Beja, James Joyce: *A Literary Life*, London: The Macmillan Press LTD., 1992, p.40.

学思想和艺术追求。他的美学思想的核心是他的"非个性化"说和"作家退出小说"理论。这是他对传统的小说理论的反拨和颠覆，也是他对现代主义小说理论的贡献。所谓"非个性化"和"作家退出小说"，就是要求作家在创作小说时，要像万物的创世主一样，隐藏在作品之中、之后、之外、之上，超然物外，修剪着指甲。换言之，作家不要做全知全能的叙述者，而要把自己融进人物，以人物的视角观察一切，并把对外部世界的感觉和印象记录下来，通过人物的口说自己的话，通过意象表现意识。乔伊斯崇尚艺术，追求艺术的美和真；他关注社会生活，但更看重生活经加工后的艺术，他把艺术看得高于一切，他要用完美的艺术创造完美的生活。

"乔伊斯把他的作品都看做是心理旅程中的驿站"，①如果是这样，那么，《肖像》则是这些驿站中的最重要的一站，因为在这一站上，我们既可以向前看，也可以向后看，既可以看到乔伊斯前面的生活和创作，也可以看到他后面的生活和创作。《肖像》是一个现实主义和现代主义的有机结合体，它既有现实主义的精髓，又有现代主义的新质，既具有写实性，更富有现代性。《肖像》的现代性体现在它的主题内容和表现手法的方方面面，而《肖像》的意义则更多地体现在它的现代性里。正是在这个基础上，乔伊斯才在后来创造出了真正意义的现代主义小说《尤利西斯》和《守灵夜》，从而铸造了意识流小说的辉煌。

阅读文学作品，就要阅读经典名著。《肖像》是英美

---

① Richard Ellmann, "James Joyce In and Out of Art", *James Joyce: A Collection of Critical Essays*, ed. by Marry T. Reynolds, New Jersey: Asimon & Schuster Company, 1993, p.24.

小说中的一部经典作品，这已成不争的事实。我们虽不能称"说不尽的《肖像》"，但我们敢大胆地说，它是一座丰富的还有待开掘和发现的矿藏。我深信，那些智慧的读者，在阅读《肖像》时，一定会享受到无穷无尽的发现的快乐。

李汝成

于青岛

Et ignotas animum dimittit in artes
*Ovid , Metamorphoses , VIII, 188*①

---

① (拉丁文)：他用他的才思致力于开拓未知的艺术领域。

奥维德：《变形记》第 8 卷, 第 188 页

奥维德(BC43—AD18), 罗马诗人。这句话是奥维德在描述迪达勒斯和儿子伊卡鲁斯从克里特岛上的迷宫出逃时所写。在希腊神话中, 迪达勒斯是发明家、雕刻家和建筑师的原型。他在为米诺斯王在克里特岛上建造了迷宫之后, 被囚禁在岛上。为了出逃, 他用蜡和羽毛自制蜡翼和儿子飞上天空。伊卡鲁斯因飞近太阳, 蜡翼遇热融化, 坠海而死。迪达勒斯逃到了西西里岛上, 继续他发明创造的艺术生涯。

目　　录

CHAPTER 1

Once upon a time and a very good time it was there was a moocow coming down along the road and this moocow[①] that was coming down along the road met a nicens little boy named baby tuckoo . . .

His father told him that story: his father looked at him through a glass[②]: he had a hairy face.

He was baby tuckoo. The moocow came down the road where Betty Byrne lived: she sold lemon platt[③].

> *O, the wild rose blossoms*
> *On the little green place.*

He sang that song. That was his song.

> *O, the green wothe botheth.*[④]

When you wet the bed,[⑤] first it is warm then it gets cold. His mother put on the oilsheet. That had the queer smell.

His mother had a nicer smell than his father. She played on the piano the sailor's hornpipe[⑥] for him to dance. He danced:

> *Tralala lala*
> *Tralala tralaladdy*
> *Tralala lala*
> *Tralala lala.*

Uncle Charles and Dante clapped. They were older than his father and mother but uncle Charles was older than Dante.

---

① moocow: 哞哞叫的奶牛　② a glass: 单片眼镜　③ lemon platt: 条形柠檬糖　④ O, the green wothe botheth: 绿色的玫瑰开放开放　⑤ When you wet the bed: 当你尿了床　⑥ hornpipe: 号笛舞(爱尔兰水手跳的一种活泼民间舞)

Dante had two brushes in her press.[①] The brush with the maroon velvet back[②] was for Michael Davitt[③] and the brush with the green velvet back was for Parnell[④]. Dante gave him a cachou[⑤] every time he brought her a piece of tissue paper[⑥].

The Vances lived in number seven. They had a different father and mother. They were Eileen's father and mother. When they were grown up he was going to marry Eileen. He hid under the table. His mother said:

— O, Stephen will apologize.

Dante said:

— O, if not, the eagles will come and pull out his eyes.

> *Pull out his eyes,*
> *Apologize,*
> *Apologize,*
> *Pull out his eyes.*
>
> *Apologize,*
> *Pull out his eyes,*
> *Pull out his eyes,*
> *Apologize.*

The wide playgrounds were swarming with boys. All were shouting and the prefects[⑦] urged them on with strong cries. The evening air was pale and chilly and after every charge and thud of the footballers the greasy leather orb flew like a heavy bird through the grey light[⑧]. He kept on the fringe of his line, out of sight of his prefect, out of the

---

① Dante had two brushes in her press: 丹特的衣橱里有两把刷子
② The brush ... velvet back: 背面是栗色丝绒的刷子　③ Michael Davitt: (1846—1906)，爱尔兰革命者，致力于爱尔兰的土地改革运动　④ Parnell: Charles Stewart Parnell(1846—1891)，爱尔兰民族运动领袖　⑤ cachou: 一种由树上的坚果做成的糖果　⑥ tissue paper: 面巾纸　⑦ the prefects: 级长　⑧ after every ... grey light: 在那些足球队员每次发动进攻，砰的踢一下球之后，那只油光光的皮球就会像只大鸟一样划过灰暗的天空。

reach of the rude feet, feigning to run now and then①. He felt his body small and weak amid the throng of players and his eyes were weak and watery. Rody Kickham was not like that: he would be captain of the third line all the fellows said.

Rody Kickham was a decent fellow but Nasty Roche was a stink②. Rody Kickham had greaves in his number and a hamper in the refectory③. Nasty Roche had big hands. He called the Friday pudding dog-in-the-blanket. And one day be had asked:

— What is your name?

Stephen had answered:

— Stephen Dedalus④.

— What kind of a name is that?

And when Stephen had not been able to answer Nasty Roche had asked:

— What is your father?

Stephen had answered:

— A gentleman.

Then Nasty Roche had asked:

— Is he a magistrate⑤?

He crept about from point to point on the fringe of his line, making little runs now and then. But his hands were bluish with cold⑥. He kept his hands in the sidepockets of his belted grey suit⑦. That was a belt round his pocket. And belt was also to give a fellow a belt. One day a fellow said to Cantwell:

— I'd give you such a belt in a second.

Cantwell had answered:

---

① feigning to run now and then: 假装跑来跑去　② a stink: 讨厌的家伙　③ had greaves . . . the refectory: 他的抽屉里有肉渣,食堂里还放着家人给他送食物的大篮子。　④ Stephen Dedalus: 基督教中有个圣徒名为 Stephen, 而姓氏 Dedalus 则来自于希腊发明家迪达勒斯。参见首页注释。　⑤ magistrate: 地方官　⑥ bluish with cold: 冻得发青　⑦ belted grey suit: 扎着腰带的灰色上衣

— Go and fight your match.① Give Cecil Thunder a belt. I'd like to see you. He'd give you a toe in the rump for yourself②.

That was not a nice expression. His mother had told him not to speak with the rough boys in the college. Nice mother! The first day in the hall of the castle when she had said goodbye she had put up her veil double to her nose to kiss him: and her nose and eyes were red. But he had pretended not to see that she was going to cry. She was a nice mother but she was not so nice when she cried. And his father had given him two fiveshilling pieces for pocket money. And his father had told him if he wanted anything to write home to him and, whatever he did, never to peach on a fellow③. Then at the door of the castle the rector had shaken hands with his father and mother, his soutane fluttering in the breeze④, and the car had driven off with his father and mother on it. They had cried to him from the car, waving their hands:

— Goodbye, Stephen, goodbye!
— Goodbye, Stephen, goodbye!

He was caught in the whirl of a scrimmage⑤ and, fearful of the flashing eyes and muddy boots, bent down to look through the legs. The fellows were struggling and groaning and their legs were rubbing and kicking and stamping. Then Jack Lawton's yellow boots dodged out the ball⑥ and all the other boots and legs ran after. He ran after them a little way and then stopped. It was useless to run on. Soon they would be going home for the holidays. After supper in the study hall he would change the number pasted up inside his desk from seventy-seven to seventy-six.

---

① Go and fight your match：去找个跟你差不多的对手打吧　② give you a toe in the rump for yourself：照你的屁股上踢一脚　③ never to peach on a fellow：永远不要出卖自己的伙伴　④ his soutane fluttering in the breeze：他的法衣在微风中飘动着　⑤ He was ... a scrimmage：他被卷入一片混战中　⑥ dodged out the ball：把球钩了出来

It would be better to be in the studyhall than out there in the cold. The sky was pale and cold but there were lights in the castle. He wondered from which window Hamilton Rowan had thrown his hat on the haha① and had there been flowerbeds at that time under the windows. One day when he had been called to the castle the butler had shown him the marks of the soldiers' slugs in the wood of the door and had given him a piece of shortbread that the community ate. It was nice and warm to see the lights in the castle②. It was like something in a book. Perhaps Leicester Abbey was like that. And there were nice sentences in Doctor Cornwell's Spelling Book. They were like poetry but they were only sentences to learn the spelling from.

> *Wolsey died in Leicester Abbey③*
> *Where the abbots④ buried him.*
> *Canker⑤ is a disease of plants,*
> *Cancer one of animals.*

It would be nice to lie on the hearthrug before the fire, leaning his head upon his hands, and think on those sentences. He shivered as if he had cold slimy water⑥ next his skin. That was mean of Wells to shoulder him into the square ditch⑦ because he would not swop his little snuff box for Wells's seasoned hacking chestnut, the conqueror of forty⑧. How cold and slimy the water had been! A fellow had once seen a big rat jump into the scum⑨. Mother was sitting at the fire with Dante waiting for Brigid to bring in the tea. She had her feet on the fender⑩ and her jewelry slippers were so hot and they had such a lovely warm smell!

---

① haha: 矮篱 ② castle: 指学校的主楼 ③ Abbey: 修道院 ④ the abbots: 修道院院长 ⑤ Canker: 植物溃疡(由霉菌、细菌或有毒物质引起的植物萎缩、脱叶的病症) ⑥ cold slimy water: 黏糊糊的水 ⑦ the square ditch: 指厕所的污水池 ⑧ because he ... of forty: 因为他不愿用他的鼻烟盒换韦尔斯那个打败 40 个对手的旧破栗子 ⑨ scum: 浮渣 ⑩ had her feet on the fender: 把脚搁在炉槛上

Dante knew a lot of things. She had taught him where the Mozambique Channel was and what was the longest river in America and what was the name of the highest mountain in the moon. Father Arnall knew more than Dante because he was a priest but both his father and uncle Charles said that Dante was a clever woman and a wellread woman. And when Dante made that noise after dinner and then put up her hand to her mouth: that was heartburn①.

A voice cried far out on the playground:

— All in!

Then other voices cried from the lower and third lines:

— All in! All in!

The players closed around, flushed and muddy②, and he went among them, glad to go in. Rody Kickham held the ball by its greasy lace. A fellow asked him to give it one last③: but he walked on without even answering the fellow. Simon Moonan told him not to because the prefect was looking. The fellow turned to Simon Moonan and said:

— We all know why you speak. You are McGlade's suck.④

Suck was a queer word. The fellow called Simon Moonan that name because Simon Moonan used to tie the prefect's false sleeves behind his back and the prefect used to let on to be angry. But the sound was ugly. Once he had washed his hands in the lavatory of the Wicklow Hotel aod his father pulled the stopper up by the chain after⑤ and the dirty water went down through the hole in the basin. And when it had all gone down slowly the hole in the basin had made a sound like that: suck. Only louder.

To remember that and the white look of the lavatory made him feel cold and then hot. There were two

---

① that was heartburn: 她又感到烧心了　② flushed and muddy: 满脸通红,浑身是泥　③ give it one last: 踢上最后一脚　④ You are McGlade's suck: 你是麦格莱德的马屁虫　⑤ pulled the stopper up by the chain after: 揪着后面的链子拉开了塞子

cocks① that you turned and water came out: cold and hot. He felt cold and then a little hot: and he could see the names printed on the cocks. That was a very queer thing.

And the air in the corridor chilled him too. It was queer and wettish. But soon the gas would be lit and in burning it made a light noise like a little song. Always the same: and when the fellows stopped talking in the play-room you could hear it.

It was the hour for sums.② Father Arnall wrote a hard sum on the board and then said:

— Now then, who will win? Go ahead, York! Go a-head, Lancaster③!

Stephen tried his best, but the sum was too hard and he felt confused. The little silk badge with the white rose on it that was pinned on the breast of his jacket began to flutter. He was no good at sums, but he tried his best so that York might not lose. Father Arnall's face looked very black, but he was not in a wax④: he was laughing. Then Jack Lawton cracked his fingers and Father Arnall looked at his copybook and said:

— Right. Bravo Lancaster! The red rose wins. Come on now, York! Forge ahead⑤!

Jack Lawton looked over from his side. The little silk badge with the red rose on it looked very rich because he had a blue sailor top on⑥. Stephen felt his own face red too, thinking of all the bets about who would get first place in elements⑦, Jack Lawton or he. Some weeks Jack Lawton got the card for first and some weeks he got the card for first. His white silk badge fluttered and fluttered as he

---

① There were two cocks: 有两个水龙头   ② It was the hour for sums: 做算术的时间   ③ York ... Lancaster: 英国 15 世纪时金雀花王朝的约克家族和兰开斯特家族，他们分别以白玫瑰和红玫瑰为其标志，两个家族为争夺王位进行了长达 30 年的战争(1455—1485)，史称玫瑰战争。这里用做比赛两组的代称。   ④ be in a wax: 发怒   ⑤ Forge ahead: 加速前进   ⑥ because he had a blue sailor top on: 因为他穿了件蓝色水手外套   ⑦ ele-ments: 基础课，包括拼写、算术、地理、历史、拉丁文和作文

worked at the next sum and heard Father Arnall's voice.
Then all his eagerness passed away and he felt his face quite
cool. He thought his face must be white because it felt so
cool. He could not get out the answer for the sum but it did
not matter. White roses and red roses: those were beautiful
colours to think of. And the cards for first place and second
place and third place were beautiful colours too: pink and
cream and lavender[1]. Lavender and cream and pink roses
were beautiful to think of. Perhaps a wild rose might be
like those colours and he remembered the song about the
wild rose blossoms on the little green place. But you could
not have a green rose. But perhaps some where in the
world you could.

The bell rang and then the classes began to file out of
the rooms and along the corridors towards the refectory.
He sat looking at the two prints of butter on his plate but
could not eat the damp bread. The tablecloth was damp
and limp[2]. But he drank off the hot weak tea which the
clumsy scullion[3], girt with a white apron, poured into his
cup. He wondered whether the scullion's apron was damp
too or whether all white things were cold and damp. Nasty
Roche and Saurin drank cocoa that their people sent them
in tins. They said they could not drink the tea; that it was
hogwash[4]. Their fathers were magistrates, the fellows
said.

All the boys seemed to him very strange. They had all
fathers and mothers and different clothes and voices. He
longed to be at home and lay his head on his mother's lap.
But he could not: and so he longed for the play and study
and prayers to be over and to be in bed.

He drank another cup of hot tea and Fleming said:

— What's up? Have you a pain or what's up with
you?

---

① cream and lavender：奶油色和淡紫色　② damp and limp：又潮又软
③ scullion：厨房帮工　④ hogwash：猪食

— I don't know, Stephen said.

— Sick in your breadbasket①, Fleming said, because your face looks white. It will go away.

— O yes, Stephen said.

But he was not sick there. He thought that he was sick in his heart if you could be sick in that place. Fleming was very decent to ask him②. He wanted to cry. He leaned his elbows on the table and shut and opened the flaps of his ears. Then he heard the noise of the refectory every time he opened the flaps of his ears. It made a roar like a train at night. And when he closed the flaps the roar was shut off like a train going into a tunnel. That night at Dalkey the train had roared like that and then, when it went into the tunnel, the roar stopped. He closed his eyes and the train went on, roaring and then stopping; roaring again, stopping. It was nice to hear it roar and stop and then roar out of the tunnel again and then stop.

Then the higher line③ fellows began to come down along the matting in the middle of the refectory, Paddy Rath and Jimmy Magee and the Spaniard who was allowed to smoke cigars and the little Portuguese who wore the woolly cap. And then the lower line tables and the tables of the third line. And every single fellow had a different way of walking.

He sat in a corner of the playroom pretending to watch a game of dominoes④ and once or twice he was able to hear for an instant the little song of the gas. The prefect was at the door with some boys and Simon Moonan was knotting his false sleeves. He was telling them something about Tullabeg.

Then he went away from the door and Wells came over to Stephen and said:

---

① breadbasket: (俚)胃   ② Fleming was ... ask him: 弗莱明还过来问候他,真是够朋友。   ③ Then the higher line: 高年级的学生   ④ a game of dominoes: 多米诺骨牌游戏

— Tell us, Dedalus, do you kiss your mother before you go to bed?

Stephen answered:

— I do.

Wells turned to the other fellows and said:

— O, I say, here's a fellow says he kisses his mother every night before he goes to bed.

The other fellows stopped their game and turned round, laughing. Stephen blushed under their eyes and said:

— I do not.

Wells said:

— O, I say, here's a fellow says he doesn't kiss his mother before he goes to bed.

They all laughed again. Stephen tried to laugh with them. He felt his whole body hot and confused in a moment. What was the right answer to the question? He had given two and still Wells laughed. But Wells must know the right answer for he was in third of grammar. He tried to think of Wells's mother but he did not dare to raise his eyes to Wells's face. He did not like Wells's face. It was Wells who had shouldered him into the square ditch the day before because he would not swop his little snuff box for Wells's seasoned hacking chestnut, the conqueror of forty. It was a mean thing to do; all the fellows said it was. And how cold and slimy the water had been! And a fellow had once seen a big rat jump plop into the scum.

The cold slime of the ditch covered his whole body; and, when the bell rang for study and the lines filed out of the playrooms, he felt the cold air of the corridor and staircase inside his clothes. He still tried to think what was the right answer. Was it right to kiss his mother or wrong to kiss his mother? What did that mean, to kiss? You put your face up like that to say goodnight and then his mother put her face down. That was to kiss. His mother put her lips on his cheek; her lips were soft and they wetted his cheek; and they made a tiny little noise: kiss. Why did people do that with their two faces?

Sitting in the studyhall he opened the lid of his desk and changed the number pasted up inside from seventy-seven to seventy-six. But the Christmas vacation was very far away: but one time it would come because the earth moved round always.

There was a picture of the earth on the first page of his geography: a big ball in the middle of clouds. Fleming had a box of crayons① and one night during free study he had coloured the earth green and the clouds maroon. That was like the two brushes in Dante's press, the brush with the green velvet back for Parnell and the brush with the maroon velvet back for Michael Davitt. But he had not told Fleming to colour them those colours. Fleming had done it himself.

He opened the geography to study the lesson; but he could not learn the names of places in America. Still they were all different places that had those different names. They were all in different countries and the countries were in continents and the continents were in the world and the world was in the universe.

He turned to the flyleaf② of the geography and read what he had written there: himself, his name and where he was.

> *Stephen Dedalus*
> *Class of Elements③*
> *Clongowes Wood College*
> *Sallins*
> *County Kildare*
> *Ireland*
> *Europe*

---

① a box of crayons: 一盒蜡笔 ② the flyleaf: 扉页 ③ Class of Elements: 基础班

The World
The Universe

That was in his writing: and Fleming one night for a cod[①] had written on the opposite page:

> *Stephen Dedalus is my name,*
> *Ireland is my nation.*
> *Clongowes is my dwellingplace*
> *And heaven my expectation.*

He read the verses backwards but then they were not poetry. Then he read the flyleaf from the bottom to the top till he came to his own name. That was he: and he read down the page again. What was after the universe? Nothing. But was there anything round the universe to show where it stopped before the nothing place began? It could not be a wall but there could be a thin line there all round everything. It was very big to think about everything and everywhere. Only God could do that. He tried to think what a big thought that must be but he could think only of God. God was God's name just as his name was Stephen. *Dieu* was the French for God and that was God's name too; and when anyone prayed to God and said *Dieu* then God knew at once that it was a French person that was praying. But though there were different names for God in all the different languages in the world and God understood what all the people who prayed said in their different languages, still God remained always the same God and God's real name was God.

It made him very tired to think that way. It made him feel his head very big. He turned over the flyleaf and looked wearily at the green round earth in the middle of the maroon clouds. He wondered which was right, to be for the green or for the maroon, because Dante had ripped the green velvet back off the brush that was for Parnell one day

---

① for a cod: 开玩笑

with her scissors and had told him that Parnell was a bad man①. He wondered if they were arguing at home about that. That was called politics. There were two sides in it: Dante was on one side and his father and Mr Casey were on the other side but his mother and uncle Charles were on no side. Every day there was something in the paper about it.

It pained him that he did not know well what politics meant and that he did not know where the universe ended. He felt small and weak. When would he be like the fellows in poetry and rhetoric? They had big voices and big boots and they studied trigonometry②. That was very far away. First came the vacation and then the next term and then vacation again and then again another term and then again the vacation. It was like a train going in and out of tunnels and that was like the noise of the boys eating in the refectory when you opened and closed the flaps of the ears. Term, vacation; tunnel, out; noise, stop. How far away it was! It was better to go to bed to sleep. Only prayers in the chapel and then bed. He shivered and yawned.③ It would be lovely in bed after the sheets got a bit hot. First they were so cold to get into. He shivered to think how cold they were first. But then they got hot and then he could sleep. It was lovely to be tired. He yawned again. Night prayers and then bed: he shivered and wanted to yawn. It would be lovely in a few minutes. He felt a warm glow creeping up from the cold shivering sheets, warmer and warmer till he felt warm all over, ever so warm; ever so warm and yet he shivered a little and still wanted to yawn.

The bell rang for night prayers and he filed out of the studyhall after the others and down the staircase and along the corridors to the chapel. The corridors were darkly lit and the chapel was darkly lit. Soon all would be dark and

---

① Parnell was a bad man: 1890 年帕内尔与奥谢夫人（Mrs. O'Shea）传出绯闻，导致他在公众中丧失威信。　② trigonometry:（数学）三角　③ He shivered and yawned: 他有些发抖，连连打着哈欠。

sleeping. There was cold night air in the chapel and the marbles① were the colour the sea was at night. The sea was cold day and night: but it was colder at night. It was cold and dark under the seawall beside his father's house. But the kettle would be on the hob to make punch②.

The prefect of the chapel prayed above his head and his memory knew the responses:

> *O Lord open our lips*
> *And our mouths shall announce Thy③ praise.*
> *Incline unto our aid, O God!*
> *O Lord, make haste to help us!*

There was a cold night smell in the chapel. But it was a holy smell. It was not like the smell of the old peasants who knelt at the back of the chapel at Sunday mass. That was a smell of air and rain and turf and corduroy④. But they were very holy peasants. They breathed behind him On his neck and sighed as they prayed. They lived in Clane, a fellow said: there were little cottages there and he had seen a woman standing at the halfdoor of a cottage with a child in her arms as the cars had come past from Sallins. It would be lovely to sleep for one night in that cottage before the fire of smoking turf⑤, in the dark lit by the fire, in the warm dark, breathing the smell of the peasants, air and rain and turf and corduroy. But, O, the road there between the trees was dark! You would be lost in the dark. It made him afraid to think of how it was.

He heard the voice of the prefect of the chapel saying the last prayers. He prayed it too against the dark outside under the trees.

> *Visit, we beseech Thee⑥, O Lord, this*

---

① marbles: 大理石 ② the kettle … make punch: 水壶放在炉旁的金属架上才能做出甜饮料来。hob 指壁炉旁边的金属平架，置锅于上可以保温，或置以开水壶保持沸腾。 ③ Thy: (古)你的 ④ corduroy: 灯芯绒 ⑤ before the fire of smoking turf: 在冒着烟的灰炭火旁 ⑥ we beseech Thee: 我们恳求你。Thee: (古)thou 的宾格。thou: (古)你。

*habitation*① *and drive away from it all the*
snares of the enemy. May Thy holy angels dwell
herein to preserve us in peace and may Thy bless-
ings be always upon us through Christ, Our
Lord. Amen.

His fingers trembled as he undressed himself in the
dormitory. He told his fingers to hurry up. He had to un-
dress and then kneel and say his own prayers and be in bed
before the gas was lowered so that he might not go to hell
when he died. He rolled his stockings off and put on his
nightshirt quickly and knelt trembling at his bedside and
repeated his prayers quickly quickly, fearing that the gas
would go down. He felt his shoulders shaking as he murmured:

> *God bless my father and my mother and*
> *spare them to me!*
> *God bless my little brothers and sisters and*
> *spare them to me!*
> *God bless Dante and uncle Charles and*
> *spare them to me!*

He blessed himself and climbed quickly into bed and,
tucking the end of the nightshirt under his feet, curled
himself together under the cold white sheets, shaking and
trembling. But he would not go to hell when he died; and
the shaking would stop. A voice bade the boys in the dormitory goodnight. He peered out for an instant over the
coverlet and saw the yellow curtains round and before his
bed that shut him off on all sides. The light was lowered
quietly.

The prefect's shoes went away. Where? Down the
staircase and along the corridors or to his room at the end?
He saw the dark. Was it true about the black dog that
walked there at night with eyes as big as carriagelamps?

---

① habitation：住所

They said it was the ghost of a murderer. A long shiver of fear flowed over his body. He saw the dark entrance hall of the castle. Old servants in old dress were in the ironingroom above the staircase. It was long ago. The old servants were quiet. There was a fire there, but the hall was still dark. A figure came up the staircase from the hall. He wore the white cloak of a marshal[①]; his face was pale and strange; he held his hand pressed to his side. He looked out of strange eyes at the old servants. They looked at him and saw their master's face and cloak and knew that he had received his deathwound. But only the dark was where they looked: only dark silent air. Their master had received his deathwound on the battlefield of Prague far away over the sea. He was standing on the field; his hand was pressed to his side; his face was pale and strange and he wore the white cloak of a marshal.

O how cold and strange it was to think of that! All the dark was cold and strange. There were pale strange faces there, great eyes like carriagelamps. They were the ghosts of murderers, the figures of marshals who had received their deathwound on battlefields far away over the sea. What did they wish to say that their faces were so strange?

Visit, we beseech Thee, O Lord, this habitation and drive away from it all ...

Going home for the holidays! That would be lovely: the fellows had told him. Getting up on the cars on the early wintry morning outside the door of the castle. The cars were rolling on the gravel[②]. Cheers for the rector!

Hurray! Hurray! Hurray!

The cars drove past the chapel and all caps were raised. They drove merrily along the country roads. The drivers pointed with their whips to Bodenstown. The fel-

---

① the white cloak of a marshal: 元帅披的白斗篷 ② on the gravel: 在碎石路上

lows cheered. They passed the farmhouse of the Jolly Farmer. Cheer after cheer after cheer. Through Clane they drove, cheering and cheered. The peasant women stood at the halfdoors, the men stood here and there. The lovely smell there was in the wintry air: the smell of Clane: rain and wintry air and turf smouldering[1] and corduroy.

The train was full of fellows: a long long chocolate train with cream facings[2]. The guards went to and fro opening, closing, locking, unlocking the doors. They were men in dark blue and silver; they had silvery whistles and their keys made a quick music: click, click: click, click.

And the train raced on over the flat lands and past the Hill of Allen. The telegraphpoles[3] were passing, passing. The train went on and on. It knew. There were coloured lanterns[4] in the hall of his father's house and ropes of green branches[5]. There were holly and ivy round the pierglass[6] and holly and ivy, green and red, twined round the chandeliers[7]. There were red holly and green ivy round the old portraits on the walls. Holly and ivy for him and for Christmas.

Lovely . . .

All the people. Welcome home, Stephen! Noises of welcome. His mother kissed him. Was that right? His father was a marshal now: higher than a magistrate. Welcome home, Stephen!

Noises . . .

There was a noise of curtainrings running back along the rods, of water being splashed in the basins. There was a noise of rising and dressing and washing in the dormitory: a noise of clapping of hands as the prefect went up and

---

① turf smouldering：闷烧着的灰炭　② a long long chocolate train with cream facings：长长的、巧克力色的火车，车头是奶油色的　③ telegraphpoles：电线杆　④ lanterns：灯笼　⑤ ropes of green branches：绿色的枝条拧成的绳子　⑥ There were holly and ivy round the pierglass：穿衣镜周围有冬青枝和常春藤环绕　⑦ chandeliers：枝形吊灯架

down telling the fellows to look sharp①. A pale sunlight showed the yellow curtains drawn back, the tossed beds. His bed was very hot and his face and body were very hot.

He got up and sat on the side of his bed. He was weak. He tried to pull on his stocking. It had a horrid rough feel. The sunlight was queer and cold.

Fleming said:

— Are you not well?

He did not know; and Fleming said:

— Get back into bed. I'll tell McGlade you're not well.

— He's sick.

— Who is?

— Tell McGlade.

— Get back into bed.

— Is he sick?

A fellow held his arms while he loosened the stocking clinging to his foot② and climbed back into the hot bed.

He crouched down between the sheets, glad of their tepid③ glow. He heard the fellows talk among themselves about him as they dressed for mass. It was a mean thing to do, to shoulder him into the square ditch, they were saying.

Then their voices ceased; they had gone. A voice at his bed said:

— Dedalus, don't spy on us, sure you won't?

Wells's face was there. He looked at it and saw that Wells was afraid.

— I didn't mean to. Sure you won't?

His father had told him, whatever he did, never to peach on a fellow. He shook his head and answered no and felt glad. Wells said:

— I didn't mean to, honour bright. It was only for

---

① look sharp: 赶快 ② the stocking clinging to his foot: 黏在脚上的袜子 ③ tepid: 微温的

cod①. I'm sorry.

The face and the voice went away. Sorry because he was afraid. Afraid that it was some disease. Canker was a disease of plants and cancer one of animals; or another different. That was a long time ago then out on the play-grounds in the evening light, creeping from point to point on the fringe of his line, a heavy bird flying low through the grey light. Leicester Abbey lit up. Wolsey died there. The abbots buried him themselves.

It was not Wells's face, it was the prefect's. He was not foxing②. No, no: he was sick really. He was not fox-ing. And he felt the prefect's hand on his forehead; and he felt his forehead warm and damp against the prefect's cold damp hand. That was the way a rat felt, slimy and damp and cold. Every rat had two eyes to look out of. Sleek slimy coats③, little little feet tucked up to jump, black slimy eyes to look out of. They could understand how to jump. But the minds of rats could not understand trigonometry. When they were dead they lay on their sides. Their coats dried then. They were only dead things.

The prefect was there again and it was his voice that was saying that he was to get up, that Father Minister had said he was to get up and dress and go to the infirmary④. And while he was dressing himself as quickly as he could the prefect said:

— We must pack off to Brother Michael because we have the collywobbles⑤! Terrible thing to have the colly-wobbles! How we wobble⑥ when we have the collywob-bles!

He was very decent to say that. That was all to make him laugh. But he could not laugh because his cheeks and

---

① I didn't ... for cod: 我不是有意的,人格担保,我只是闹着玩。
② He was not foxing: 他不是装病 ③ Sleek slimy coats: 光滑黏糊的皮毛
④ the infirmary: 学校的医务室 ⑤ collywobbles: [口]肚子咕噜噜叫
⑥ wobble: 摇晃

lips were all shivery: and then the prefect had to laugh by himself.

The prefect cried:

— Quick march[1]! Hayfoot! Strawfoot[2]!

They went together down the staircase and along the corridor and past the bath. As he passed the door he remembered with a vague fear the warm turfcoloured bogwater, the warm moist air, the noise of plunges, the smell of the towels, like medicine.

Brother Michael was standing at the door of the infirmary and from the door of the dark cabinet on his right came a smell like medicine. That came from the bottles on the shelves. The prefect spoke to Brother Michael and Brother Michael answered and called the prefect sir. He had reddish hair mixed with grey and a queer look. It was queer that he would always be a brother[3]. It was queer too that you could not call him sir because he was a brother and had a different kind of look. Was he not holy enough or why could he not catch up on the others?

There were two beds in the room and in one bed there was a fellow: and when they went in he called out:

— Hello! It's young Dedalus! What's up?

— The sky is up, Brother Michael said.

He was a fellow out of the third of grammar and, while Stephen was undressing, he asked Brother Michael to bring him a round of buttered toast[4].

— Ah, do! he said.

— Butter you up! said Brother Michael. You'll get your walking papers in the morning when the doctor comes.[5]

---

① Quick march: 快步走！（模仿军队口令） ② Hayfoot! Strawfoot!： 模仿新兵军训时的口令(训练行军时，新兵的左腿绑上干草，右腿绑上麦秸) ③ brother: 耶稣会兄弟，无须接受成为教士所应接受的宗教教育，在耶稣会里只承担一些诸如管理房间之类的工作。 ④ bring him a round of buttered toast: 给他带来一涂了奶油的烤面包圈。 ⑤ You'll get ... doctor comes: 一会儿医生来了，他会给你开个证明让你上午就走。

— Will I? the fellow said. I'm not well yet.

Brother Michael repeated:

— You'll get your walking papers. I tell you.

He bent down to rake the fire①. He had a long back like the long back of a tramhorse②. He shook the poker③ gravely and nodded his head at the fellow out of third of grammar.

Then Brother Michael went away and after a while the fellow out of third of grammar turned in towards the wall and fell asleep.

That was the infirmary. He was sick then. Had they written home to tell his mother and father? But it would be quicker for one of the priests to go himself to tell them. Or he would write a letter for the priest to bring.

> Dear Mother,
>   I am sick. I want to go home. Please come and take me home. I am in the infirmary.
>   Your fond son,
>   Stephen

How far away they were! There was cold sunlight outside the window. He wondered if he would die. You could die just the same on a sunny day. He might die before his mother came. Then he would have a dead mass④ in the chapel like the way the fellows had told him it was when Little had died. All the fellows would be at the mass, dressed in black, all with sad faces. Wells too would be there but no fellow would look at him. The rector⑤ would be there in a cope of black and gold⑥ and there would be tall yellow candles on the altar⑦ and round the catafalque⑧. And they would carry the coffin out of the chapel slowly and he

---

　　① to rake the fire: 扒一扒火　② tramhorse: 拉车的马　③ poker: 拨火棍　④ a dead mass: 葬礼弥撒　⑤ rector: (宗教学校的)校长　⑥ in a cope of black and gold: 穿着一件饰有金线的黑色法衣　⑦ altar: 圣坛　⑧ the catafalque: 灵柩车

would be buried in the little graveyard of the community off the main avenue of limes①. And Wells would be sorry then for what he had done. And the bell would toll slowly.

He could hear the tolling. He said over to himself the song that Brigid had taught him.

> *Dingdong! The castle bell!*
> *Farewell, my mother!*
> *Bury me in the old churchyard*
> *Beside my eldest brother.*
> *My coffin shall be black,*
> *Six angels at my back,*
> *Two to sing and two to pray*
> *And two to carry my soul away.*

How beautiful and sad that was! How beautiful the words were where they said *Bury me in the old churchyard*! A tremor passed over his body. How sad and how beautiful! He wanted to cry quietly but not for himself: for the words, so beautiful and sad, like music. The bell! The bell! Farewell! O farewell!

The cold sunlight was weaker and Brother Michael was standing at his bedside with a bowl of beeftea. He was glad for his mouth was hot and dry. He could hear them playing on the playgrounds. And the day was going on in the college just as if he were there.

Then Brother Michael was going away and the fellow out of third of grammar told him to be sure and come back and tell him all the news in the paper. He told Stephen that his name was Athy and that his father kept a lot of racehorses that were spiffing jumpers② and that his father would give a good tip to Brother Michael any time he wanted it because Brother Michael was very decent and always told him the news out of the paper they got every day up in the castle. There was every kind of news in the paper: ac-

---

① off the main avenue of limes: 在用石灰石铺成的大路旁　② kept a … spiffing jumpers: 养了很多赛马，并且都是些顶呱呱的能跳栏的马

cidents, shipwrecks[①], sports, and politics.

— Now it is all about politics in the papers, he said. Do your people talk about that too?

— Yes, Stephen said.

— Mine too, he said.

Then he thought for a moment and said:

— You have a queer name[②], Dedalus, and I have a queer name too, Athy. My name is the name of a town. Your name is like Latin.

Then he asked:

— Are you good at riddles?

Stephen answered:

— Not very good.

Then he said:

— Can you answer me this one? Why is the county Kildare like the leg of a fellow's breeches[③]?

Stephen thought what could be the answer and then said:

— I give it up.

— Because there is a thigh in it, he said. Do you see the joke? Athy is the town in the county Kildare and a thigh is the other thigh.

— O, I see, Stephen said.

— That's an old riddle, he said.

After a moment he said:

— I say!

— What? asked Stephen.

— You know, he said, you can ask that riddle another way.

— Can you? said Stephen.

— The same riddle, he said. Do you know the other way to ask it?

— No, said Stephen.

---

① shipwrecks: 船只失事 ② a queer name: 古怪的名字 ③ like the leg of a fellow's breeches: 像一条裤腿

— Can you not think of the other way? he said.

He looked at Stephen over the bedclothes as he spoke. Then he lay back on the pillow and said:

— There is another way but I won't tell you what it is.

Why did he not tell it? His father, who kept the race-horses, must be a magistrate too like Saurin's father and Nasty Roche's father. He thought of his own father, of how he sang songs while his mother played and of how he always gave him a shilling when he asked for sixpence and he felt sorry for him that he was not a magistrate like the other boys' fathers. Then why was he sent to that place with them? But his father had told him that he would be no stranger there because his granduncle had presented an address to the liberator there fifty years before[①]. You could know the people of that time by their old dress. It seemed to him a solemn time: and he wondered if that was the time when the fellows in Clongowes wore blue coats with brass buttons and yellow waistcoats and caps of rabbitskin and drank beer like grownup people and kept greyhounds of their own to course the hares with[②].

He looked at the window and saw that the daylight had grown weaker. There would be cloudy grey light over the playgrounds. There was no noise on the playgrounds. The class must be doing the themes[③] or perhaps Father Arnall was reading a legend out of the book.

It was queer that they had not given him any medicine. Perhaps Brother Michael would bring it back when he came. They said you got stinking stuff[④] to drink when you were in the infirmary. But he felt better now than before. It would be nice getting better slowly. You could get a book then. There was a book in the library

---

① because his ... years before: 因为他的伯祖父曾在 50 年前给那个地方的解放者演讲过 ② kept greyhounds ... hares with: 各自都养着猎狗, 用以追赶野兔。 ③ must be doing the themes: 一定在写作文 ④ stinking stuff: 发臭的东西

about Holland. There were lovely foreign names in it and pictures of strangelooking cities and ships. It made you feel so happy.

How pale the light was at the window! But that was nice. The fire rose and fell on the wall. It was like waves. Someone had put coal on and he heard voices. They were talking. It was the noise of the waves. Or the waves were talking among themselves as they rose and fell.

He saw the sea of waves[①], long dark waves rising and falling, dark under the moonless night. A tiny light twinkled at the pierhead[②] where the ship was entering: and he saw a multitude of people gathered by the water's edge to see the ship that was entering their harbour. A tall man stood on the deck, looking out towards the flat dark land: and by the light at the pierhead he saw his face, the sorrowful face of Brother Michael.

He saw him lift his hand towards the people and heard him say in a loud voice of sorrow over the waters:

— He is dead. We saw him lying upon the catafalque. A wail of sorrow went up from the people.

— Parnell! Parnell! He is dead!

They fell upon their knees, moaning in sorrow.

And he saw Dante in a maroon velvet dress and with a green velvet mantle hanging from her shoulders walking proudly and silently past the people who knelt by the water's edge.

A great fire, banked high and red, flamed in the grate[③] and under the ivytwined branches of the chandelier the Christmas table was spread. They had come home a little late and still dinner was not ready: but it would be ready in a jiffy[④], his mother had said. They were waiting

---

① He saw the sea of waves … : 这是帕内尔于 1891 年 10 月 6 日在英格兰死去后，尸体运抵都柏林时的情景。 ② at the pierhead: 在码头前端 ③ in the grate: 在壁炉里 ④ in a jiffy: 即刻

for the door to open and for the servants to come in, holding the big dishes covered with their heavy metal covers.

All were waiting: uncle Charles, who sat far away in
the shadow of the window, Dante and Mr Casey, who sat
in the easychairs① at either side of the hearth, Stephen,
seated on a chair between them, his feet resting on the
toasted boss②. Mr Dedalus looked at himself in the pierglass above the mantelpiece③, waxed out his moustache-
ends and then, parting his coattails, stood with his back to
the glowing fire: and still, from time to time, he withdrew
a hand from his coattail to wax out one of his moustache-
ends④. Mr Casey leaned his head to one side and, smiling,
tapped the gland of his neck with his fingers. And Stephen
smiled too for he knew now that it was not true that Mr
Casey had a purse of silver⑤ in his throat. He smiled to
think how the silvery noise which Mr Casey used to make
had deceived him. And when he had tried to open Mr
Casey's hand to see if the purse of silver was hidden there
he had seen that the fingers could not be straightened out:
and Mr Casey had told him that he had got those three
cramped fingers⑥ making a birthday present for Queen
Victoria.

Mr Casey tapped the gland of his neck and smiled at
Stephen with sleepy eyes: and Mr Dedalus said to him:

— Yes. Well now, that's all right. O, we had a good
walk, hadn't we, John? Yes ... I wonder if there's any
likelihood of dinner this evening. Yes ... O, well now,
we got a good breath of ozone⑦ round the Head⑧ today.
Ay, bedad.

He turned to Dante and said:

---

① easychairs: 安乐椅　② his feet resting on the toasted boss: 他的脚搭
在壁炉前温暖的金属架上　③ the pierglass above the mantelpiece: 壁炉台上
的穿衣镜　④ to wax out one of his moustache ends: 捻着自己的八字胡
⑤ a purse of silver: 一小袋银币　⑥ cramped fingers: 肌肉麻痹的手指
⑦ ozone: 海边的新鲜空气　⑧ the Head: 指 Bray Head, 一座海边的石山,
位于都柏林东南部 12 英里处。

— You didn't stir out at all, Mrs Riordan?

Dante frowned and said shortly:

— No.

Mr Dedalus dropped his coattails and went over to the sideboard①. He brought forth a great stone jar of whisky from the locker and filled the decanter slowly②, bending now and then to see how much he had poured in. Then replacing the jar in the locker he poured a little of the whisky into two glasses, added a little water and came back with them to the fireplace.

— A thimbleful③, John, he said, just to whet your appetite④.

Mr Casey took the glass, drank, and placed it near him on the mantelpiece. Then he said:

— Well, I can't help thinking of our friend Christopher manufacturing ...

He broke into a fit of laughter and coughing and added: — ... manufacturing that champagne for those fellows.

Mr Dedalus laughed loudly.

— Is it Christy? he said. There's more cunning in one of those warts on his bald head than in a pack of jack foxes⑤.

He inclined his head, closed his eyes, and, licking his lips profusely⑥, began to speak with the voice of the hotel keeper.

— And he has such a soft mouth when he's speaking to you, don't you know. He's very moist and watery about the dewlaps⑦, God bless him.

---

① sideboard：餐具桌(通常有抽屉和食柜) ② He brought ... decanter slowly：他从食柜里拿出一个装着威士忌的大石罐, 然后慢慢地往酒瓶里倒酒 ③ A thimbleful：一小口 ④ just to whet your appetite：给你开开胃 ⑤ There's more ... jack foxes：他光头上一个瘊子里装的诡计就比一群公狐狸的加起来还要多 ⑥ licking his lips profusely：使劲舔着嘴唇 ⑦ dewlaps：喉袋

Mr Casey was still struggling through his fit of coughing and laughter. Stephen, seeing and hearing the hotel keeper through his father's face and voice, laughed.

Mr Dedalus put up his eyeglass and, staring down at him, said quietly and kindly:

— What are you laughing at, you little puppy, you?

The servants entered and placed the dishes on the table. Mrs Dedalus followed and the places were arranged.

— Sit over, she said.

Mr Dedalus went to the end of the table and said:

— Now, Mrs Riordan, sit over. John, sit you down, my hearty.

He looked round to where uncle Charles sat and said:

— Now then, sir, there's a bird here waiting for you.

When all had taken their seats he laid his hand on the cover and then said quickly, withdrawing it:

— Now, Stephen.

Stephen stood up in his place to say the grace before meals[1]:

Bless us, O Lord, and these Thy gifts which through Thy bounty[2] we are about to receive through Christ Our Lord. Amen.

All blessed themselves and Mr Dedalus with a sigh of pleasure lifted from the dish the heavy cover pearled around the edge with glistening drops[3].

Stephen looked at the plump turkey which had lain, trussed and skewered[4], on the kitchen table. He knew that his father had paid a guinea[5] for it in Dunn's of D'Olier Street and that the man had prodded[6] it often at the breastbone to show how good it was: and he remembered the man's voice when he had said:

---

① say the grace before meals: 对着饭菜感恩祈祷 ② Thy bounty: 你的恩惠 ③ pearled around ... glistening drops: 盖子周围的水珠闪闪发光，像珍珠一样。 ④ trussed and skewered: 已经捆紧用和用烤肉叉叉起来了 ⑤ guinea: 几尼(旧英国金币) ⑥ prodded: 戳

— Take that one, sir. That's the real Ally Daly[1].

Why did Mr Barrett in Clongowes call his pandybat a turkey[2]? But Clongowes was far away: and the warm heavy smell of turkey and ham and celery[3] rose from the plates and dishes and the great fire was banked high and red in the grate and the green ivy and red holly made you feel so happy and when dinner was ended the big plumpudding would be carried in, studded with peeled almonds and sprigs of holly[4], with bluish fire running around it[5] and a little green flag flying from the top.

It was his first Christmas dinner and he thought of his little brothers and sisters who were waiting in the nursery, as he had often waited, till the pudding came. The deep low collar and the Eton jacket made him feel queer and oldish: and that morning when his mother had brought him down to the parlour, dressed for mass, his father had cried. That was because he was thinking of his own father. And uncle Charles had said so too.

Mr Dedalus covered the dish and began to eat hungrily. Then he said:

— Poor old Christy, he's nearly lopsided now with roguery[6].

— Simon, said Mrs Dedalus, you haven't given Mrs Riordan any sauce.

Mr Dedalus seized the sauceboat.

— Haven't I? he cried. Mrs Riordan, pity the poor blind.

Dante covered her plate with her hands and said:

— No, thanks.

Mr Dedalus turned to uncle Charles.

---

[1] Ally Daly: 最好的 [2] call his pandybat a turkey: 巴雷特先生把戒尺叫做火鸡(因为戒尺能把手心打得通红，像火鸡一样。英语中有一习语: be as red as a turkey-cock)。 [3] celery: 芹菜 [4] the big ... of holly: 大盘葡萄干布丁会端上来,上面点缀着剥了皮的杏仁和冬青树枝。 [5] with bluish fire running around it: 四周流动着蓝色的火焰(有些西餐在上菜时,浇上白兰地用火点着) [6] he's nearly ... with roguery: 因为老做坏事,他的腿都快被打瘸了。

— How are you off, sir?

— Right as the mail, Simon.

— You, John?

— I'm all right. Go on yourself.

— Mary? Here, Stephen, here's something to make your hair curl.

He poured sauce freely over Stephen's plate and set the boat again on the table. Then he asked uncle Charles was it tender. Uncle Charles could not speak because his mouth was full, but he nodded that it was.

— That was a good answer our friend made to the canon. What? said Mr Dedalus.

— I didn't think he had that much in him, said Mr Casey.

— *I'll pay you your dues* ①, *father*, *when you cease turning the house of God into a pollingbooth* ② .

— A nice answer, said Dante, for any man calling himself a catholic to give to his priest.

— They have only themselves to blame, said Mr Dedalus suavely. If they took a fool's advice they would confine their attention to religion.

— It is religion, Dante said. They are doing their duty in warning the people.

— We go to the house of God, Mr Casey said, in all humility to pray to our Maker and not to hear election addresses.

— It is religion, Dante said again. They are right. They must direct their flocks. ③

— And preach politics from the altar, is it? asked Mr Dedalus.

— Certainly, said Dante. It is a question of public morality. A priest would not be a priest if he did not tell his flock what is right and what is wrong.

---

① pay you your dues: 支付你的费用　② pollingbooth: 投票站
③ They must direct their flocks: 他们得教导教民

Mrs Dedalus laid down her knife and fork, saying:

— For pity's sake[①] and for pity sake let us have no political discussion on this day of all days in the year.

— Quite right, ma'am, said uncle Charles. Now, Simon, that's quite enough now. Not another word now.

— Yes, yes, said Mr Dedalus quickly.

He uncovered the dish boldly and said:

— Now then, who's for more turkey?

Nobody answered. Dante said:

— Nice language for any catholic to use!

— Mrs Riordan, I appeal to you, said Mrs Dedalus, to let the matter drop now.

Dante turned on her and said:

— And am I to sit here and listen to the pastors of my church being flouted[②]?

— Nobody is saying a word against them, said Mr Dedalus, so long as they don't meddle in politics[③].

— The bishops and priests of Ireland have spoken, said Dante, and they must be obeyed.

— Let them leave politics alone, said Mr Casey, or the people may leave their church alone.

— You hear? said Dante, turning to Mrs Dedalus.

— Mr Casey! Simon! said Mrs Dedalus, let it end now.

— Too bad! Too bad! said uncle Charles.

— What? cried Mr Dedalus. Were we to desert him at the bidding of the English people?[④]

— He was no longer worthy to lead, said Dante. He

---

① For pity's sake: 发发慈悲　② listen to ... being flouted: 听任我教堂里的牧师遭受蔑视　③ so long as ... in politics: 只要他们不搅在政治里。(这场争吵因爱尔兰民族运动领袖帕内尔之死而起。1890 年，帕内尔由于与奥谢夫人的绯闻，在公众中丧失威信，同时遭到天主教教会反对，帕内尔 1891 年死去，这样爱尔兰人民盼望了 30 年的民族解放就此告终。斯蒂芬的父亲迪达拉斯先生一直是帕内尔的支持者，他认为是天主教的那帮教棍把帕内尔逼上死路的。而斯蒂芬的姨妈丹特则站在教会一边。)
④ Were we ... English people: 难道我们要听从英格兰人的吩咐，把他(帕内尔)抛弃吗？

was a public sinner[①].

— We are all sinners and black sinners, said Mr Casey coldly.

— *Woe be to the man by whom the scandal cometh*![②] said Mrs Riordan. *It would be better for him that a millstone were tied about his neck and that he were cast into the depths of the sea rather than that he should scandalize one of these*, *my least little ones*. That is the language of the Holy Ghost.

— And very bad language if you ask me, said Mr Dedalus coolly.

— Simon! Simon! said uncle Charles. The boy.

— Yes, yes, said Mr Dedalus. I meant about the ... I was thinking about the bad language of that railway porter. Well now, that's all right. Here, Stephen, show me your plate, old chap. Eat away now. Here.

He heaped up the food on Stephen's plate and served uncle Charles and Mr Casey to large pieces of turkey and splashes of sauce. Mrs Dedalus was eating little and Dante sat with her hands in her lap. She was red in the face. Mr Dedalus rooted with the carvers[③] at the end of the dish and said:

— There's a tasty bit here we call the pope's nose. If any lady or gentleman ...

He held a piece of fowl up on the prong of the carving-fork[④]. Nobody spoke. He put it on his own plate, saying:

— Well, you can't say but you were asked. I think I had better eat it myself because I'm not well in my health lately.

He winked at Stephen and, replacing the dishcover, began to eat again.

There was a silence while he ate. Then he said:

— Well now, the day kept up fine after all. There

---

① He was a public sinner: 他(帕内尔)是公众的罪人 ② Woe ... scandal cometh: 让那些制造谣言的人见鬼去吧 ③ carvers: 切肉刀 ④ He held ... carvingfork: 他把一块火鸡挑在切肉叉的叉尖上

were plenty of strangers down too.

Nobody spoke. He said again:

— I think there were more strangers down than last Christmas.

He looked round at the others whose faces were bent towards their plates and, receiving no reply, waited for a moment and said bitterly:

— Well, my Christmas dinner has been spoiled anyhow.

— There could be neither luck nor grace, Dante said, in a house where there is no respect for the pastors of the church.

Mr Dedalus threw his knife and fork noisily on his plate.

— Respect! he said. Is it for Billy with the lip[1] or for the tub of guts up in Armagh[2]? Respect!

— Princes of the church, said Mr Casey with slow scorn.

— Lord Leitrim's coachman, yes, said Mr Dedalus.

— They are the Lord's anointed[3], Dante said. They are an honour to their country.

— Tub of guts, said Mr Dedalus coarsely. He has a handsome face, mind you, in repose[4]. You should see that fellow lapping up[5] his bacon and cabbage of a cold winter's day. O Johnny!

He twisted his features into a grimace of heavy bestiality[6] and made a lapping noise with his lips.

— Really, Simon, said Mrs Dedalus, you should not speak that way before Stephen. It's not right.

— O, he'll remember all this when he grows up, said

---

① Billy with the lip: 指从 1885 年到 1921 年任职于都柏林的大主教 William J. Walsh(1841—1921)　② the tub of guts up in Armagh: 阿尔玛的草包。指从 1887 年到 1924 年任职于阿尔玛的大主教。以上两个人在许多问题上与帕内尔作对。　③ the Lord's anointed: 救世主　④ in repose: 在安静的时候　⑤ lapping up: 贪婪地吃　⑥ He twisted ... heavy bestiality: 他扭曲着脸,作出一副凶恶的怪相

Dante hotly — the language he heard against God and religion and priests in his own home.

— Let him remember too, cried Mr Casey to her from across the table, the language with which the priests and the priests' pawns[①] broke Parnell's heart and hounded him into his grave[②]. Let him remember that too when he grows up.

— Sons of bitches[③]! cried Mr Dedalus. When he was down they turned on him to betray him and rend him like rats in a sewer[④]. Lowlived dogs! And they look it! By Christ, they look it!

— They behaved rightly, cried Dante. They obeyed their bishops and their priests. Honour to them!

— Well, it is perfectly dreadful to say that not even for one day in the year, said Mrs Dedalus, can we be free from these dreadful disputes!

Uncle Charles raised his hands mildly and said:

— Come now, come now, come now! Can we not have our opinions whatever they are without this bad temper and this bad language? It is too bad surely.

Mrs Dedalus spoke to Dante in a low voice but Dante said loudly:

— I will not say nothing. I will defend my church and my religion when it is insulted and spit on by renegade catholics[⑤].

Mr Casey pushed his plate rudely into the middle of the table and, resting his elbows before him, said in a hoarse voice to his host:

— Tell me, did I tell you that story about a very famous spit?

— You did not, John, said Mr Dedalus.

---

① the priests' pawns: 教士的爪牙　② hounded him into his grave: 把他逼进坟墓　③ Sons of bitches: 狗娘养的　④rend him like rats in a sewer: 像对待阴沟里的耗子一样,把他扯得粉碎　⑤ when it ... renegade catholics: 当它受到侮辱和被变节的天主教徒吐唾沫的时候

— Why, then, said Mr Casey, it is a most instructive story. It happened not long ago in the county Wicklow where we are now.

He broke off and, turning towards Dante, said with quiet indignation[①]:

— And I may tell you, ma'am, that I, if you mean me, am no renegade catholic. I am a catholic as my father was and his father before him and his father before him again, when we gave up our lives rather than sell our faith.

— The more shame to you now, Dante said, to speak as you do.

— The story, John, said Mr Dedalus smiling. Let us have the story anyhow.

— Catholic indeed! repeated Dante ironically. The blackest protestant[②] in the land would not speak the language I have heard this evening.

Mr Dedalus began to sway his head to and fro, crooning[③] like a country singer.

— I am no protestant, I tell you again, said Mr Casey, flushing.

Mr Dedalus, still crooning and swaying his head, began to sing in a grunting nasal tone:

> O, come all you Roman catholics
> That never went to mass.

He took up his knife and fork again in good humour[④] and set to eating, saying to Mr Casey:

— Let us have the story, John. It will help us to digest.

Stephen looked with affection at Mr Casey's face which stared across the table over his joined hands. He liked to sit near him at the fire, looking up at his dark

---

① indignation: 愤慨   ② The blackest protestant: 最邪恶的新教教徒。(在爱尔兰,新教教徒和天主教教徒是对立的两派。下文提到,丹特姨妈甚至不愿让斯蒂芬和新教教徒艾琳一起玩)   ③ croon: 低声哼唱   ④ in good humour: 好情绪地

fierce face. But his dark eyes were never fierce and his slow voice was good to listen to. But why was he then against the priests? Because Dante must be right then. But he had heard his father say that she was a spoiled nun① and that she had come out of the convent② in the Alleghanies when her brother had got the money from the savages for the trinkets and the chainies③. Perhaps that made her severe against Parnell. And she did not like him to play with Eileen because Eileen was a protestant and when she was young she knew children that used to play with protestants and the protestants used to make fun of the litany④ of the Blessed Virgin. *Tower of Ivory*, they used to say, *House of Gold*! How could a woman be a tower of ivory or a house of gold? Who was right then? And he remembered the evening in the infirmary in Clongowes, the dark waters, the light at the pierhead and the moan of sorrow from the people when they had heard.

Eileen had long white hands. One evening when playing tig she had put her hands over his eyes: long and white and thin and cold and soft. That was ivory: a cold white thing. That was the meaning of *Tower of Ivory*.

— The story is very short and sweet, Mr Casey said. It was one day down in Arklow, a cold bitter day, not long before the chief⑤ died. May God have mercy on him!

He closed his eyes wearily and paused. Mr Dedalus took a bone from his plate and tore some meat from it with his teeth, saying:

— Before he was killed, you mean.

Mr Casey opened his eyes, sighed and went on:

— It was down in Arklow one day. We were down there at a meeting and after the meeting was over we had to make our way to the railway station through the crowd.

---

① a spoiled nun: 被宠坏的修女　②convent: 女修道院　③her brother ... the chainies: 她的哥哥把一些不值钱的小玩意儿和破瓷器卖给野蛮人, 弄到一点儿钱。　④litany: 应答祈祷　⑤the chief: 指帕内尔

Such booing① and baaing②, man, you never heard. They called us all the names in the world.③ Well there was one old lady, and a drunken old harridan④ she was surely, that paid all her attention to me. She kept dancing along beside me in the mud bawling⑤ and screaming into my face: *Priest-hunter*! *The Paris Funds*!⑥ *Mr Fox*!⑦ *Kitty O'Shea*!⑧

— And what did you do, John? asked Mr Dedalus.

— I let her bawl away, said Mr Casey. It was a cold day and to keep up my heart⑨ I had (saving your presence, ma'am⑩) a quid of Tullamore in my mouth and sure I couldn't say a word in any case because my mouth was full of tobacco juice.

— Well, John?

— Well. I let her bawl away, to her heart's content⑪, *Kitty O'Shea* and the rest of it till at last she called that lady a name that I won't sully⑫ this Christmas board nor your ears, ma'am, nor my own lips by repeating.

He paused. Mr Dedalus, lifting his head from the bone, asked:

— And what did you do, John?

— Do! said Mr Casey. She stuck her ugly old face up at me when she said it and I had my mouth full of tobacco juice. I bent down to her and *Phth*! says I to her like that.

He turned aside and made the act of spitting.

— *Phth*! says I to her like that, right into her eye.

He clapped a hand to his eye and gave a hoarse scream of pain.

---

① boo: 发出呸的声音 ② baa: 咩 (羊叫声) ③ They called ... the world: 他们把世界上最难听的话都骂尽了 ④ a drunken old harridan: 一个喝得醉醺醺的老母夜叉 ⑤ bawling: 高声叫喊 ⑥ The Paris Funds: 巴黎基金。帕内尔曾在巴黎募捐,后来也是这笔钱的托管人 ⑦ Mr Fox: 指帕内尔 ⑧ Kitty O'Shea: 即奥谢夫人 ⑨ to keep up my heart: 为了提神 ⑩ saving your presence, ma'am: 恕我冒昧,夫人 ⑪ to her heart's content: 让她骂了个痛快 ⑫ sully: 弄脏

— *O Jesus, Mary and Joseph! says she. I'm blind-ed! I'm blinded and drownded!*

He stopped in a fit of coughing and laughter, repeating:

— *I'm blinded entirely.*

Mr Dedalus laughed loudly and lay back in his chair while uncle Charles swayed his head to and fro①.

Dante looked terribly angry and repeated while they laughed:

— Very nice! Ha! Very nice!

It was not nice about the spit in the woman's eye. But what was the name the woman had called Kitty O'Shea that Mr Casey would not repeat? He thought of Mr Casey walking through the crowds of people and making speeches from a wagonette②. That was what he had been in prison for and he remembered that one night Sergeant O'Neill had come to the house and had stood in the hall, talking in a low voice with his father and chewing nervously at the chinstrap of his cap③. And that night Mr Casey had not gone to Dublin by train but a car had come to the door and he had heard his father say something about the Cabinteely road④.

He was for Ireland and Parnell and so was his father: and so was Dante too for one night at the band on the esplanade⑤ she had hit a gentleman on the head with her umbrella because he had taken off his hat when the band played *God save the Queen*⑥ at the end.

Mr Dedalus gave a snort of contempt⑦.

— Ah, John, he said. It is true for them. We are an unfortunate priestridden race⑧ and always were and always

---

① to and fro: 来回地   ② wagonette: 小马车   ③ the chinstrap of his cap: 帽子上的带子   ④ the Cabinteely road: 一条到都柏林的偏僻小路   ⑤ esplanade: 广场   ⑥ God save the Queen: 《天佑吾王》，英国国歌   ⑦ a snort of contempt: 轻蔑的咕噜声   ⑧ We are ... priestridden race: 我们是个不幸的受尽教士祸害的民族

will be till the end of the chapter[①].

Uncle Charles shook his head, saying:

— A bad business! A bad business!

Mr Dedalus repeated:

— A priestridden Godforsaken race[②]!

He pointed to the portrait of his grandfather on the wall to his right.

— Do you see that old chap up there, John? he said. He was a good Irishman when there was no money in the job. He was condemned to death as a whiteboy[③]. But he had a saying about our clerical friends[④], that he would never let one of them put his two feet under his mahogany[⑤].

Dante broke in angrily:

— If we are a priestridden race we ought to be proud of it! They are the apple of God's eye[⑥]. *Touch them not, says Christ, for they are the apple of My eye.*

— And can we not love our country then? asked Mr Casey. Are we not to follow the man that was born to lead us?

— A traitor to his country! replied Dante. A traitor, an adulterer! The priests were right to abandon him. The priests were always the true friends of Ireland.

— Were they, faith? said Mr Casey.

He threw his fist on the table and, frowning angrily, protruded one finger after another[⑦].

— Didn't the bishops of Ireland betray us in the time of the union when bishop Lanigan presented an address of

---

① till the end of the chapter: 直到历史上这个重要的时代结束　② A priestridden Godforsaken race: 一个受教士祸害、被上帝遗弃的民族　③ whiteboy: 反动青年。19 世纪上半期, 他们(whiteboys)起来反对提高地租的地主和顺从交租的农民(blacklegs), 因晚上穿着易辨认的白色衣服而得名。　④ clerical friends: 牧师朋友　⑤ put his two feet under his mahogany: 来自习语 have one's knees under sb's mahogany(在某人家吃饭), mahogany 为餐桌之意。　⑥ the apple of God's eye: 上帝的宝贝　⑦ protruded one finger after another: 一个接一个地伸出手指

loyalty to the Marquess Cornwallis? Didn't the bishops and priests sell the aspirations of their country in 1829 in return for catholic emancipation①? Didn't they denounce the Fenian movement② from the pulpit and in the confession box? And didn't they dishonour the ashes of Terence Bellew MacManus③?

His face was glowing with anger and Stephen felt the glow rise to his own cheek as the spoken words thrilled him. Mr Dedalus uttered a guffaw of coarse scorn④.

— O, by God, he cried, I forgot little old Paul Cullen⑤! Another apple of God's eye!

Dante bent across the table and cried to Mr Casey:

— Right! Right! They were always right! God and morality and religion come first.

Mrs Dedalus, seeing her excitement, said to her:

— Mrs Riordan, don't excite yourself answering them.

— God and religion before everything! Dante cried. God and religion before the world.

Mr Casey raised his clenched fist and brought it down on the table with a crash.

— Very well, then, he shouted hoarsely⑥, if it comes to that, no God for Ireland!

— John! John! cried Mr Dedalus, seizing his guest by the coatsleeve.

Dante stared across the table, her cheeks shaking. Mr Casey struggled up from his chair and bent across the table towards her, scraping the air from before his eyes with one hand as though he were tearing aside a cobweb⑦.

— No God for Ireland! he cried. We have had too

---

① emancipation: 解放　② Fenian movement: 芬尼亚运动。指 19 世纪在爱尔兰出现的、致力于建立独立的爱尔兰共和国的运动　③ Terence Bellew MacManus: (1823—1860)，爱尔兰爱国者　④ uttered a guffaw of coarse scorn: 发出一阵轻蔑粗鲁的狂笑　⑤ Paul Cullen: (1803—1878)，1852 年到 1878 年间都柏林的大主教，曾镇压过芬尼亚运动。　⑥ he shouted hoarsely: 他哑着嗓子喊　⑦ cobweb: 蜘蛛网

much God in Ireland. Away with God!

— Blasphemer[①]! Devil! screamed Dante, starting to her feet and almost spitting in his face.

Uncle Charles and Mr Dedalus pulled Mr Casey back into his chair again, talking to him from both sides reasonably. He stared before him out of his dark flaming eyes, repeating:

— Away with God, I say!

Dante shoved her chair violently aside[②] and left the table, upsetting her napkinring[③] which rolled slowly along the carpet and came to rest against the foot of an easychair. Mrs Dedalus rose quickly and followed her towards the door. At the door Dante turned round violently and shouted down the room, her cheeks flushed and quivering with rage:

— Devil out of hell[④]! We won! We crushed him to death! Fiend!

The door slammed behind her.

Mr Casey, freeing his arms from his holders, suddenly bowed his head on his hands with a sob of pain.

— Poor Parnell! he cried loudly. My dead king!

He sobbed loudly and bitterly.

Stephen, raising his terrorstricken face, saw that his father's eyes were full of tears.

The fellows talked together in little groups.

One fellow said:

— They were caught near the Hill of Lyons.

— Who caught them?

— Mr Gleeson and the minister. They were on a car.

The same fellow added:

— A fellow in the higher line told me.

Fleming asked:

---

① Blasphemer: 亵渎 ② Dante shoved ... violently aside: 丹特把椅子猛推到一边。 ③ napkinring: 束餐巾的环 ④ Devil out of hell: 来自地狱的魔鬼

— But why did they run away, tell us?

— I know why, Cecil Thunder said. Because they had fecked cash out of the rector's room[①].

— Who fecked?

— Kickham's brother. And they all went shares in it.

— But that was stealing. How could they have done that?

— A fat lot[②] you know about it, Thunder! Wells said. I know why they scut[③].

— Tell us why.

— I was told not to, Wells said.

— O, go on, Wells, all said. You might tell us. We won't let it out.

Stephen bent forward his head to hear. Wells looked round to see if anyone was coming. Then he said secretly:

— You know the altar wine they keep in the press in the sacristy[④]?

— Yes.

— Well, they drank that and it was found out who did it by the smell. And that's why they ran away, if you want to know.

And the fellow who had spoken first said:

— Yes, that's what I heard too from the fellow in the higher line.

The fellows were all silent. Stephen stood among them, afraid to speak, listening. A faint sickness of awe made him feel weak[⑤]. How could they have done that? He thought of the dark silent sacristy. There were dark wooden presses there where the crimped surplices[⑥] lay quietly folded. It was not the chapel but still you had to speak un-

---

① they had ... rector's room：他们从校长的房间里偷了钱 ② A fat lot：(作反语用；字面上说"多的"而实际上指)很少 ③ scut：本意为兔子的尾巴，此处意为逃跑。 ④ You know ... the sacristy：你知道他们在圣器收藏室的柜橱里存放着圣坛上用的酒吗? ⑤ A faint ... feel weak：一阵因恐惧而引起的轻微的不适 ⑥ the crimped surplices：有褶皱的宽大白色法衣

der your breath①. It was a holy place. He remembered the
summer evening he had been there to be dressed as boat-
bearer, the evening of the procession to the little altar in
the wood②. A strange and holy place. The boy that held
the censer had swung it gently to and fro near the door
with the silvery cap lifted by the middle chain to keep the
coals lighting. That was called charcoal: and it had burned
quietly as the fellow had swung it gently and had given off
a weak sour smell③. And then when all were vested he had
stood holding out the boat to the rector and the rector had
put a spoonful of incense in it and it had hissed on the red
coals.

The fellows were talking together in little groups here
and there on the playground. The fellows seemed to him to
have grown smaller: that was because a sprinter④ had
knocked him down the day before, a fellow out of second of
grammar⑤. He had been thrown by the fellow's machine
lightly on the cinderpath⑥ and his spectacles had been broken in three pieces and some of the grit of the cinders had
gone into his mouth.

That was why the fellows seemed to him smaller and
farther away and the goalposts so thin and far and the soft
grey sky so high up. But there was no play on the football
grounds for cricket was coming: and some said that Barnes
would be prof and some said it would be Flowers. And all
over the playgrounds they were playing rounders and bowling twisters and lobs⑦. And from here and from there
came the sounds of the cricketbats through the soft grey
air. They said: pick, pack, pock, puck: little drops of water in a fountain slowly falling in the brimming bowl.

Athy, who had been silent, said quietly:

---

① you had to speak under your breath: 你必须得低声说话　② the
evening ... the wood: 列队到树林里的小圣坛去的那个傍晚　③ had given
off a weak sour smell: 发出一种轻微的酸味　④ sprinter: 短跑运动员　⑤ a
fellow out of second of grammar: 文法二班的学生　⑥ cinderpath: 煤渣路
⑦ they were ... and lobs: 他们在玩圆场棒球,打吊球和高球

— You are all wrong.

All turned towards him eagerly.

— Why?

— Do you know?

— Who told you?

— Tell us, Athy.

Athy pointed across the playground to where Simon Moonan was walking by himself kicking a stone before him.

— Ask him, he said.

The fellows looked there and then said:

— Why him?

— Is he in it?

— Tell us, Athy. Go on. You might if you know.

Athy lowered his voice and said:

— Do you know why those fellows scut? I will tell you but you must not let on you know.

He paused for a moment and then said mysteriously:

— They were caught with Simon Moonan and Tusker Boyle in the square① one night.

The fellows looked at him and asked:

— Caught?

— What doing?

Athy said:

— Smugging②.

All the fellows were silent; and Athy said:

— And that's why.

Stephen looked at the faces of the fellows but they were all looking across the playground. He wanted to ask somebody about it. What did that mean about the smugging in the square? Why did the five fellows out of the higher line run away for that? It was a joke, he thought. Simon Moonan had nice clothes and one night he had

---

① in the square: 指在学校的厕所里 ② smugging: 干些偷偷摸摸见不得人的事

shown him a ball of creamy sweets that the fellows of the football fifteen had rolled down to him along the carpet in the middle of the refectory when he was at the door. It was the night of the match against the Bective Rangers; and the ball was made just like a red and green apple only it opened and it was full of the creamy sweets. And one day Boyle had said that an elephant had two tuskers instead of two tusks and that was why he was called Tusker Boyle but some fellows called him Lady Boyle because he was always at his nails, paring them①.

Eileen had long thin cool white hands too because she was a girl. They were like ivory; only soft. That was the meaning of *Tower of Ivory* but protestants could not understand it and made fun of it. One day he had stood beside her looking into the hotel grounds. A waiter was running up a trail of bunting on the flagstaff② and a fox terrier③ was scampering to and fro on the sunny lawn. She had put her hand into his pocket where his hand was and he had felt how cool and thin and soft her hand was. She had said that pockets were funny things to have: and then all of a sudden she had broken away and had run laughing down the sloping curve of the path. Her fair hair had streamed out behind her like gold in the sun. *Tower of Ivory*. *House of Gold*. By thinking of things you could understand them.

But why in the square? You went there when you wanted to do something. It was all thick slabs④ of slate and water trickled all day out of tiny pinholes and there was a queer smell of stale water there. And behind the door of one of the closets there was a drawing in red pencil of a bearded man in a Roman dress with a brick in each hand and underneath was the name of the drawing:

*Balbus*⑤ *was building a wall*.

---

① because he . . . paring them: 因为他总是在修指甲   ② A waiter was running up a trail of bunting on the flagstaff: 一个侍者正在往旗杆上升一面旗   ③ a fox terrier: 捕狐的猎狗   ④ thick slabs: 厚石板   ⑤ Balbus: 巴尔巴斯。西班牙人，后来成为罗马公民。在恺撒离开罗马参加高卢战役时，他曾被指派保卫恺撒的财产。

Some fellow had drawn it there for a cod. It had a funny face but it was very like a man with a beard. And on the wall of another closet there was written in backhand in beautiful writing:

Julius Caesar wrote The Calico Belly[1].

Perhaps that was why they were there because it was a place where some fellows wrote things for cod. But all the same it was queer what Athy said and the way he said it. It was not a cod because they had run away. He looked with the others in silence across the playground and began to feel afraid.

At last Fleming said:

— And we are all to be punished for what other fellows did?

— I won't come back, see if I do, Cecil Thunder said. Three days' silence in the refectory and sending us up for six and eight every minute[2].

— Yes, said Wells. And old Barrett has a new way of twisting the note so that you can't open it and fold it again to see how many ferulae you are to get[3]. I won't come back too.

— Yes, said Cecil Thunder, and the prefect of studies[4] was in second of grammar this morning.

— Let us get up a rebellion, Fleming said. Will we?

All the fellows were silent. The air was very silent and you could hear the cricketbats but more slowly than before: pick, pock.

Wells asked:

— What is going to be done to them?

— Simon Moonan and Tusker are going to be flogged[5], Athy said, and the fellows in the higher line got

---

① Julius Caesar wrote The Calico Belly：恺撒曾写过《高卢之战》(*De Bello Gallico*)一书, 此处学生戏改为《白布肚皮》　② sending us up for six and eight every minute：叫我们上去, 每分钟挨六到八板　③ how many ferulae you are to get：你手心要挨多少下打　④ the prefect of studies：教导主任 ⑤ to be flogged：遭受鞭打

their choice of flogging or being expelled[①].

— And which are they taking? asked the fellow who had spoken first.

— All are taking expulsion[②] except Corrigan, Athy answered. He's going to be flogged by Mr Gleeson.

— Is it Corrigan that big fellow? said Fleming. Why, he'd be able for two of Gleeson!

— I know why, Cecil Thunder said. He is right and the other fellows are wrong because a flogging wears off after a bit but a fellow that has been expelled from college is known all his life on account of it. Besides Gleeson won't flog him hard.

— It's best of his play not to, Fleming said.

— I wouldn't like to be Simon Moonan and Tusker, Cecil Thunder said. But I don't believe they will be flogged. Perhaps they will be sent up for twice nine[③].

— No, no, said Athy. They'll both get it on the vital spot.

Wells rubbed himself and said in a crying voice:

— Please, sir, let me off[④]!

Athy grinned and turned up the sleeves of his jacket, saying:

> *It can't be helped ;*
> *It must be done .*
> *So down with your breeches*
> *And out with your bum .*[⑤]

The fellows laughed; but he felt that they were a little afraid. In the silence of the soft grey air he heard the cricketbats from here and from there: pock. That was a sound to hear but if you were hit then you would feel a pain. The pandybat made a sound too but not like that. The fellows said it was made of whalebone and leather with lead inside[⑥]: and he wondered what was the pain like. There

---

① being expelled: 被开除   ② All are taking expulsion: 都选择被开除
③ be sent up for twice nine: 被叫上去挨两个九板   ④ let me off: 饶了我吧
⑤ So down ... your bum: 所以马上脱下裤子/露出屁股来   ⑥ made of ... lead inside: 用鲸鱼骨和牛皮做成,里面还灌了铅

were different kinds of pains for all the different kinds of sounds. A long thin cane would have a high whistling sound and he wondered what was that pain like. It made him shivery to think of it and cold: and what Athy said too. But what was there to laugh at in it? It made him shivery: but that was because you always felt like a shiver when you let down your trousers. It was the same in the bath when you undressed yourself. He wondered who had to let them down, the master or the boy himself. O how could they laugh about it that way?

He looked at Athy's rolledup sleeves and knuckly inky hands①. He had rolled up his sleeves to show how Mr Gleeson would roll up his sleeves. But Mr Gleeson had round shiny cuffs② and clean white wrists and fattish white hands and the nails of them were long and pointed. Perhaps he pared them too like Lady Boyle. But they were terribly long and pointed nails. So long and cruel they were, though the white fattish hands were not cruel but gentle. And though he trembled with cold and fright to think of the cruel long nails and of the high whistling sound of the cane and of the chill you felt at the end of your shirt when you undressed yourself yet he felt a feeling of queer quiet pleasure inside him to think of the white fattish hands, clean and strong and gentle. And he thought of what Cecil Thunder had said; that Mr Gleeson would not flog Corrigan hard. And Fleming had said he would not because it was best of his play not to. But that was not why

A voice from far out on the playground cried:
— All in!
And other voices cried:
— All in! All in!
During the writing lesson he sat with his arms folded, listening to the slow scraping of the pens③. Mr Harford

---

① rolledup sleeves and knuckly inky hands: 卷起的袖子和沾满墨水的大骨节的手 ② shiny cuffs: 发光的护腕 ③ listening to the slow scraping of the pens: 倾听着别人的笔在本子上慢慢划过的声音

went to and fro making little signs in red pencil and sometimes sitting beside the boy to show him how to hold the pen. He had tried to spell out the headline for himself though he knew already what it was for it was the last of the book. *Zeal without prudence is like a ship adrift*. But the lines of the letters were like fine invisible threads and it was only by closing his right eye tight and staring out of the left eye that he could make out the full curves of the capital[1].

But Mr Harford was very decent and never got into a wax. All the other masters got into dreadful waxes. But why were they to suffer for what fellows in the higher line did? Wells had said that they had drunk some of the altar wine out of the press in the sacristy and that it had been found out who had done it by the smell. Perhaps they had stolen a monstrance[2] to run away with it and sell it somewhere. That must have been a terrible sin, to go in there quietly at night, to open the dark press and steal the flashing gold thing into which God was put on the altar in the middle of flowers and candles at benediction[3] while the incense went up in clouds at both sides as the fellow swung the censer and Dominic Kelly sang the first part by himself in the choir. But God was not in it of course when they stole it. But still it was a strange and a great sin even to touch it. He thought of it with deep awe; a terrible and strange sin: it thrilled him to think of it in the silence when the pens scraped lightly. But to drink the altar wine out of the press and be found out by the smell was a sin too: but it was not terrible and strange. It only made you feel a little sickish on account of the smell of the wine. Because on the day when he had made his first holy communion[4] in the chapel he had shut his eyes and opened his mouth and put

---

① he could ... the capital: 他才能辨别出大写字母的曲线　② monstrance: 圣餐盒　③ benediction: (天主教)祝福式　④ holy communion: 圣餐

out his tongue a little : and when the rector had stooped down① to give him the holy communion he had smelt a faint winy smell off the rector's breath after the wine of the mass. The word was beautiful: wine. It made you think of dark purple because the grapes were dark purple that grew in Greece outside houses like white temples. But the faint smell of the rector's breath had made him feel a sick feeling on the morning of his first communion. The day of your first communion was the happiest day of your life. And once a lot of generals had asked Napoleon what was the happiest day of his life. They thought he would say the day he won some great battle or the day he was made an emperor. But he said:

— Gentlemen, the happiest day of my life was the day on which I made my first holy communion.

Father Arnall came in and the Latin lesson began and he remained still, leaning on the desk with his arms folded. Father Arnall gave out the themebooks② and he said that they were scandalous and that they were all to be written out again with the corrections at once. But the worst of all was Fleming's theme because the pages were stuck together by a blot: and Father Arnall held it up by a corner and said it was an insult to any master to send him up such a theme. Then he asked Jack Lawton to decline the noun *mare*③ and Jack Lawton stopped at the ablative④ singular and could not go on with the plural.

— You should be ashamed of yourself, said Father Arnall sternly. You, the leader of the class!

Then he asked the next boy and the next and the next. Nobody knew. Father Arnall became very quiet, more and more quiet as each boy tried to answer and could not. But his face was blacklooking and his eyes were staring though his voice was so quiet. Then he asked Fleming

---

① stooped down: 弯腰   ② themebooks: 作文本   ③ mare: (拉丁文) 海   ④ ablative: (拉丁文语法)夺格的

and Fleming said that that word had no plural. Father Arnall suddenly shut the book and shouted at him:

— Kneel out there in the middle of the class. You are one of the idlest boys I ever met. Copy out your themes again the rest of you.

Fleming moved heavily out of his place and knelt between the two last benches. The other boys bent over their themebooks and began to write. A silence filled the classroom and Stephen, glancing timidly at Father Arnall's dark face, saw that it was a little red from the wax he was in.

Was that a sin for Father Arnall to be in a wax or was he allowed to get into a wax when the boys were idle because that made them study better or was he only letting on to be in a wax? It was because he was allowed, because a priest would know what a sin was and would not do it. But if he did it one time by mistake what would he do to go to confession?① Perhaps he would go to confession to the minister. And if the minister did it he would go to the rector: and the rector to the provincial: and the provincial to the general of the jesuits. That was called the order②: and he had heard his father say that they were all clever men. They could all have become highup people③ in the world if they had not become jesuits. And he wondered what Father Arnall and Paddy Barrett would have become and what Mr McGlade and Mr Gleeson would have become if they had not become jesuits. It was hard to think what because you would have to think of them in a different way with different coloured coats and trousers and with beards and moustaches and different kinds of hats.

The door opened quietly and closed. A quick whisper ran through the class: the prefect of studies. There was an instant of dead silence and then the loud crack of a pandy-

---

① But if . . . to confession: 但是如果他一时疏忽，犯了某种罪行，他该怎样进行忏悔呢？　② the order: 圣职人员的等级　③ highup people: 社会地位高的人

bat on the last desk①. Stephen's heart leapt up in fear.

— Any boys want flogging here, Father Arnall? cried the prefect of studies. Any lazy idle loafers that want flogging in this class?

He came to the middle of the class and saw Fleming on his knees.

— Hoho! he cried. Who is this boy? Why is he on his knees? What is your name, boy?

— Fleming, sir.

— Hoho, Fleming! An idler of course. I can see it in your eye. Why is he on his knees, Father Arnall?

— He wrote a bad Latin theme, Father Arnall said, and he missed all the questions in grammar.

— Of course he did! cried the prefect of studies, of course he did! A born idler②! I can see it in the corner of his eye.

He banged his pandybat down on the desk and cried:

— Up, Fleming! Up, my boy!

Fleming stood up slowly.

— Hold out③! cried the prefect of studies.

Fleming held out his hand. The pandybat came down on it with a loud smacking sound: one, two, three, four, five, six.

— Other hand!

The pandybat came down again in six loud quick smacks④.

— Kneel down! cried the prefect of studies.

Fleming knelt down, squeezing his hands under his armpits⑤, his face contorted with pain⑥, but Stephen knew how hard his hands were because Fleming was always

---

① the loud crack of a pandybat on the last desk: 啪地一声, 传来戒尺拍在后面桌子上的声音 ② A born idler: 天生的懒蛋 ③ Hold out: 伸出手来 ④ six loud quick smacks: 六下又响又快的拍击声 ⑤ squeezing his hands under his armpits: 他把两手放在胳肢窝下, 使劲地压着 ⑥ his face contorted with pain: 他的脸因为痛苦而扭曲

rubbing rosin into them①. But perhaps he was in great pain for the noise of the pandies was terrible. Stephen's heart was beating and fluttering.

— At your work, all of you! shouted the prefect of studies. We want no lazy idle loafers here, lazy idle little schemers②. At your work, I tell you. Father Dolan will be in to see you every day. Father Dolan will be in tomorrow.

He poked one of the boys in the side with his pandy-bat, saying:

— You, boy! When will Father Dolan be in again?

— Tomorrow, sir, said Tom Furlong's voice.

— Tomorrow and tomorrow and tomorrow, said the prefect of studies. Make up your minds for that. Every day Father Dolan. Write away. You, boy, who are you?

Stephen's heart jumped suddenly.

— Dedalus, sir.

— Why are you not writing like the others?

— I ... my ...

He could not speak with fright.

— Why is he not writing, Father Arnall?

— He broke his glasses, said Father Arnall, and I exempted him from work③.

— Broke? What is this I hear? What is this your name is! said the prefect of studies.

— Dedalus, sir.

— Out here, Dedalus. Lazy little schemer. I see schemer in your face. Where did you break your glasses?

Stephen stumbled into the middle of the class, blinded by fear and haste④.

— Where did you break your glasses? repeated the prefect of studies.

— The cinderpath, sir.

---

① rubbing rosin into them: 往手心里擦松香 ② lazy idle little schemers: 无所事事、懒惰的小阴谋家 ③ I exempted him from work: 我准许他免写作业 ④ Stephen stumbled ... and haste: 斯蒂芬跌跌绊绊地走到教室中间,因为恐慌而感到眼前一片漆黑。

— Hoho! The cinderpath! cried the prefect of studies. I know that trick.①

Stephen lifted his eyes in wonder and saw for a moment Father Dolan's whitegrey not young face, his baldy whitegrey head with fluff at the sides of it②, the steel rims of his spectacles③ and his nocoloured eyes looking through the glasses. Why did he say he knew that trick?

— Lazy idle little loafer! cried the prefect of studies. Broke my glasses! An old schoolboy trick! Out with your hand this moment!

Stephen closed his eyes and held out in the air his trembling hand with the palm upwards. He felt the prefect of studies touch it for a moment at the fingers to straighten it and then the swish of the sleeve of the soutane④ as the pandybat was lifted to strike. A hot burning stinging tingling blow⑤ like the loud crack of a broken stick made his trembling hand crumple together like a leaf in the fire⑥: and at the sound and the pain scalding tears⑦ were driven into his eyes. His whole body was shaking with fright, his arm was shaking and his crumpled burning livid⑧ hand shook like a loose leaf in the air. A cry sprang to his lips, a prayer to be let off. But though the tears scalded his eyes and his limbs quivered with pain and fright he held back the hot tears and the cry that scalded his throat.

— Other hand! shouted the prefect of studies.

Stephen drew back his maimed and quivering right arm⑨ and held out his left hand. The soutane sleeve swished again as the pandybat was lifted and a loud crashing sound and a fierce maddening tingling burning pain

---

① I know that trick: 我可知道你的鬼把戏 ② his baldy ... of it: (看到)他的灰白色秃头及其两边的汗毛 ③ the steel rims of his spectacles: 眼镜的金属边 ④ the swish of the sleeve of the soutane: 法衣袖子飕飕的声音 ⑤ A hot burning stinging tingling blow: 火辣辣的针扎般刺痛的一击 ⑥ crumple together like a leaf in the fire: 像火中的树叶一样皱作一团 ⑦ scalding tears: 热泪(伤心泪) ⑧ livid: 青黑色的(指皮肉被打伤而呈现的颜色) ⑨ drew back ... right arm: 抽回他受伤的哆哆嗦嗦的右手

made his hand shrink together with the palms and fingers in a livid quivering mass. The scalding water burst forth from his eyes and, burning with shame and agony and fear, he drew back his shaking arm in terror and burst out into a whine of pain[1]. His body shook with a palsy of fright and in shame and rage he felt the scalding cry come from his throat and the scalding tears falling out of his eyes and down his flaming cheeks.

— Kneel down, cried the prefect of studies.

Stephen knelt down quickly pressing his beaten hands to his sides. To think of them beaten and swollen with pain all in a moment made him feel so sorry for them as if they were not his own but someone else's that he felt sorry for. And as he knelt, calming the last sobs in his throat and feeling the burning tingling pain pressed into his sides, he thought of the hands which he had held out in the air with the palms up and of the firm touch of the prefect of studies when he had steadied the shaking fingers and of the beaten swollen reddened mass of palm and fingers[2] that shook helplessly in the air.

— Get at your work, all of you, cried the prefect of studies from the door. Father Dolan will be in every day to see if any boy, any lazy idle little loafer wants flogging. Every day. Every day.

The door closed behind him.

The hushed class[3] continued to copy out the themes. Father Arnall rose from his seat and went among them, helping the boys with gentle words and telling them the mistakes they had made. His voice was very gentle and soft. Then he returned to his seat and said to Fleming and Stephen:

— You may return to your places, you two.

Fleming and Stephen rose and, walking to their seats,

---

① burst out into a whine of pain: 呜呜地痛哭起来　② the beaten swollen reddened mass of palm and fingers: 被打得红肿成一团的手掌和手指　③ The hushed class: 班里鸦雀无声

sat down. Stephen, scarlet with shame[①], opened a book quickly with one weak hand and bent down upon it, his face close to the page.

It was unfair and cruel because the doctor had told him not to read without glasses and he had written home to his father that morning to send him a new pair. And Father Arnall had said that he need not study till the new glasses came. Then to be called a schemer before the class and to be pandied when he always got the card for first or second and was the leader of the Yorkists! How could the prefect of studies know that it was a trick? He felt the touch of the prefect's fingers as they had steadied his hand and at first he had thought he was going to shake hands with him because the fingers were soft and firm: but then in an instant he had heard the swish of the soutane sleeve and the crash. It was cruel and unfair to make him kneel in the middle of the class then: and Father Arnall had told them both that they might return to their places without making any difference between them. He listened to Father Arnall's low and gentle voice as he corrected the themes. Perhaps he was sorry now and wanted to be decent. But it was unfair and cruel. The prefect of studies was a priest but that was cruel and unfair. And his whitegrey face and the nocoloured eyes behind the steelrimmed spectacles were cruel looking because he had steadied the hand first with his firm soft fingers and that was to hit it better and louder.

— It's a stinking mean thing[②], that's what it is, said Fleming in the corridor as the classes were passing out in file to the refectory, to pandy a fellow for what is not his fault.

— You really broke your glasses by accident, didn't you? Nasty Roche asked.

Stephen felt his heart filled by Fleming's words and did not answer.

---

① scarlet with shame: 因为受到羞辱,脸涨得通红 ② It's a stinking mean thing: 真是卑鄙下流、令人不齿。

— Of course he did! said Fleming. I wouldn't stand it. I'd go up and tell the rector on him.

— Yes, said Cecil Thunder eagerly, and I saw him lift the pandybat over his shoulder and he's not allowed to do that.

— Did they hurt much? Nasty Roche asked.

— Very much, Stephen said.

— I wouldn't stand it, Fleming repeated, from Baldyhead or any other Baldyhead. It's a stinking mean low trick, that's what it is. I'd go straight up to the rector and tell him about it after dinner.

— Yes, do. Yes, do, said Cecil Thunder.

— Yes, do. Yes, go up and tell the rector on him, Dedalus, said Nasty Roche, because he said that he'd come in tomorrow again to pandy you.

— Yes, yes. Tell the rector, all said.

And there were some fellows out of second of grammar listening and one of them said:

— The senate and the Roman people declared that[1] Dedalus had been wrongly punished.

It was wrong; it was unfair and cruel: and, as he sat in the refectory, he suffered time after time in memory the same humiliation until he began to wonder whether it might not really be that there was something in his face which made him look like a schemer and he wished he had a little mirror to see. But there could not be; and it was unjust and cruel and unfair.

He could not eat the blackish fish fritters[2] they got on Wednesdays in Lent[3] and one of his potatoes had the mark of the spade[4] in it. Yes, he would do what the fellows had told him. He would go up and tell the rector that he had been wrongly punished. A thing like that had been done before by somebody in history, by some great person whose

① The senate ... declared that: 模仿罗马元老院颁布法令　② the blackish fish fritters: 发黑的鱼肉煎饼　③ Lent: 四旬斋(复活节前四十日, 在此期间星期日时须斋戒和忏悔)　④ the mark of the spade: 黑桃印记

head was in the books of history. And the rector would declare that he had been wrongly punished because the senate and the Roman people always declared that the men who did that had been wrongly punished. Those were the great men whose names were in Richmal Magnall's Questions[1]. History was all about those men and what they did and that was what Peter Parley's[2] Tales about Greece and Rome were all about. Peter Parley himself was on the first page in a picture. There was a road over a heath[3] with grass at the side and little bushes: and Peter Parley had a broad hat like a protestant minister and a big stick and he was walking fast along the road to Greece and Rome.

It was easy what he had to do. All he had to do was when the dinner was over and he came out in his turn to go on walking but not out to the corridor but up the staircase on the right that led to the castle. He had nothing to do but that: to turn to the right and walk fast up the staircase and in half a minute he would be in the low dark narrow corridor that led through the castle to the rector's room. And every fellow had said that it was unfair, even the fellow out of second of grammar who had said that about the senate and the Roman people.

What would happen?

He heard the fellows of the higher line stand up at the top of the refectory and heard their steps as they came down the matting[4]: Paddy Rath and Jimmy Magee and the Spaniard and the Portuguese and the fifth was big Corrigan who was going to be flogged by Mr Gleeson. That was why the prefect of studies had called him a schemer and pandied him for nothing: and, straining his weak eyes[5], tired with the tears, he watched big Corrigan's

---

① Richmal Magnall's Questions：Richmal Magnall(1769—1820)，英国女教师，她的关于历史、地理方面的问答手册在 19 世纪很受学生欢迎。这里斯蒂芬把她的名字拼错了。　② Peter Parley：(1793—1860)，美国出版商，是一系列儿童书籍的主编。　③ heath：荒地　④ matting：地席　⑤ straining his weak eyes：眯起他视力模糊的双眼

broad shoulders and big hanging black head passing in the file. But he had done something and besides Mr Gleeson would not flog him hard: and he remembered how big Corrigan looked in the bath. He had skin the same colour as the turfcoloured bogwater① in the shallow end of the bath and when he walked along the side his feet slapped loudly on the wet tiles and at every step his thighs shook a little because he was fat②.

The refectory was half empty and the fellows were still passing out in file. He could go up the staircase because there was never a priest or a prefect outside the refectory door. But he could not go. The rector would side with the prefect of studies and think it was a schoolboy trick and then the prefect of studies would come in every day the same only it would be worse because he would be dreadfully waxy at any fellow going up to the rector about him. The fellows had told him to go but they would not go themselves. They had forgotten all about it. No, it was best to forget all about it and perhaps the prefect of studies had Only said he would come in. No, it was best to hide out of the way because when you were small and young you could often escape that way.

The fellows at his table stood up. He stood up and passed out among them in the file. He had to decide. He was coming near the door. If he went on with the fellows he could never go up to the rector because he could not leave the playground for that. And if he went and was pandied all the same all the fellows would make fun and talk about young Dedalus going up to the rector to tell on the prefect of studies.

He was walking down along the matting and he saw the door before him. It was impossible: he could not. He thought of the baldy head of the prefect of studies with the cruel nocoloured eyes looking at him and he heard the voice

---

① turfcoloured bogwater: 泥炭色的污水　② at every ... was fat: 由于太胖, 他每走一步大腿上的肉都会哆嗦一下。

of the prefect of studies asking him twice what his name
was. Why could he not remember the name when he was
told the first time? Was he not listening the first time or
was it to make fun out of the name? The great men in the
history had names like that and nobody made fun of them.
It was his own name that he should have made fun of if he
wanted to make fun. Dolan: it was like the name of a
woman who washed clothes.

He had reached the door and, turning quickly up to
the right, walked up the stairs and, before he could make
up his mind to come back, he had entered the low dark
narrow corridor that led to the castle. And as he crossed
the threshold of the door of the corridor he saw, without
turning his head to look, that all the fellows were looking
after him as they went filing by.

He passed along the narrow dark corridor, passing little doors that were the doors of the rooms of the community. He peered in front of him and right and left through the
gloom and thought that those must be portraits. It was
dark and silent and his eyes were weak and tired with tears
so that he could not see. But he thought they were the portraits of the saints and great men of the order who were
looking down on him silently as he passed: saint Ignatius
Loyola[1] holding an open book and pointing to the words
Ad Majorem Dei Gloriam[2] in it; saint Francis Xavier
pointing to his chest; Lorenzo Ricci with his berretta on his
head like one of the prefects of the lines, the three patrons
of holy youth, saint Stanislaus Kostka, saint Aloysius Gonzaga and blessed John Berchmans, all with young faces because they died when they were young, and Father Peter
Kenny[3] sitting in a chair wrapped in a big cloak.

---

① Ignatius Loyola: 西班牙教士 (1491—1556), 耶稣会创始人。
② Ad Majorem Dei Gloriam: (拉丁文) 为了上帝更大的荣光。这是耶稣会
会员的座右铭, 耶稣会学校的学生把这四个词的首字母 A. M. D. G. 写在练
习本顶部, 以提醒自己学习的目的。 ③ Father Peter Kenny: 耶稣会神父,
这所学校的创办人。

He came out on the landing above the entrance hall and looked about him. That was where Hamilton Rowan had passed and the marks of the soldiers' slugs were there[①]. And it was there that the old servants had seen the ghost in the white cloak of a marshal.

An old servant was sweeping at the end of the landing. He asked him where was the rector's room and the old servant pointed to the door at the far end and looked after him as he went on to it and knocked.

There was no answer. He knocked again more loudly and his heart jumped when he heard a muffled voice[②] say:

— Come in!

He turned the handle and opened the door and fumbled for the handle of the green baize door inside[③]. He found it and pushed it open and went in.

He saw the rector sitting at a desk writing. There was a skull on the desk and a strange solemn smell in the room like the old leather of chairs.

His heart was beating fast on account of the solemn place he was in and the silence of the room: and he looked at the skull and at the rector's kindlooking face.

— Well, my little man, said the rector, what is it?

Stephen swallowed down[④] the thing in his throat and said:

— I broke my glasses, sir.

The rector opened his mouth and said:

— O!

Then he smiled and said:

— Well, if we broke our glasses we must write home for a new pair.

— I wrote home, sir, said Stephen, and Father Arnall said I am not to study till they come.

---

① the marks ... were there: 那里有士兵的子弹留下的痕迹　② a muffled voice: 低沉的声音　③ fumbled for the handle of the green baize door inside: 胡乱摸索着寻找里面那道绿毛呢面的门的把手　④ swallowed down: 吞下

— Quite right! said the rector.

Stephen swallowed down the thing again and tried to keep his legs and his voice from shaking.

— But, sir . . .

— Yes?

— Father Dolan came in today and pandied me because I was not writing my theme.

The rector looked at him in silence and he could feel the blood rising to his face and the tears about to rise to his eyes.

The rector said:

— Your name is Dedalus, isn't it?

— Yes, sir.

— And where did you break your glasses?

— On the cinderpath, sir. A fellow was coming out of the bicycle house and I fell and they got broken. I don't know the fellow's name.

The rector looked at him again in silence. Then he smiled and said:

— O, well, it was a mistake; I am sure Father Dolan did not know.

— But I told him I broke them, sir, and he pandied me.

— Did you tell him that you had written home for a new pair? the rector asked.

— No, sir.

— O well then, said the rector, Father Dolan did not understand. You can say that I excuse you from your lessons for a few days.

Stephen said quickly for fear his trembling would prevent him:

— Yes, sir, but Father Dolan said he will come in tomorrow to pandy me again for it.

— Very well, the rector said, it is a mistake and I shall speak to Father Dolan myself. Will that do now?

Stephen felt the tears wetting his eyes and murmured:

— O yes sir, thanks.

The rector held his hand across the side of the desk where the skull was and Stephen, placing his hand in it for a moment, felt a cool moist palm[①].

— Good day now, said the rector, withdrawing his hand and bowing.

— Good day, sir, said Stephen.

He bowed and walked quietly out of the room, closing the doors carefully and slowly.

But when he had passed the old servant on the landing and was again in the low narrow dark corridor he began to walk faster and faster. Faster and faster he hurried on through the gloom excitedly. He bumped his elbow against the door at the end[②], and hurrying down the staircase, walked quickly through the two corridors and out into the air.

He could hear the cries of the fellows on the playgrounds. He broke into a run and, running quicker and quicker, ran across the cinderpath and reached the third line playground, panting.

The fellows had seen him running. They closed round him in a ring, pushing one against another to hear.

— Tell us! Tell us!

— What did he say?

— Did you go in?

— What did he say?

— Tell us! Tell us!

He told them what he had said and what the rector had said and, when he had told them, all the fellows flung their caps spinning up into the air[③] and cried:

— Hurroo!

They caught their caps and sent them up again spinning skyhigh and cried again:

---

① felt a cool moist palm: 感到他的手掌又凉又潮　② He bumped his elbow against the door at the end: 在楼梯拐角处, 他的胳臂肘撞到了门。
③ flung their caps spinning up into the air: 把帽子旋转着向空中扔去

— Hurroo! Hurroo!

They made a cradle of their locked hands and hoisted him up[①] among them and carried him along till he struggled to get free. And when he had escaped from them they broke away in all directions, flinging their caps again into the air and whistling as they went spinning up and crying:

— Hurroo!

And they gave three groans for Baldyhead Dolan and three cheers for Conmee and they said he was the decentest rector that was ever in Clongowes.

The cheers died away in the soft grey air. He was alone. He was happy and free: but he would not be anyway proud with Father Dolan. He would be very quiet and obedient: and he wished that he could do something kind for him to show him that he was not proud.

The air was soft and grey and mild and evening was coming. There was the smell of evening in the air, the smell of the fields in the country where they digged up turnips[②] to peel them and eat them when they went out for a walk to Major Barton's, the smell there was in the little wood beyond the pavilion where the gallnuts were[③].

The fellows were practising long shies and bowling lobs and slow twisters. In the soft grey silence he could hear the bump of the balls: and from here and from there through the quiet air the sound of the cricketbats[④]: pick, pack, pock, puck: like drops of water in a fountain falling softly in the brimming bowl.

---

① They made a cradle of their locked hands and hoisted him up: 他们把手搭成个摇篮,把他抬了起来。 ② turnips: 萝卜 ③ the smell ... gallnuts were: 空气里还有亭子那边的小树林的味道,那里长着五倍子。 ④ the sound of the cricket bats: 板球棒的声音

CHAPTER 2 65

CHAPTER 2

Uncle Charles smoked such black twist that at last his nephew suggested to him to enjoy his morning smoke in a little outhouse at the end of the garden.

— Very good, Simon. All serene, Simon, said the old man tranquilly. Anywhere you like. The outhouse will do me nicely: it will be more salubrious①.

— Damn me, said Mr Dedalus frankly, if I know how you can smoke such villainous awful tobacco. It's like gunpowder, by God.

— It's very nice, Simon, replied the old man. Very cool and mollifying②.

Every morning, therefore, uncle Charles repaired to his outhouse but not before he had creased and brushed scrupulously his back hair and brushed and put on his tall hat. While he smoked the brim of his tall hat and the bowl of his pipe③ were just visible beyond the jambs④ of the outhouse door. His arbour, as he called the reeking outhouse which he shared with the cat and the garden tools, served him also as a sounding box⑤: and every morning he hummed contentedly one of his favourite songs: *O, twine me a bower*⑥ or *Blue Eyes and Golden Hair* or *The Groves of Blarney*⑦ while the grey and blue coils of smoke⑧ rose slowly from his pipe and vanished in the pure air.

During the first part of the summer in Blackrock uncle Charles was Stephen's constant companion. Uncle Charles was a hale old man⑨ with a welltanned skin, rugged fea-

---

① it will be more salubrious：它会更有益于健康。 ② cool and mollifying：清凉而且能使人平静下来 ③ the bowl of his pipe：烟斗的烟锅 ④ jambs：门的侧壁 ⑤ sounding box：共鸣箱 ⑥ *O, twine me a bower*：《哦，请为我搭间小屋》 ⑦ *The Groves of Blarney*：《布拉尼的小树林》 ⑧ the grey and blue coils of smoke：灰蓝色的烟圈儿 ⑨ a hale old man：精神矍铄的老人

tures and white side whiskers. On week days he did mes-
sages between the house in Carysfort Avenue and those
shops in the main street of the town with which the family
dealt. Stephen was glad to go with him on these errands for
uncle Charles helped him very liberally to handfuls of whatever was exposed in open boxes and barrels outside the
counter. He would seize a handful of grapes and sawdust①
or three or four American apples and thrust them generous-
ly into his grandnephew's hand while the shopman smiled
uneasily; and, on Stephen's feigning reluctance to take
them, he would frown and say:

— Take them, sir. Do you hear me, sir? They're
good for your bowels②.

When the order list③ had been booked the two would
go on to the park where an old friend of Stephen's father,
Mike Flynn, would be found seated on a bench, waiting
for them. Then would begin Stephen's run round the park.
Mike Flynn would stand at the gate near the railway station, watch in hand, while Stephen ran round the track in
the style Mike Flynn favoured, his head high lifted, his
knees well lifted and his hands held straight down by his
sides. When the morning practice was over the trainer
would make his comments and sometimes illustrate them by
shuffling along for a yard or so comically in an old pair of
blue canvas shoes. A small ring of wonderstruck children
and nursemaids would gather to watch him④ and linger
even when he and uncle Charles had sat down again and
were talking athletics and politics. Though he had heard
his father say that Mike Flynn had put some of the best
runners of modern times through his hands Stephen often
glanced with mistrust at his trainer's flabby stubblecovered
face⑤, as it bent over the long stained fingers⑥ through

---

① a handful of grapes and sawdust: 一大把带着锯末的葡萄　② good
for your bowels: 对你的肠胃有好处　③ the order list: 订货单　④ A small
... watch him: 一群惊讶不已的孩子和保姆站成一圈儿, 盯着他看。
⑤ flabby stubblecovered face: 皱褶且布满胡子茬儿的脸　⑥ stained fingers:
被烟熏黄的手指

which he rolled his cigarette, and with pity at the mild lustreless blue eyes which would look up suddenly from the task and gaze vaguely into the blue distance while the long swollen fingers ceased their rolling and grains and fibres of tobacco fell back into the pouch①.

On the way home uncle Charles would often pay a visit to the chapel and, as the font② was above Stephen's reach, the old man would dip his hand and then sprinkle the water briskly about Stephen's clothes and on the floor of the porch. While he prayed he knelt on his red handkerchief and read above his breath③ from a thumbblackened prayerbook④ wherein catchwords were printed at the foot of every page. Stephen knelt at his side respecting, though he did not share, his piety. He often wondered what his granduncle prayed for so seriously. Perhaps he prayed for the souls in purgatory⑤ or for the grace of a happy death or perhaps he prayed that God might send him back a part of the big fortune he had squandered in Cork⑥.

On Sundays Stephen with his father and his granduncle took their constitutional⑦. The old man was a nimble walker in spite of his corns⑧ and often ten or twelve miles of the road were covered. The little village of Stillorgan was the parting of the ways. Either they went to the left towards the Dublin mountains or along the Goatstown road and thence into Dundrum, coming home by Sandyford. Trudging along the road or standing in some grimy wayside publichouse his elders spoke constantly of the subjects nearer their hearts, of Irish politics, of Munster⑨ and of the legends of their own family, to all of which Stephen lent an avid ear. Words which he did not understand he said over and over to himself till he had learnt them by heart: and through them he had glimpses of the real world about him. The hour when he too would take part in the life of that

---

① grains and fibres of tobacco fell back into the pouch：那些松散的烟丝重又掉回到烟草袋里　② font：圣水器　③ read above his breath：高声地朗读　④ a thumbblackened prayerbook：被手指翻黑了的祈祷书　⑤ prayed for the souls in purgatory：为在炼狱中涤罪的灵魂祈祷　⑥ the big ... in Cork：他在科克镇挥霍掉的大笔财产　⑦ took their constitutional：去散步　⑧ corns：鸡眼　⑨ Munster：迪达勒斯先生的家乡科克镇所在的省

world seemed drawing near and in secret he began to make ready for the great part which he felt awaited him the nature of which he only dimly apprehended.

His evenings were his own; and he pored over a ragged translation of *The Count of Monte Cristo*[①]. The figure of that dark avenger stood forth in his mind for whatever he had heard or divined in childhood of the strange and terrible. At night he built up on the parlour table an image of the wonderful island cave out of transfers and paper flowers and coloured tissue paper and strips of the silver and golden paper in which chocolate is wrapped. When he had broken up this scenery, weary of its tinsel[②], there would come to his mind the bright picture of Marseilles[③], of sunny trellises[④] and of Mercedes[⑤]. Outside Blackrock, on the road that led to the mountains, stood a small whitewashed house in the garden of which grew many rosebushes: and in this house, he told himself, another Mercedes lived. Both on the outward and on the homeward journey he measured distance by this landmark: and in his imagination he lived through a long train of adventures, marvellous as those in the book itself, towards the close of which there appeared an image of himself, grown older and sadder, standing in a moonlit garden with Mercedes who had so many years before slighted his love, and with a sadly proud gesture of refusal, saying:

— Madam, I never eat muscatel grapes[⑥].

He became the ally of a boy named Aubrey Mills and founded with him a gang of adventurers in the avenue. Aubrey carried a whistle dangling from his buttonhole and a bicycle lamp attached to his belt while the others had short sticks thrust daggerwise through theirs[⑦]. Stephen, who

---

① he pored ... *Monte Cristo*：全神贯注地读一本破烂的《基督山伯爵》英译本 ② weary of its tinsel：厌倦了它的华而不实 ③ Marseilles：马塞（法国港市） ④ sunny trellises：阳光下的藤蔓 ⑤ Mercedes：《基督山伯爵》中的女主人公 ⑥ muscatel grapes：麝香葡萄干 ⑦ the others ... through theirs：其他孩子把短棍儿当匕首插在皮带上

had read of Napoleon's plain style of dress, chose to remain unadorned and thereby heightened for himself the pleasure of taking counsel with his lieutenant before giving orders[1]. The gang made forays[2] into the gardens of old maids or went down to the castle and fought a battle on the shaggy weedgrown rocks, coming home after it weary stragglers with the stale odours of the foreshore in their nostrils and the rank oils of the seawrack upon their hands and in their hair[3].

Aubrey and Stephen had a common milkman and often they drove out in the milkcar to Carrickmines where the cows were at grass. While the men were milking the boys would take turns in riding the tractable mare[4] round the field. But when autumn came the cows were driven home from the grass: and the first sight of the filthy cowyard at Stradbrook with its foul green puddles[5] and clots of liquid dung and steaming brantroughs[6], sickened Stephen's heart. The cattle which had seemed so beautiful in the country on sunny days revolted him and he could not even look at the milk they yielded.

The coming of September did not trouble him this year for he was not to be sent back to Clongowes. The practice in the park came to an end when Mike Flynn went into hospital. Aubrey was at school and had only an hour or two free in the evening. The gang fell asunder[7] and there were no more nightly forays or battles on the rocks. Stephen sometimes went round with the car which delivered the evening milk: and these chilly drives blew away his memory of the filth of the cowyard and he felt no repugnance[8] at

---

① taking counsel . . . giving orders：在下命令之前和他的下级军官商议
② made forays：发动袭击　③ with the . . . their hair：鼻孔里带着一股海边前滩陈腐的味道，手上、头发上粘满海上沉船的臭油污。　④ the tractable mare：容易驾驭的母马　⑤ foul green puddles：发绿的臭水坑　⑥ clots of liquid dung and steaming brantroughs：一块块稀牛粪和冒着热气的饲料槽
⑦ The gang fell asunder：那帮孩子也解散了　⑧ felt no repugnance：不觉得厌恶

seeing the cowhairs and hayseeds on the milkman's coat.
Whenever the car drew up before a house he waited to
catch a glimpse of a well-scrubbed kitchen or of a softly-
lighted hall and to see how the servant would hold the jug
and how she would close the door. He thought it should be
a pleasant life enough, driving along the roads every
evening to deliver milk, if he had warm gloves and a fat
bag of gingernuts in his pocket to eat from. But the same
foreknowledge① which had sickened his heart and made his
legs sag suddenly as he raced round the park, the same intuition which had made him glance with mistrust at his
trainer's flabby stubblecovered face as it bent heavily over
his long stained fingers, dissipated any vision of the fu-
ture②. In a vague way he understood that his father was in
trouble and that this was the reason why he himself had not
been sent back to Clongowes. For some time he had felt the
slight changes in his house; and those changes in what he
had deemed unchangeable were so many slight shocks to his
boyish conception of the world. The ambition which he felt
astir at times in the darkness of his soul sought no outlet. A
dusk like that of the outer world obscured his mind as he
heard the mare's hoofs clattering along the tramtrack on the
Rock Road and the great can swaying and rattling behind
him.

He returned to Mercedes and, as he brooded upon her
image, a strange unrest crept into his blood. Sometimes a
fever gathered within him and led him to rove alone in the
evening along the quiet avenue. The peace of the gardens
and the kindly lights in the windows poured a tender influence into his restless heart. The noise of children at play
annoyed him and their silly voices made him feel, even
more keenly than he had felt at Clongowes, that he was
different from others. He did not want to play. He wanted
to meet in the real world the unsubstantial image③ which

---

① foreknowledge: 预知 ② dissipated any vision of the future: 使他对
自己的前途感到茫然 ③ the unsubstantial image: 虚幻的形象

his soul so constantly beheld. He did not know where to seek it or how: but a premonition[1] which led him on told him that this image would, without any overt act of his[2], encounter him. They would meet quietly as if they had known each other and had made their tryst[3], perhaps at one of the gates or in some more secret place. They would be alone, surrounded by darkness and silence: and in that moment of supreme tenderness he would be transfigured. He would fade into something impalpable[4] under her eyes and then in a moment, he would be transfigured. Weakness and timidity and inexperience would fall from him in that magic moment.

Two great yellow caravans had halted one morning before the door and men had come tramping into the house to dismantle it. The furniture had been hustled out[5] through the front garden which was strewn with wisps of straw and rope ends[6] and into the huge vans at the gate. When all had been safely stowed the vans had set off noisily down the avenue: and from the window of the railway carriage, in which he had sat with his red-eyed mother, Stephen had seen them lumbering heavily along the Merrion Road.

The parlour fire[7] would not draw that evening and Mr Dedalus rested the poker against the bars of the grate to attract the flame[8]. Uncle Charles dozed in a corner of the half furnished uncarpeted room and near him the family portraits leaned against the wall. The lamp on the table shed a weak light over the boarded floor, muddied by the feet of the vanmen[9]. Stephen sat on a footstool beside his

① premonition：预感　② without any overt act of his：无须他公开地做些什么　③ tryst：约会　④ fade into something impalpable：变得不可捉摸　⑤ The furniture had been hustled out：家具被费力地搬出来　⑥ strewn with wisps of straw and rope ends：撒满乱草绳和绳子头　⑦ The parlour fire：客厅的炉火　⑧ rested the ... the flame：把拨火棍支在壁炉栅的横杆上，以让火烧得旺些　⑨ muddied by the feet of the vanmen：被赶车的人踩得满地是泥

father listening to a long and incoherent monologue. He understood little or nothing of it at first but he became slowly aware that his father had enemies and that some fight was going to take place. He felt too that he was being enlisted for the fight, that some duty was being laid upon his shoulders. The sudden flight from the comfort and revery of Blackrock, the passage through the gloomy foggy city, the thought of the bare cheerless house in which they were now to live made his heart heavy: and again an intuition or foreknowledge of the future came to him. He understood also why the servants had often whispered together in the hall and why his father had often stood on the hearthrug, with his back to the fire, talking loudly to uncle Charles who urged him to sit down and eat his dinner.

— There's a crack of the whip left in me yet, Stephen, old chap, said Mr Dedalus, poking at the dull fire with fierce energy. We're not dead yet, sonny. No, by the Lord Jesus (God forgive me) nor half dead.

Dublin was a new and complex sensation. Uncle Charles had grown so witless that he could no longer be sent out on errands and the disorder in settling in the new house left Stephen freer than he had been in Blackrock. In the beginning he contented himself with circling timidly round the neighbouring square or, at most, going half way down one of the side streets: but when he had made a skeleton map of the city in his mind he followed boldly one of its central lines until he reached the custom house. He passed unchallenged among the docks and along the quays[1] wondering at the multitude of corks[2] that lay bobbing on the surface of the water in a thick yellow scum, at the crowds of quay porters and the rumbling carts and the ill-dressed bearded policeman. The vastness and strangeness of the life suggested to him by the bales of merchandise[3]

---

① He passed . . . the quays: 沿着码头在船坞间闲逛　② multitude of corks: 大量的浮漂　③ bales of merchandise: 一包包货物

stocked along the walls or swung aloft out of the holds of steamers wakened again in him the unrest which had sent him wandering in the evening from garden to garden in search of Mercedes. And amid this new bustling life he might have fancied himself in another Marseille but that he missed the bright sky and the sumwarmed trellises of the wineshops. A vague dissatisfaction grew up within him as he looked on the quays and on the river and on the lowering skies and yet he continued to wander up and down day after day as if he really sought someone that eluded him①.

He went once or twice with his mother to visit their relatives: and, though they passed a jovial array of shops lit up and adorned② for Christmas, his mood of embittered silence did not leave him. The causes of his embitterment were many, remote and near. He was angry with himself for being young and the prey of restless foolish impulses, angry also with the change of fortune which was reshaping the world about him into a vision of squalor and insincerity③. Yet his anger lent nothing to the vision. He chronicled with patience what he saw, detaching himself from it and tasting its mortifying flavour in secret④.

He was sitting on the backless chair in his aunt's kitchen. A lamp with a reflector hung on the japanned wall⑤ of the fireplace and by its light his aunt was reading the evening paper that lay on her knees. She looked a long time at a smiling picture that was set in it and said musingly:

— The beautiful Mabel Hunter⑥!

A ringletted girl⑦ stood on tiptoe to peer at the picture and said softly:

— What is she in, mud?

---

① as if . . . eluded him: 仿佛他真想找一个想要避开他的什么人 ② a jovial . . . and adorned: 一排排张灯结彩的店铺 ③ a vision of squalor and insincerity: 悲惨而虚妄的前景 ④ tasting its mortifying flavour in secret: 偷偷地品尝受伤的滋味 ⑤ the japanned wall: 平滑发光的墙 ⑥ Mabel Hunter: 当时的一位著名演员 ⑦ A ringletted girl: 一个满头卷发的女孩儿

— In a pantomime①, love.

The child leaned her ringletted head against her mother's sleeve, gazing on the picture, and murmured as if fascinated:

— The beautiful Mabel Hunter!

As if fascinated, her eyes rested long upon those demurely taunting eyes② and she murmured again devotedly:

— Isn't she an exquisite creature?

And the boy who came in from the street, stamping crookedly under his stone of coal③, heard her words. He dropped his load promptly on the floor and hurried to her side to see. But she did not raise her easeful head to let him see. He mauled the edges of the paper④ with his reddened and blackened hands, shouldering her aside and complaining that he could not see.

He was sitting in the narrow breakfast room high up in the old darkwindowed house. The firelight flickered on the wall and beyond the window a spectral dusk⑤ was gathering upon the river. Before the fire an old woman was busy making tea and, as she bustled at the task, she told in a low voice of what the priest and the doctor had said. She told too of certain changes she had seen in her of late and of her odd ways and sayings. He sat listening to the words and following the ways of adventure that lay open in the coals, arches and vaults⑥ and winding galleries and jagged caverns⑦.

Suddenly he became aware of something in the doorway. A skull appeared suspended in the gloom of the doorway. A feeble creature like a monkey was there, drawn thither by the sound of voices at the fire. A whining voice came from the door asking:

---

① pantomime：哑剧 ② those demurely taunting eyes：那双严肃而又带些嘲弄的眼睛 ③ stamping crookedly under his stone of coal：扛着一袋煤，歪歪斜斜地走进来 ④ mauled the edges of the paper：粗手粗脚地扒拉报纸沿儿 ⑤ spectral dusk：鬼魅般的黄昏 ⑥ arches and vaults：拱门和地窖 ⑦ jagged caverns：坑坑洼洼的山洞

— Is that Josephine?

The old bustling woman answered cheerily from the fireplace:

— No, Ellen. It's Stephen.

— O . . . O, good evening, Stephen.

He answered the greeting and saw a silly smile break over the face in the doorway.

— Do you want anything, Ellen? asked the old woman at the fire.

But she did not answer the question and said:

— I thought it was Josephine. I thought you were Josephine, Stephen.

And, repeating this several times, she fell to laughing feebly.

He was sitting in the midst of a children's party at Harold's Cross①. His silent watchful manner had grown upon him and he took little part in the games. The children, wearing the spoils of their crackers②, danced and romped noisily and, though he tried to share their merriment, he felt himself a gloomy figure amid the gay cocked hats and sunbonnets.

But when he had sung his song and withdrawn into a snug corner③ of the room he began to taste the joy of his loneliness. The mirth, which in the beginning of the evening had seemed to him false and trivial, was like a soothing air to him, passing gaily by his senses, hiding from other eyes the feverish agitation④ of his blood while through the circling of the dancers and amid the music and laughter her glance travelled to his corner, flattering, taunting, searching, exciting his heart.

In the hall the children who had stayed latest were putting on their things: the party was over. She had thrown a shawl about her and, as they went together to-

---

① Harold's Cross：位于都柏林南部郊区　② wearing the spoils of their crackers：带着他们在晚会上得来的小礼物　③ a snug corner：舒适的角落　④ feverish agitation：焦灼不安

wards the tram, sprays of her fresh warm breath flew gaily above her cowled head[1] and her shoes tapped blithely on the glassy road[2].

It was the last tram. The lank brown horses[3] knew it and shook their bells to the clear night in admonition. The conductor talked with the driver, both nodding often in the green light of the lamp. On the empty seats of the tram were scattered a few coloured tickets. No sound of footsteps came up or down the road. No sound broke the peace of the night save when the lank brown horses rubbed their noses together and shook their bells.

They seemed to listen, he on the upper step and she on the lower. She came up to his step many times and went down to hers again between her phrases and once or twice stood close beside him for some moments on the upper step, forgetting to go down, and then went down. His heart danced upon her movements like a cork upon a tide.[4] He heard what her eyes said to him from beneath their cowl and knew that in some dim past, whether in life or in revery, he had heard their tale before. He saw her urge her vanities[5], her fine dress and sash and long black stockings, and knew that he had yielded to them a thousand times. Yet a voice within him spoke above the noise of his dancing heart, asking him would he take her gift to which he had only to stretch out his hand. And he remembered the day when he and Eileen had stood looking into the hotel grounds, watching the waiters running up a trail of bunting on the flagstaff and the fox terrier scampering to and fro on the sunny lawn, and how, all of a sudden, she had broken out into a peal of laughter and had run down the sloping curve of the path. Now, as then, he stood listlessly in his place, seemingly a tranquil watcher of the scene before him.

---

① cowled head：罩着围巾的头　② tapped blithely on the glassy road：轻快地踏在光滑的路上　③ The lank brown horses：高瘦的棕色马　④ His heart … a tide：他的心脏和着她的动作跳动着，宛如浮漂浮在海面上。⑤ urge her vanities：摆弄她的手袋

— She too wants me to catch hold of her, he thought. That's why she came with me to the tram. I could easily catch hold of her when she comes up to my step: nobody is looking. I could hold her and kiss her.

But he did neither: and, when he was sitting alone in the deserted tram, he tore his ticket into shreds and stared gloomily at the corrugated footboard①.

The next day he sat at his table in the bare upper room for many hours. Before him lay a new pen, a new bottle of ink and a new emerald exercise②. From force of habit he had written at the top of the first page the initial letters of the jesuit motto③: A. M. D. G.④ On the first line of the page appeared the title of the verses he was trying to write: To E — C — . He knew it was right to begin so for he had seen similar titles in the collected poems of Lord Byron⑤. When he had written this title and drawn an ornamental line⑥ underneath he fell into a daydream and began to draw diagrams on the cover of the book. He saw himself sitting at his table in Bray the morning after the discussion at the Christmas dinnertable, trying to write a poem about Parnell on the back of one of his father's second moiety notices⑦. But his brain had then refused to grapple with the theme, and desisting, he had covered the page with the names and addresses of certain of his classmates:

Roderick Kickham
John Lawton
Anthony MacSwiney
Simon Moonan

Now it seemed as if he would fail again but, by dint of brooding on the incident⑧, he thought himself into confi-

---

① the corrugated footboard: 起皱的地板　② a new emerald exercise: 一本新的绿色练习本　③ the jesuit motto: 耶稣会的座右铭　④ A. M. D. G.: 拉丁文 Ad Majorem Dei Gloriam 的缩写，参见前文注释。　⑤ Byron: 拜伦 (1788－1824)，英国浪漫主义时期诗人。　⑥ an ornamental line: 装饰线　⑦ second moiety notices: 关于破产程序的法律通知　⑧ by dint of brooding on the incident: 由于想到那次事件

dence. During this process all those elements which he deemed common and insignificant fell out of the scene. There remained no trace of the tram itself nor of the trammen nor of the horses: nor did he and she appear vividly. The verses told only of the night and the balmy breeze[①] and the maiden lustre of the moon. Some undefined sorrow was hidden in the hearts of the protagonists[②] as they stood in silence beneath the leafless trees and when the moment of farewell had come the kiss, which had been withheld by one, was given by both. After this the letters L. D. S.[③] were written at the foot of the page and, having hidden the book, he went into his mother's bedroom and gazed at his face for a long time in the mirror of her dressingtable.

But his long spell of leisure and liberty was drawing to its end. One evening his father came home full of news which kept his tongue busy all through dinner. Stephen had been awaiting his father's return for there had been mutton hash[④] that day and he knew that his father would make him dip his bread in the gravy. But he did not relish the hash for the mention of Clongowes had coated his palate with a scum of disgust.

— I walked bang into him[⑤], said Mr Dedalus for the fourth time, just at the corner of the square.

— Then I suppose, said Mrs Dedalus, he will be able to arrange it. I mean about Belvedere.

— Of course he will, said Mr Dedalus. Don't I tell you he's provincial[⑥] of the order now?

— I never liked the idea of sending him to the christian brothers[⑦] myself, said Mrs Dedalus.

— Christian brothers be damned! said Mr Dedalus. Is it with Paddy Stink and Micky Mud? No, let him stick to

---

① the balmy breeze：温和的风　② the protagonists：主角　③ L. D. S.：拉丁文 Laus Deo Semper 的缩写，意为"永远颂扬上帝"。　④ mutton hash：羊肉羹　⑤ I walked bang into him：我无意中和他碰了面　⑥ provincial：管辖教区的大主教　⑦ the christian brothers：基督教兄弟会

the jesuits in God's name since he began with them. They'll be of service to him in after years. Those are the fellows that can get you a position.

— And they're a very rich order, aren't they, Simon?

— Rather. They live well, I tell you. You saw their table at Clongowes. Fed up, by God, like gamecocks.

Mr Dedalus pushed his plate over to Stephen and bade him finish what was on it.

— Now then, Stephen, he said, you must put your shoulder to the wheel, old chap. You've had a fine long holiday.

— O, I'm sure he'll work very hard now, said Mrs Dedalus, especially when he has Maurice with him.

— O, Holy Paul, I forgot about Maurice, said Mr Dedalus. Here, Maurice! Come here, you thickheaded ruffian①! Do you know I'm going to send you to a college where they'll teach you to spell c. a. t. cat. And I'll buy you a nice little penny handkerchief to keep your nose dry. Won't that be grand fun?

Maurice grinned at his father and then at his brother.

Mr Dedalus screwed his glass into his eye and stared hard at both his sons. Stephen mumbled his bread without answering his father's gaze.

— By the bye, said Mr Dedalus at length, the rector, or provincial, rather, was telling me that story about you and Father Dolan. You're an impudent② thief, he said.

— O, he didn't, Simon!

— Not he! said Mr Dedalus. But he gave me a great account of the whole affair. We were chatting, you know, and one word borrowed another. And, by the way, who do you think he told me will get that job in the corporation? But I'll tell you that after. Well, as I was saying, we were chatting away quite friendly and he asked me did our friend

---

① you thickheaded ruffian：你这个没头没脑的小浑蛋 ② impudent：厚颜无耻的

here wear glasses still and then he told me the whole story.

— And was he annoyed, Simon?

— Annoyed? Not he! *Manly little chap*! [1] he said.

Mr Dedalus imitated the mincing nasal tone of the provincial.

Father Dolan and I, when I told them all at dinner about it, Father Dolan and I had a great laugh over it. *You better mind yourself Father Dolan*, said I, *or young Dedalus will send you up for twice nine*. We had a famous laugh together over it. Ha! Ha! Ha!

Mr Dedalus turned to his wife and interjected in his natural voice:

— Shows you the spirit in which they take the boys there. O, a jesuit for your life, for diplomacy!

He reassumed the provincial's voice and repeated:

— *I told them all at dinner about it and Father Dolan and I and all of us we had a hearty laugh together over it*. Ha! Ha! Ha!

The night of the Whitsuntide play[2] had come and Stephen from the window of the dressingroom looked out on the small grassplot across which lines of Chinese lanterns[3] were stretched. He watched the visitors come down the steps from the house and pass into the theatre. Stewards in evening dress, old Belvhedereans, loitered in groups about the entrance to the theatre and ushered in the visitors with ceremony. Under the sudden glow of a lantern he could recognize the smiling face of a priest.

The Blessed Sacrament had been removed from the tabernacle[4] and the first benches had been driven back so as to leave the dais of the altar[5] and the space before it free. Against the walls stood companies of barbells and In-

---

① *Manly little chap*：有男子汉气的小家伙　② the Whitsuntide play：降灵节的游艺晚会。　③ Chinese lanterns：中国式灯笼　④ The Blessed Sacrament had been removed from the tabernacle：圣餐台已从教堂里移了出去　⑤ the dais of the altar：祭坛的讲台

dian clubs[1]; the dumbbells were piled in one corner: and in the midst of countless hillocks of gymnasium shoes and sweaters and singlets in untidy brown parcels[2] there stood the stout leatherjacketed vaulting horse[3] waiting its turn to be carried up on the stage. A large bronze shield, tripped with silver, leaned against the panel of the altar also waiting its turn to be carried up on the stage and set in the middle of the winning team at the end of the gymnastic display[4].

Stephen, though in deference to[5] his reputation for essay-writing he had been elected secretary to the gymnasium, had had no part in the first section of the programme but in the play which formed the second section he had the chief part, that of a farcical pedagogue[6]. He had been cast for it on account of his stature and grave manners for he was now at the end of his second year at Belvedere and in number two.

A score of the younger boys in white knickers and singlets came pattering down from the stage, through the vestry and into the chapel. The vestry and chapel were peopled with eager masters and boys. The plump bald sergeantmajor[7] was testing with his foot the springboard of the vaulting horse. The lean young man in a long overcoat, who was to give a special display of intricate club swinging, stood near watching with interest, his silvercoated clubs peeping out of his deep sidepockets. The hollow rattle of the wooden dumbbells was heard as another team made ready to go up on the stage: and in another moment the excited prefect was hustling the boys through the vestry like a flock of geese, flapping the wings of his soutane nervously and crying to the laggards to make haste[8]. A little troop of

---

① barbells and Indian clubs：杠铃和体操用的棍棒　② in the ... brown parcels：在堆成山的运动鞋、运动服及用脏乎乎的棕色纸包裹着的汗衫中　③ the stout leatherjacketed vaulting horse：皮面的高大跳马　④ the gymnastic display：体育表演　⑤ in deference to：遵从　⑥ a farcical pedagogue：滑稽可笑的教员　⑦ The plump bald sergeantmajor：秃头的胖军士长　⑧ flapping the ... make haste：紧张地拍着法衣的袖子，催促落在后面的孩子加快脚步。

Neapolitan peasants were practising their steps at the end of the chapel, some circling their arms above their heads, some swaying their baskets of paper violets and curtseying[①]. In a dark corner of the chapel at the gospel side of the altar a stout old lady knelt amid her copious black skirts. When she stood up a pinkdressed figure, wearing a curly golden wig and an oldfashioned straw sunbonnet, with black pencilled eyebrows and cheeks delicately rouged and powdered, was discovered. A low murmur of curiosity ran round the chapel at the discovery of this girlish figure. One of the prefects, smiling and nodding his head, approached the dark corner and, having bowed to the stout old lady, said pleasantly:

— Is this a beautiful young lady or a doll that you have here, Mrs Tallon?

Then, bending down to peer at the smiling painted face under the leaf of the bonnet, he exclaimed:

— No! Upon my word I believe it's little Bertie Tallon after all!

Stephen at his post by the window heard the old lady and the priest laugh together and heard the boys' murmur of admiration behind him as they passed forward to see the little boy who had to dance the sunbonnet dance by himself. A movement of impatience escaped him. He let the edge of the blind fall and, stepping down from the bench on which he had been standing, walked out of the chapel.

He passed out of the schoolhouse and halted under the shed that flanked the garden. From the theatre opposite came the muffled noise of the audience and sudden brazen clashes of the soldiers' band[②]. The light spread upwards from the glass roof making the theatre seem a festive ark[③], anchored among the hulks of houses, her frail cables of lanterns looping her to her moorings. A sidedoor of the theatre opened suddenly and a shaft of light[④] flew across the

---

① some swaying ... and curtseying：摇晃着他们用紫罗兰纸花做成的花篮，行屈膝礼。　② sudden brazen clashes of the soldiers' band：士兵乐队演奏时铜乐器突然相碰的声音　③ a festive ark：节日方舟　④ a shaft of light：一束光线

grassplots. A sudden burst of music issued from the ark, the prelude of a waltz: and when the sidedoor closed again the listener could hear the faint rhythm of the music. The sentiment of the opening bars, their languor and supple movement, evoked the incommunicable emotion which had been the cause of all his day's unrest and of his impatient movement of a moment before. His unrest issued from him like a wave of sound: and on the tide of flowing music the ark was journeying, trailing her cables of lanterns in her wake. Then a noise like dwarf artillery① broke the movement. It was the clapping that greeted the entry of the dumbbell team on the stage.

At the far end of the shed near the street a speck of pink light showed in the darkness and as he walked towards it he became aware of a faint aromatic odour②. Two boys were standing in the shelter of a doorway, smoking, and before he reached them he had recognized Heron by his voice.

— Here comes the noble Dedalus! cried a high throaty voice. Welcome to our trusty friend!

This welcome ended in a soft peal of mirthless laughter as Heron salaamed③ and then began to poke the ground with his cane.

— Here I am, said Stephen, halting and glancing from Heron to his friend.

The latter was a stranger to him but in the darkness, by the aid of the glowing cigarettetips, he could make out a pale dandyish face④, over which a smile was travelling slowly, a tall overcoated figure and a hard hat. Heron did not trouble himself about an introduction but said instead:

— I was just telling my friend Wallis what a lark it would be tonight if you took off the rector in the part of the schoolmaster. It would be a ripping good joke.

---

① like dwarf artillery: 仿佛隆隆的小炮声　② a faint aromatic odour: 一股淡淡的幽香　③ Heron salaamed: 赫伦向他行额手礼　④ a pale dandyish face: 一张苍白的、花花公子的脸

Heron made a poor attempt to imitate for his friend Wallis the rector's pedantic bass① and then, laughing at his failure, asked Stephen to do it.

— Go on, Dedalus, he urged, you can take him off rippingly②. *He that will not hear the churcha let him be to theea as the heathena and the publicana*.

The imitation was prevented by a mild expression of anger from Wallis in whose mouthpiece the cigarette had become too tightly wedged.

— Damn this blankety blank holder, he said, taking it from his mouth and smiling and frowning upon it tolerantly. It's always getting stuck like that. Do you use a holder?

— I don't smoke, answered Stephen.

— No, said Heron, Dedalus is a model youth. He doesn't smoke and he doesn't go to bazaars and he doesn't flirt and he doesn't damn anything or damn all.

Stephen shook his head and smiled in his rival's flushed and mobile face, beaked like a bird's③. He had often thought it strange that Vincent Heron had a bird's face as well as a bird's name④. A shock of pale hair lay on the forehead like a ruffled crest: the forehead was narrow and bony and a thin hooked nose stood out between the closest prominent eyes which were light and inexpressive. The rivals were school friends. They sat together in class, knelt together in the chapel, talked together after beads over their lunches⑤. As the fellows in number one were undistinguished dullards⑥ Stephen and Heron had been during the year the virtual heads of the school. It was they who went up to the rector together to ask for a free day or to get a fellow off⑦.

— O by the way, said Heron suddenly, I saw your

---

① pedantic bass: 卖弄学问的低沉的声音　② you can take him off rippingly: 你模仿他绝对会惟妙惟肖　③ beaked like a bird's: 嘴尖得像鸟嘴一样　④ a bird's name: 因为 heron 在英语中是"苍鹭"的意思　⑤ after beads over their lunches: 在午饭祷告后　⑥ undistinguished dullards: 不起眼的笨孩子　⑦ to get a fellow off: 请求饶恕某个同学

governor going in.

The smile waned on Stephen's face. Any illusion made to his father by a fellow or by a master put his calm to rout in a moment. He waited in timorous silence[①] to hear what Heron might say next. Heron, however, nudged him expressively with his elbow and said:

— You're a sly dog, Dedalus!

— Why so? said Stephen.

— You'd think butter wouldn't melt in your mouth said Heron. But I'm afraid you're a sly dog.

— Might I ask you what you are talking about? said Stephen urbanely.

— Indeed you might, answered Heron. We saw her, Wallis, didn't we? And deucedly pretty[②] she is too. And so inquisitive! *And what part does Stephen take, Mr Dedalus? And will Stephen not sing, Mr Dedalus?* Your governor was staring at her through that eyeglass of his for all he was worth so that I think the old man has found you out too. I wouldn't care a bit, by Jove. She's ripping[③], isn't she, Wallis?

— Not half bad, answered Wallis quietly as he placed his holder once more in a corner of his mouth.

A shaft of momentary anger flew through Stephen's mind at these indelicate allusions in the hearing of a stranger. For him there was nothing amusing in a girl's interest and regard. All day he had thought of nothing but their leavetaking on the steps of the tram at Harold's Cross, the stream of moody emotions it had made to course through him and the poem he had written about it. All day he had imagined a new meeting with her for he knew that she was to come to the play. The old restless moodiness had again filled his breast as it had done on the night of the party but had not found an outlet in verse. The growth and knowledge of two years of boyhood stood between then and

---

① He waited in timorous silence：他怯生生地、默默地等着　② deucedly pretty：漂亮极了　③ She's ripping：她真棒

now, forbidding such an outlet: and all day the stream of gloomy tenderness within him had started forth and returned upon itself in dark courses and eddies, wearying him in the end until the pleasantry of the prefect and the painted little boy had drawn from him a movement of impatience.

— So you may as well admit, Heron went on, that we've fairly found you out this time. You can't play the saint on me any more, that's one sure five.

A soft peal of mirthless laughter escaped from his lips and, bending down as before, he struck Stephen lightly across the calf of the leg① with his cane, as if in jesting reproof.

Stephen's movement of anger had already passed. He was neither flattered nor confused, but simply wished the banter② to end. He scarcely resented what had seemed to him at first a silly indelicateness for he knew that the adventure in his mind stood in no danger from these words: and his face mirrored his rival's false smile.

— Admit! repeated Heron, striking him again with his cane across the calf of the leg.

The stroke was playful but not so lightly given as the first had been. Stephen felt the skin tingle and glow slightly and almost painlessly; and bowing submissively, as if to meet his companion's jesting mood, began to recite the *Confiteor*③. The episode ended well, for both Heron and Wallis laughed indulgently at the irreverence④.

The confession came only from Stephen's lips and, while they spoke the words, a sudden memory had carried him to another scene called up, as if by magic, at the moment when he had noted the faint cruel dimples⑤ at the corners of Heron's smiling lips and had felt the familiar

---

① the calf of the leg: 小腿 ② banter: 取笑 ③ *Confiteor*: 信徒在做忏悔之前通常要背的祈祷词 ④ laughed indulgently at the irreverence: 对这种不敬的行为(他们)纵声大笑起来 ⑤ dimples: 笑窝

stroke of the cane against his calf and had heard the familiar word of admonition[1]:

— Admit.

It was towards the close of his first term in the college when he was in number six. His sensitive nature was still smarting under the lashes of an undivined and squalid way of life[2]. His soul was still disquieted and cast down by the dull phenomenon of Dublin. He had emerged from a two years' spell of revery to find himself in the midst of a new scene, every event and figure of which affected him intimately, disheartened him or allured and, whether alluring or disheartening, filled him always with unrest and bitter thoughts. All the leisure which his school life left him was passed in the company of subversive writers[3] whose gibes and violence of speech set up a ferment in his brain before they passed out of it into his crude writings.

The essay was for him the chief labour of his week and every Tuesday, as he marched from home to the school, he read his fate in the incidents of the way, pitting himself against some figure ahead of him and quickening his pace to outstrip it before a certain goal was reached or planting his steps scrupulously[4] in the spaces of the patchwork of the footpath and telling himself that he would be first and not first in the weekly essay.

On a certain Tuesday the course of his crossed triumphs was rudely broken. Mr Tate, the English master, pointed his finger at him and said bluntly:

— This fellow has heresy in his essay[5].

A hush fell on the class[6]. Mr Tate did not break it but dug with his hand between his crossed thighs while his heavily starched linen creaked about his neck and wrists[7].

---

① admonition：劝戒　② squalid way of life：贫穷的生活方式　③ subversive writers：具有反抗性的作家　④ scrupulously：一丝不苟地　⑤ This fellow ... his essay：这个学生在他的作文里宣扬了异端邪说　⑥ A hush fell on the class：教室里顿时鸦雀无声　⑦ his heavily ... and wrists：他浆得硬邦邦的亚麻衬衣在颈部和腰部嘎嘎作响

Stephen did not look up. It was a raw spring morning and his eyes were still smarting and weak. He was conscious of failure and of detection, of the squalor of his own mind and home, and felt against his neck the raw edge of his turned and jagged collar.

A short loud laugh from Mr Tate set the class more at ease.

— Perhaps you didn't know that, he said.

— Where? asked Stephen.

Mr Tate withdrew his delving hand and spread out the essay.

— Here. It's about the Creator and the soul. Rrm . . . rrm . . . rrm . . . Ah! *without a possibility of ever approaching nearer*. That's heresy.

Stephen murmured:

— I meant *without a possibility of ever reaching*.

It was a submission and Mr Tate, appeased, folded up the essay and passed it across to him, saying:

— O . . . Ah! *ever reaching*. That's another story.

But the class was not so soon appeased. Though nobody spoke to him of the affair after class he could feel about him a vague general malignant joy[1].

A few nights after this public chiding he was walking with a letter along the Drumcondra Road when he heard a voice cry:

— Halt!

He turned and saw three boys of his own class coming towards him in the dusk. It was Heron who had called out and, as he marched forward between his two attendants, he cleft the air before him with a thin cane, in time to their steps[2]. Boland, his friend, marched beside him, a large grin on his face, while Nash came on a few steps behind, blowing from the pace[3] and wagging his great red head.

---

① he could ... malignant joy: 他觉出周围的同学有一种隐隐的幸灾乐祸的情绪 ② he cleft ... their steps: 他边走边晃动着手杖, 为他们的脚步打着拍子。 ③ blowing from the pace: 由于跟不上而呼呼直喘气

As soon as the boys had turned into Clonliffe Road together they began to speak about books and writers, saying what books they were reading and how many books there were in their fathers' bookcases at home. Stephen listened to them in some wonderment for Boland was the dunce① and Nash the idler of the class. In fact, after some talk about their favourite writers, Nash declared for Captain Marryat② who, he said, was the greatest writer.

— Fudge! said Heron. Ask Dedalus. Who is the greatest writer, Dedalus?

Stephen noted the mockery in the question and said:

— Of prose do you mean?

— Yes.

— Newman③, I think.

— Is it Cardinal Newman? asked Boland.

— Yes, answered Stephen.

The grin broadened on Nash's freckled face as he turned to Stephen and said:

— And do you like Cardinal Newman, Dedalus?

— O, many say that Newman has the best prose style, Heron said to the other two in explanation. Of course he's not a poet.

— And who is the best poet, Heron? asked Boland.

— Lord Tennyson④, of course, answered Heron.

— O, yes, Lord Tennyson, said Nash. We have all his poetry at home in a book.

At this Stephen forgot the silent vows⑤ he had been making and burst out:

— Tennyson a poet! Why, he's only a rhymester⑥!

— O, get out! said Heron. Everyone knows that

---

① dunce: 笨人　② Captain Marryat: Frederick Marryat (1792－1848)，英国皇家海军军官，写了一些适合男孩口味的海上冒险故事。　③ Newman: 约翰·亨利·纽曼(1801－1890)，英国传教士，后被罗马天主教任命为红衣主教，他的关于宗教的文章，风格优雅而雄辩。　④ Lord Tennyson: 丁尼生(1809－1892)，英国维多利亚时期诗人。　⑤ forgot the silent vows: 忘记了要保持沉默的誓言　⑥ rhymester: 作打油诗的人

Tennyson is the greatest poet.

— And who do you think is the greatest poet? asked Boland, nudging his neighbour.

— Byron, of course, answered Stephen.

Heron gave the lead and all three joined in a scornful laugh[1].

— What are you laughing at? asked Stephen.

— You, said Heron. Byron the greatest poet! He's only a poet for uneducated people.

— He must be a fine poet! said Boland.

— You may keep your mouth shut, said Stephen, turning on him boldly. All you know about poetry is what you wrote up on the slates in the yard[2] and were going to be sent to the loft for.

Boland, in fact, was said to have written on the slates in the yard a couplet about a classmate of his who often rode home from the college on a pony:

As Tyson was riding into Jerusalem
He fell and hurt his Alec Kafoozelum.

This thrust put the two lieutenants to silence but Heron went on:

— In any case Byron was a heretic and immoral[3] too.

— I don't care what he was, cried Stephen hotly.

— You don't care whether he was a heretic or not? said Nash.

— What do you know about it? shouted Stephen. You never read a line of anything in your life except a trans, or Boland either.

— I know that Byron was a bad man, said Boland.

— Here, catch hold of this heretic, Heron called out.

In a moment Stephen was a prisoner.

— Tate made you buck up the other day, Heron went

---

① a scornful laugh: 一阵讥讽的大笑 ② the slates in the yard: 学校院子里的石板 ③ Byron was a heretic and immoral: 拜伦是个异端分子而且还不道德。

on, about the heresy in your essay.

— I'll tell him tomorrow, said Boland.

— Will you? said Stephen. You'd be afraid to open your lips.

— Afraid?

— Ay. Afraid of your life.

— Behave yourself! cried Heron, cutting at Stephen's legs with his cane.

It was the signal for their onset[①]. Nash pinioned his arms behind while Boland seized a long cabbage stump which was lying in the gutter. Struggling and kicking under the cuts of the cane and the blows of the knotty stump Stephen was borne back against a barbed wire fence[②].

— Admit that Byron was no good.

— No.

— Admit.

— No.

— Admit.

— No. No.

At last after a fury of plunges he wrenched himself free[③]. His tormentors set off towards Jones's Road, laughing and jeering at him, while he, torn and flushed and panting, stumbled after them half blinded with tears, clenching his fists madly and sobbing.

While he was still repeating the *Confiteor* amid the indulgent laughter of his hearers and while the scenes of that malignant episode were still passing sharply and swiftly before his mind he wondered why he bore no malice now to those who had tormented him. He had not forgotten a whit of their cowardice and cruelty but the memory of it called forth no anger from him. All the descriptions of fierce love and hatred which he had met in books had seemed to him

---

① It was the signal for their onset: 这是他们发起攻击的信号。   ② a barbed wire fence: 有刺的铁丝网栅栏   ③ At last after a fury of plunges he wrenched himself free: 经过一番拼命挣扎，他终于挣脱了。

therefore unreal. Even that night as he stumbled home-
wards along Jones's Road he had felt that some power was
divesting him of that suddenwoven anger① as easily as a
fruit is divested of its soft ripe peel.

He remained standing with his two companions at the
end of the shed listening idly to their talk or to the bursts of
applause in the theatre. She was sitting there among the
others perhaps waiting for him to appear. He tried to recall
her appearance but could not. He could remember only that
she had worn a shawl about her head like a cowl② and that
her dark eyes had invited and unnerved him. He wondered
had he been in her thoughts as she had been in his. Then in
the dark and unseen by the other two he rested the tips of
the fingers of one hand upon the palm of the other hand,
scarcely touching it and yet pressing upon it lightly. But
the pressure of her fingers had been lighter and steadier:
and suddenly the memory of their touch traversed his brain
and body like an invisible warm wave.

A boy came towards them, running along under the
shed. He was excited and breathless.

— O, Dedalus, he cried, Doyle is in a great bake
about you③. You're to go in at once and get dressed for the
play. Hurry up, you better.

— He's coming now, said Heron to the messenger
with a haughty drawl④, when he wants to.

The boy turned to Heron and repeated:

— But Doyle is in an awful bake.

— Will you tell Doyle with my best compliments that
I damned his eyes? answered Heron.

— Well, I must go now, said Stephen, who cared little for such points of honour.

— I wouldn't, said Heron, damn me if I would.

---

① some power was divesting him of that suddenwoven anger: 某种力量正
在从他身上剥去他那种突然发怒的情绪 ② she had worn a shawl about her
head like a cowl: 她曾把披肩当作头巾罩在头上 ③ is in a great bake about
you: 正因为你而大为恼火 ④ a haughty drawl: 傲慢的拉长的声音

That's no way to send for one of the senior boys. In a bake, indeed! I think it's quite enough that you're taking a part in his bally old play①.

This spirit of quarrelsome comradeship which he had observed lately in his rival had not seduced Stephen from his habits of quiet obedience. He mistrusted the turbulence and doubted the sincerity of such comradeship which seemed to him a sorry anticipation of manhood②. The question of honour here raised was, like all such questions, trivial to him. While his mind had been pursuing its intangible phantoms③ and turning in irresolution from such pursuit he had heard about him the constant voices of his father and of his masters, urging him to be a gentleman above all things and urging him to be a good catholic above all things. These voices had now come to be hollowsounding in his ears. When the gymnasium had been opened he had heard another voice urging him to be strong and manly and healthy and when the movement towards national revival had begun to be felt in the college yet another voice had bidden him be true to his country and help to raise up her fallen language and tradition④. In the profane world, as he foresaw, a worldly voice would bid him raise up his father's fallen state by his labours and, meanwhile, the voice of his school comrades urged him to be a decent fellow, to shield others from blame or to beg them off⑤ and to do his best to get free days for the school. And it was the din of all these hollowsounding voices that made him halt irresolutely in the pursuit of phantoms. He gave them ear only for a time but he was happy only when he was far from them, beyond their call, alone or in the company of phantasmal comrades.

---

① it's quite ... old play：你肯在他那部老破戏里演一个角色就已经够意思了。 ② which seemed to him a sorry anticipation of manhood：这让他难过地预知到成年后的情形 ③ intangible phantoms：触摸不到的幻象 ④ help to raise up her fallen language and tradition：帮助复兴爱尔兰失落的语言和传统 ⑤ beg them off：替他们说情

In the vestry a plump freshfaced jesuit and an elderly man, in shabby blue clothes, were dabbling in a case of paints and chalks①. The boys who had been painted walked about or stood still awkwardly, touching their faces in a gingerly fashion with their furtive fingertips. In the middle of the vestry a young jesuit, who was then on a visit to the college, stood rocking himself rhythmically from the tips of his toes to his heels and back again, his hands thrust well forward into his sidepockets. His small head set off with glossy red curls and his newly shaven face agreed well with the spotless decency of his soutane and with his spotless shoes.

As he watched this swaying form and tried to read for himself the legend of the priest's mocking smile there came into Stephen's memory a saying which he had heard from his father before he had been sent to Clongowes, that you could always tell a jesuit by the style of his clothes. At the same moment he thought he saw a likeness between his father's mind and that of this smiling welldressed priest: and he was aware of some desecration② of the priest's office or of the vestry itself, whose silence was now routed by loud talk and joking and its air pungent with the smells of the gasjets and the grease③.

While his forehead was being wrinkled and his jaws painted black and blue by the elderly man, he listened distractedly to the voice of the plump young jesuit which bade him speak up and make his points clearly. He could hear the band playing *The Lily of Killarney*④ and knew that in a few moments the curtain would go up. He felt no stage fright⑤ but the thought of the part he had to play humiliated him. A remembrance of some of his lines made a sudden flush rise to his painted cheeks. He saw her serious alluring

---

① were dabbling in a case of paints and chalks：正在一个盒子里调油彩和白粉　② desecration：亵渎　③ its air pungent with the smells of the gasjets and the grease：空气混杂了煤气灯和油彩发出的刺鼻的味道　④ *The Lily of Killarney*：《基拉尔尼的百合花》　⑤ stage fright：怯场

eyes watching him from among the audience and their image at once swept away his scruples, leaving his will compact①. Another nature seemed to have been lent him: the infection of the excitement and youth about him entered into and transformed his moody mistrustfulness. For one rare moment he seemed to be clothed in the real apparel of boyhood: and, as he stood in the wings among the other players, he shared the common mirth amid which the drop scene was hauled upwards by two ablebodied priests with violent jerks and all awry②.

A few moments after he found himself on the stage amid the garish gas③ and the dim scenery, acting before the innumerable faces of the void. It surprised him to see that the play which he had known at rehearsals for a disjointed lifeless thing had suddenly assumed a life of its own. It seemed now to play itself, he and his fellow actors aiding it with their parts. When the curtain fell on the last scene he heard the void filled with applause and, through a rift in the side scene, saw the simple body before which he had acted magically deformed, the void of faces breaking at all points and falling asunder into busy groups.

He left the stage quickly and rid himself of his mummery④ and passed out through the chapel into the college garden. Now that the play was over his nerves cried for some further adventure. He hurried onwards as if to overtake it. The doors of the theatre were all open and the audience had emptied out. On the lines which he had fancied the moorings of an ark a few lanterns swung in the night breeze, flickering cheerlessly. He mounted the steps from the garden in haste, eager that some prey should not elude him, and forced his way through the crowd in the hall and past the two jesuits who stood watching the exodus⑤ and

---

① leaving his will compact: 使他的意志坚强起来 ② awry: 歪歪斜斜的 ③ amid the garish gas: 在五光十色的煤气灯下 ④ rid himself of his mummery: 抛开逗乐的表演 ⑤ the exodus: 成群离去的观众

bowing and shaking hands with the visitors. He pushed onward nervously, feigning a still greater haste and faintly conscious of the smiles and stares and nudges which his powdered head left in its wake.

When he came out on the steps he saw his family waiting for him at the first lamp. In a glance he noted that every figure of the group was familiar and ran down the steps angrily.

— I have to leave a message down in George's Street, he said to his father quickly. I'll be home after you.

Without waiting for his father's questions he ran across the road and began to walk at breakneck speed[①] down the hill. He hardly knew where he was walking. Pride and hope and desire like crushed herbs in his heart sent up vapours of maddening incense before the eyes of his mind. He strode down the hill amid the tumult of sudden-risen vapours of wounded pride and fallen hope and baffled desire. They streamed upwards before his anguished eyes in dense and maddening fumes and passed away above him till at last the air was clear and cold again.

A film still veiled his eyes but they burned no longer. A power, akin to that which had often made anger or resentment fall from him, brought his steps to rest. He stood still and gazed up at the sombre porch of the morgue[②] and from that to the dark cobbled laneway[③] at its side. He saw the word *Lotts* on the wall of the lane and breathed slowly the rank heavy air[④].

— That is horse piss and rotted straw[⑤], he thought. It is a good odour to breathe. It will calm my heart. My heart is quite calm now. I will go back.

Stephen was once again seated beside his father in the corner of a railway carriage at Kingsbridge. He was travel-

---

① at breakneck speed: 以危险的高速 ② the sombre porch of the morgue: 陈尸所阴暗的门廊 ③ the dark cobbled laneway: 铺着鹅卵石的黑暗的小巷 ④ the rank heavy air: 发着腥臭的阴沉的空气 ⑤ That is horse piss and rotted straw: 那是马尿和烂稻草的味道。

ling with his father by the night mail to Cork. As the train steamed out of the station he recalled his childish wonder of years before and every event of his first day at Clongowes. But he felt no wonder now. He saw the darkening lands slipping past him, the silent telegraphpoles passing his window swiftly every four seconds, the little glimmering stations, manned by a few silent sentries①, flung by the mail behind her② and twinkling for a moment in the darkness like fiery grains flung backwards by a runner.

He listened without sympathy to his father's evocation of Cork and of scenes of his youth, a tale broken by sighs or draughts from his pocketflask③ whenever the image of some dead friend appeared in it or whenever the evoker remembered suddenly the purpose of his actual visit. Stephen heard but could feel no pity. The images of the dead were all strange to him save that of uncle Charles, an image which had lately been fading out of memory. He knew, however, that his father's property was going to be sold by auction④ and in the manner of his own dispossession⑤ he felt the world give the lie rudely to his phantasy.

At Maryborough he fell asleep. When he awoke the train had passed out of Mallow and his father was stretched asleep on the other seat. The cold light of the dawn lay over the country, over the unpeopled fields and the closed cottages. The terror of sleep fascinated his mind as he watched the silent country or heard from time to time his father's deep breath or sudden sleepy movement. The neighbourhood of unseen sleepers filled him with strange dread as though they could harm him; and he prayed that the day might come quickly. His prayer, addressed neither to God nor saint, began with a shiver, as the chilly morning breeze crept through the chink of the carriage door⑥ to

---

① sentries: 警卫　② flung by the mail behind her: 被邮车抛在后面　③ broken by ... pocketflask: 被几声叹息或从口袋里掏出酒瓶喝上几口的动作所打断　④ be sold by auction: 被拍卖出售　⑤ in the manner of his own dispossession: 这样做也是在剥夺他的所有权　⑥ the chink of the carriage door: 车厢门口的缝隙

his feet, and ended in a trail of foolish words which he made to fit the insistent rhythm of the train; and silently, at intervals of four seconds, the telegraphpoles held the galloping notes of the music between punctual bars. This furious music allayed his dread[1] and, leaning against the windowledge, he let his eyelids close again.

They drove in a jingle[2] across Cork while it was still early morning and Stephen finished his sleep in a bedroom of the Victoria Hotel. The bright warm sunlight was streaming through the window and he could hear the din of traffic[3]. His father was standing before the dressingtable, examining his hair and face and moustache with great care, craning his neck across the waterjug and drawing it back sideways to see the better. While he did so he sang softly to himself with quaint accent and phrasing:

> 'Tis youth and folly
> Makes young men marry,
> So here, my love, I'll
>   No longer stay.
> What can't be cured, sure,
> Must be injured, sure,
>   So I'll go to
>   Amerikay.

> My love she's handsome,
> My love she's bonny[4]:
> She's like good whisky
>   When it is new;
> But when 'tis old
> And growing cold
> It fades and dies like
> The mountain dew.

The consciousness of the warm sunny city outside his

---

① allayed his dread: 减轻了他的恐惧　② jingle: 有顶两轮马车
③ the din of traffic: 交通的喧闹声　④ bonny: 美丽的

window and the tender tremors[1] with which his father's voice festooned the strange sad happy air, drove off all the mists of the night's ill humour from Stephen's brain. He got up quickly to dress and, when the song had ended, said:

— That's much prettier than any of your other *come-all-yous*[2].

— Do you think so? asked Mr Dedalus.

— I like it, said Stephen.

— It's a pretty old air, said Mr Dedalus, twirling the points of his moustache. Ah, but you should have heard Mick Lacy sing it! Poor Mick Lacy! He had little turns for it, grace notes that he used to put in that I haven't got. That was the boy who could sing a *come-all-you*, if you like.

Mr Dedalus had ordered drisheens for breakfast and during the meal he crossexamined the waiter for local news[3]. For the most part they spoke at crosspurposes[4] when a name was mentioned, the waiter having in mind the present holder and Mr Dedalus his father or perhaps his grandfather.

— Well, I hope they haven't moved the Queen's College anyhow, said Mr Dedalus, for I want to show it to this youngster of mine.

Along the Mardyke the trees were in bloom. They entered the grounds of the college and were led by the garrulous porter across the quadrangle[5]. But their progress across the gravel was brought to a halt after every dozen or so paces by some reply of the porter's.

— Ah, do you tell me so? And is poor Pottlebelly dead?

— Yes, sir. Dead, sir.

---

① the tender tremors: 柔和的颤音　② *come-all-yous*: 指街头流浪艺人唱的歌　③ crossexamined the waiter for local news: 仔细向侍者询问了当地的新闻　④ crosspurposes: 相互误解　⑤ led by the garrulous porter across the quadrangle: 一个唠唠叨叨的工友带着他们穿过广场

During these halts Stephen stood awkwardly behind the two men, weary of the subject and waiting restlessly for the slow march to begin again. By the time they had crossed the quadrangle his restlessness had risen to fever. He wondered how his father, whom he knew for a shrewd suspicious man[1], could be duped[2] by the servile manners of the porter; and the lively southern speech which had entertained him all the morning now irritated his ears.

They passed into the anatomy theatre[3] where Mr Dedalus, the porter aiding him, searched the desks for his initials. Stephen remained in the background, depressed more than ever by the darkness and silence of the theatre and by the air it wore of jaded and formal study. On the desk he read the word *Foetus*[4] cut several times in the dark stained wood. The sudden legend startled his blood: he seemed to feel the absent students of the college about him and to shrink from their company. A vision of their life, which his father's words had been powerless to evoke, sprang up before him out of the word cut in the desk. A broadshouldered student with a moustache was cutting in the letters with a jackknife, seriously. Other students stood or sat near him laughing at his handiwork. One jogged his elbow[5]. The big student turned on him, frowning. He was dressed in loose grey clothes and had tan boots.

Stephen's name was called. He hurried down the steps of the theatre so as to be as far away from the vision as he could be and, peering closely at his father's initials, hid his flushed face.

But the word and the vision capered before his eyes[6] as he walked back across the quadrangle and towards the college gate. It shocked him to find in the outer world a trace of what he had deemed till then a brutish and individ-

---

① a shrewd suspicious man: 一个精明多疑的人　② be duped: 被愚弄
③ the anatomy theatre: 解剖示范室　④ *Foetus*:. 胎儿　⑤ One jogged his elbow: 一个学生轻碰了一下他的胳膊肘　⑥ capered before his eyes: 在他眼前跳跃

ual malady of his own mind. His recent monstrous reveries came thronging into his memory. They too had sprung up before him, suddenly and furiously, out of mere words. He had soon given into them and allowed them to sweep across and abase his intellect, wondering always where they came from, from what den of monstrous images[①], and always weak and humble towards others, restless and sickened of himself when they had swept over him.

— Ay, bedad! And there's the Groceries[②] sure e-nough! cried Mr Dedalus. You often heard me speak of the Groceries, didn't you, Stephen. Many's the time we went down there when our names had been marked, a crowd of us, Harry Peard and little Jack Mountain and Bob Dyas and Maurice Moriarty, the Frenchman, and Tom O'Grady and Mick Lacy that I told you of this morning and Joey Corbet and poor little goodhearted Johnny Keevers of the Tantiles.

The leaves of the trees along the Mardyke were astir and whispering in the sunlight. A team of cricketers passed, agile young men in flannels and blazers[③], one of them carrying the long green wicketbag. In a quiet bystreet a German band of five players in faded uniforms and with battered brass instruments[④] was playing to an audience of street arabs and leisurely messenger boys. A maid in a white cap and apron was watering a box of plants on a sill which shone like a slab of limestone[⑤] in the warm glare. From another window open to the air came the sound of a piano, scale after scale rising into the treble[⑥].

Stephen walked on at his father's side, listening to stories he had heard before, hearing again the names of the scattered and dead revellers who had been the companions

---

① from what den of monstrous images: 来自于一个产生怪异形象的什么洞穴 ② the Groceries: 指可以卖酒的食品杂货店 ③ A team ... and blazers: 一队板球队员走了过去, 他们是一帮穿着法兰绒上衣和运动装的活泼的年轻人。 ④ battered brass instruments: 破旧的铜管乐器 ⑤ a slab of limestone: 石灰石石板 ⑥ scale after scale rising into the treble: 一个音阶一个音阶地高上去, 直到最高音部。

of his father's youth. And a faint sickness sighed in his heart. He recalled his own equivocal position in Belvedere, a free boy, a leader afraid of his own authority, proud and sensitive and suspicious, battling against the squalor of his life and against the riot of his mind. The letters cut in the stained wood of the desk stared upon him, mocking his bodily weakness and futile enthusiasms and making him loathe himself for his own mad and filthy orgies[1]. The spittle in his throat grew bitter and fowl to swallow and the faint sickness climbed to his brain so that for a moment he closed his eyes and walked on in darkness.

He could still hear his father's voice.

— When you kick out for yourself, Stephen — as I daresay you will one of these days — remember, whatever you do, to mix with gentlemen. When I was a young fellow I tell you I enjoyed myself. I mixed with fine decent fellows. Everyone of us could do something. One fellow had a good voice, another fellow was a good actor, another could sing a good comic song, another was a good oarsman or a good racketplayer, another could tell a good story and so on. We kept the ball rolling[2] anyhow and enjoyed ourselves and saw a bit of life and we were none the worse of it either. But we were all gentlemen, Stephen — at least I hope we were — and bloody good honest Irishmen too. That's the kind of fellows I want you to associate with, fellows of the right kidney[3]. I'm talking to you as a friend, Stephen, I don't believe in playing the stern father. I don't believe a son should be afraid of his father. No, I treat you as your grandfather treated me when I was a young chap. We were more like brothers than father and son. I'll never forget the first day he caught me smoking. I was standing at the end of the South Terrace one day with some maneens like myself and sure we thought we were grand fellows be-

---

① filthy orgies：污秽的放荡行为　② kept the ball rolling：不使活动中
断　③ fellows of the right kidney：一些好脾气的人

cause we had pipes stuck in the corners of our mouths. Suddenly the governor passed. He didn't say a word, or stop even. But the next day, Sunday, we were out for a walk together and when we were coming home he took out his cigar case and said: *By the by, Simon, I didn't know you smoked* : or something like that. — Of course I tried to carry it off as best I could[①]. *If you want a good smoke*, he said, *try one of these cigars. An American captain made me a present of them last night in Queenstown*.

Stephen heard his father's voice break into a laugh which was almost a sob.

— He was the handsomest man in Cork at that time, by God he was! The women used to stand to look after him in the street.

He heard the sob passing loudly down his father's throat and opened his eyes with a nervous impulse. The sunlight breaking suddenly on his sight turned the sky and clouds into a fantastic world of sombre masses with lakelike spaces of dark rosy light. His very brain was sick and powerless. He could scarcely interpret the letters of the signboards of the shops[②]. By his monstrous way of life he seemed to have put himself beyond the limits of reality. Nothing moved him or spoke to him from the real world unless he heard in it an echo of the infuriated cries within him[③]. He could respond to no earthly human appeal, dumb and insensible to the call of summer and gladness and companionship, wearied and dejected by his father's voice. He could scarcely recognize as his own thoughts, and repeated slowly to himself:

— I am Stephen Dedalus. I am walking beside my father whose name is Simon Dedalus. We are in Cork, in Ireland. Cork is a city. Our room is in the Victoria Hotel.

---

① I tried to carry it off as best I could: 我尽量装作若无其事地应付过去。 ② the signboards of the shops: 商店的广告牌 ③ an echo of the infuriated cries within him: 他内心狂喊的回音

Victoria and Stephen and Simon. Simon and Stephen and Victoria. Names.

The memory of his childhood suddenly grew dim. He tried to call forth some of its vivid moments but could not. He recalled only names: Dante, Parnell, Clane, Clongowes. A little boy had been taught geography by an old woman who kept two brushes in her wardrobe①. Then he had been sent away from home to a college. In the college he had made his first communion and eaten slim jim out of his cricket cap and watched the firelight leaping and dancing on the wall of a little bedroom in the infirmary and dreamed of being dead, of mass being said for him by the rector in a black and gold cope, of being buried then in the little graveyard of the community off the main avenue of limes. But he had not died then. Parnell had died. There had been no mass for the dead in the chapel and no procession. He had not died but he had faded out like a film in the sun. He had been lost or had wandered out of existence for he no longer existed. How strange to think of him passing out of existence in such a way, not by death but by fading out in the sun or by being lost and forgotten somewhere in the universe! It was strange to see his small body appear again for a moment: a little boy in a grey belted suit. His hands were in his sidepockets and his trousers were tucked in at the knees by elastic bands②.

On the evening of the day on which the property was sold Stephen followed his father meekly about the city from bar to bar. To the sellers in the market, to the barmen and barmaids, to the beggars who importuned him for a lob③ Mr Dedalus told the same tale, that he was an old Corkonian, that he had been trying for thirty years to get rid of his Cork accent up in Dublin and that Peter Pickackafax beside

---

① who kept two brushes in her wardrobe: 她的衣柜里有两把刷子
② elastic bands: 松紧带 ③ the beggars who importuned him for a lob: 缠着他向他讨点儿小钱的乞丐

him was his eldest son but that he was only a Dublin jack-een[①].

They had set out early in the morning from Newcombe's coffeehouse, where Mr Dedalus's cup had rattled noisily against its saucer, and Stephen had tried to cover that shameful sign of his father's drinkingbout[②] of the night before by moving his chair and coughing. One humiliation had succeeded another : the false smiles of the market sellers, the curvettings and oglings of the barmaids with whom his father flirted[③], the compliments and encouraging words of his father's friends. They had told him that he had a great look of his grandfather and Mr Dedalus had agreed that he was an ugly likeness. They had unearthed traces of a Cork accent in his speech and made him admit that the Lee was a much finer river than the Liffey. One of them in order to put his Latin to the proof had made him translate short passages from Dilectus[④] and asked him whether it was correct to say: *Tempora mutantur nos et mutamur in illis*[⑤] or *Tempora mutantur et nos mutamur in illis*[⑥]. Another, a brisk old man, whom Mr Dedalus called Johnny Cashman, had covered him with confusion by asking him to say which were prettier, the Dublin girls or the Cork girls.

— He's not that way built, said Mr Dedalus. Leave him alone. He's a levelheaded thinking boy[⑦] who doesn't bother his head about that kind of nonsense.

— Then he's not his father's son, said the little old man.

— I don't know, I'm sure, said Mr Dedalus, smiling complacently[⑧].

---

① a Dublin jackeen: 一个都柏林的无名小卒 ② drinkingbout: 酒宴 ③ the curvetings ... father flirted: 和向他抛媚眼的酒吧女招待调情 ④ Dilectus: 一本拉丁文摘选 ⑤ *Tempora ... in illis*: (拉丁文)时代改变了我们,同时我们也改变了。 ⑥ *Tempora ... in illis*: 这一句的音韵是正确的。意为: 时代变了,而我们也随着有所改变。 ⑦ He's a levelheaded thinking boy: 他是个头脑冷静、爱思考的孩子。 ⑧ smiling complacently: 得意地笑着

— Your father, said the little old man to Stephen, was the boldest flirt in the city of Cork in his day. Do you know that?

Stephen looked down and studied the tiled floor① of the bar into which they had drifted.

— Now don't be putting ideas into his head, said Mr Dedalus. Leave him to his Maker②.

— Yerra, sure I wouldn't put any ideas into his head. I'm old enough to be his grandfather. And I am a grandfather, said the little old man to Stephen. Do you know that?

— Are you? asked Stephen.

— Bedad I am, said the little old man. I have two bouncing grandchildren out at Sunday's Well. Now then! What age do you think I am? And I remember seeing your grandfather in his red coat riding out to hounds③. That was before you were born.

— Ay, or thought of, said Mr Dedalus.

— Bedad I did, repeated the little old man. And, more than that, I can remember even your greatgrandfather, old John Stephen Dedalus, and a fierce old fireeater he was④. Now then! There's a memory for you!

— That's three generations — four generations, said another of the company. Why, Johnny Cashman, you must be nearing the century⑤.

— Well, I'll tell you the truth, said the little old man. I'm just twenty-seven years of age.

— We're as old as we feel, Johnny, said Mr Dedalus. And just finish what you have there, and we'll have another. Here, Tim or Tom or whatever your name is, give us the same again here. By God, I don't feel more than eighteen myself. There's that son of mine there not half my age

---

① the tiled floor: 砖地   ② Leave him to his Maker: 让上帝去教导他吧。   ③ riding out to hounds: 骑马纵狗打猎   ④ a fierce old fireeater he was: 一个有着火爆脾气的老人。   ⑤ you must be nearing the century: 你一定快一百岁了。

and I'm a better man than he is any day of the week.

— Draw it mild now, Dedalus. I think it's time for you to take a back seat, said the gentleman who had spoken before.

— No, by God! asserted Mr Dedalus. I'll sing a tenor song against him or I'll vault a fivebarred gate against him① or I'll run with him after the hounds across the country as I did thirty years ago along with the Kerry Boy and the best man for it.

— But he'll beat you here, said the little old man, tapping his forehead and raising his glass to drain it.

— Well, I hope he'll be as good a man as his father. That's all I can say, said Mr Dedalus.

— If he is, he'll do, said the little old man.

— And thanks be to God, Johnny, said Mr Dedalus, that we lived so long and did so little harm.

— But did so much good, Simon, said the little old man gravely. Thanks be to God we lived so long and did so much good.

Stephen watched the three glasses being raised from the counter as his father and his two cronies② drank to the memory of their past. An abyss of fortune or of temperament sundered him from them③. His mind seemed older than theirs: it shone coldly on their strifes and happiness and regrets like a moon upon a younger earth. No life or youth stirred in him as it had stirred in them. He had known neither the pleasure of companionship with others nor the vigour of rude male health nor filial piety④. Nothing stirred within his soul but a cold and cruel and loveless lust. His childhood was dead or lost and with it his soul capable of simple joys, and he was drifting amid life like the barren shell of the moon.

---

① I'll sing ... against him：我可以跟他比赛唱一支男高音的歌，或比赛跳一个有五道杠的大门。　② cronies：老朋友　③ sundered him from them：把他与他们分开　④ nor filial piety：更不知道什么父子之道

Art thou pale for weariness
Of climbing heaven and gazing on the earth,
Wandering companionless ... ?

He repeated to himself the lines of Shelley's[①] fragment. Its alternation of sad human ineffectualness with vast inhuman cycles of activity chilled him, and he forgot his own human and ineffectual grieving.

Stephen's mother and his brother and one of his cousins waited at the corner of quiet Foster Place while he and his father went up the steps and along the colonnade[②] where the Highland sentry was parading. When they had passed into the great hall and stood at the counter Stephen drew forth his orders[③] on the governor of the bank of Ireland for thirty and three pounds; and these sums, the moneys of his exhibition and essay prize, were paid over to him rapidly by the teller in notes and in coin respectively[④]. He bestowed them in his pockets with feigned composure[⑤] and suffered the friendly teller, to whom his father chatted, to take his hand across the broad counter and wish him a brilliant career in after life. He was impatient of their voices and could not keep his feet at rest. But the teller still deferred the serving of others[⑥] to say he was living in changed times and that there was nothing like giving a boy the best education that money could buy. Mr Dedalus lingered in the hall gazing about him and up at the roof and telling Stephen, who urged him to come out, that they were standing in the house of commons of the old Irish parliament.

— God help us! he said piously, to think of the men of those times, Stephen, Hely Hutchinson and Flood and Henry Grattan and Charles Kendal Bushe, and the noble-

---

① Shelley：雪莱(1792－1822)，英国浪漫主义时期诗人。　② colonnade：柱廊　③ orders：汇票　④ by the ... respectively：由出纳员分别用纸币和硬币付给他　⑤ with feigned composure：装作不在乎的样子　⑥ deferred the serving of others：迟迟不接待别的顾客

men we have now, leaders of the Irish people at home and abroad. Why, by God, they wouldn't be seen dead in a ten-acre field with them. No, Stephen, old chap, I'm sorry to say that they are only as I roved out[①] one fine May morning in the merry month of sweet July.

A keen October wind was blowing round the bank. The three figures standing at the edge of the muddy path had pinched cheeks and watery eyes. Stephen looked at his thinly clad mother and remembered that a few days before he had seen a mantle[②] priced at twenty guineas in the windows of Barnardo's.

— Well that's done, said Mr Dedalus.

— We had better go to dinner, said Stephen. Where?

— Dinner? said Mr Dedalus. Well, I suppose we had better, what?

— Some place that's not too dear, said Mrs Dedalus.

— Underdone's?

— Yes. Some quiet place.

— Come along, said Stephen quickly. It doesn't matter about the dearness.

He walked on before them with short nervous steps, smiling. They tried to keep up with him, smiling also at his eagerness.

— Take it easy like a good young fellow, said his father. We're not out for the half mile, are we?

For a swift season of merrymaking the money of his prizes ran through Stephen's fingers. Great parcels of groceries and delicacies and dried fruits arrived from the city. Every day he drew up a bill of fare for the family and every night led a party of three or four to the theatre to see *Ingomar* or *The Lady of Lyons*. In his coat pockets he carried squares of Vienna chocolate for his guests while his trousers' pocket bulged with masses of silver and copper coins. He bought presents for everyone, overhauled his

---

① roved out：出去闲逛　② mantle：披风

room, wrote out resolutions①, marshalled his books up and down their shelves, pored upon all kinds of price lists, drew up a form of commonwealth for the household by which every member of it held some office, opened a loan bank for his family② and pressed loans on willing borrowers so that he might have the pleasure of making out receipts and reckoning the interests on the sums lent. When he could do no more he drove up and down the city in trams. Then the season of pleasure came to an end. The pot of pink enamel paint gave out③ and the wainscot of his bedroom remained with its unfinished and illplastered coat④.

His household returned to its usual way of life. His mother had no further occasion to upbraid him for squandering his money. He too returned to his old life at school and all his novel enterprises⑤ fell to pieces. The commonwealth fell, the loan bank closed its coffers and its books on a sensible loss, the rules of life which he had drawn about himself fell into desuetude⑥.

How foolish his aim had been! He had tried to build a breakwater of order and elegance⑦ against the sordid tide of life without him and to dam up, by rules of conduct and active interest and new filial relations, the powerful recurrence of the tides within him. Useless. From without as from within the waters had flowed over his barriers: their tides began once more to jostle fiercely above the crumbled mole⑧.

He saw clearly too his own futile isolation. He had not gone one step nearer the lives he had sought to approach nor bridged the restless shame and rancour⑨ that had divided him from mother and brother and sister. He felt that he

---

① wrote out resolutions：制定了决心计划　② opened a loan bank for his family：为家人开设了一个贷款银行　③ The pot ... gave out：盛粉红色瓷漆的罐子已经空了。　④ the wainscot ... illplastered coat：他卧室的护墙板还没刷完，而且到处是翘起的墙皮。　⑤ novel enterprises：新奇的事业　⑥ fell into desuetude：废弃　⑦ a breakwater of order and elegance：一道整齐而又优美的堤坝　⑧ the crumbled mole：崩溃的堤坝　⑨ rancour：积怨

was hardly of the one blood with them but stood to them rather in the mystical kinship of fosterage, fosterchild and fosterbrother.

He turned to appease the fierce longings of his heart before which everything else was idle and alien. He cared little that he was in mortal sin, that his life had grown to be a tissue of subterfuge and falsehood①. Beside the savage desire within him to realize the enormities which he brooded on nothing was sacred. He bore cynically with the shameful details of his secret riots in which he exulted to defile with patience whatever image had attracted his eyes②. By day and by night he moved among distorted images of the outer world. A figure that had seemed to him by day demure and innocent came towards him by night through the winding darkness of sleep, her face transfigured by a lecherous cunning③, her eyes bright with brutish joy. Only the morning pained him with its dim memory of dark orgiastic riot, its keen and humiliating sense of transgression.

He returned to his wanderings. The veiled autumnal evenings led him from street to street as they had led him years before along the quiet avenues of Blackrock. But no vision of trim front gardens or of kindly lights in the windows poured a tender influence upon him now. Only at times, in the pauses of his desire, when the luxury that was wasting him gave room to a softer languor④, the image of Mercedes traversed the background of his memory. He saw again the small white house and the garden of rosebushes on the road that led to the mountains and he remembered the sadly proud gesture of refusal which he was to make there, standing with her in the moonlit garden after years of estrangement and adventure. At those moments

---

① a tissue of subterfuge and falsehood: 一连串逃避和欺骗　② he exulted ... his eyes: 他极有耐性地亵渎一切吸引他的形象，并因此而狂喜。
③ her face transfigured by a lecherous cunning: 她的脸变得淫荡而狡猾。
④ gave room to a softer languor: 被柔和的温情所替代

the soft speeches of Claude Melnotte[1] rose to his lips and eased his unrest. A tender premonition touched him of the tryst he had then looked forward to and, in spite of the horrible reality which lay between his hope of then and now, of the holy encounter he had then imagined at which weakness and timidity and inexperience were to fall from him.

Such moments passed and the wasting fires of lust sprang up again. The verses passed from his lips and the inarticulate cries[2] and the unspoken brutal words rushed forth from his brain to force a passage. His blood was in revolt. He wandered up and down the dark slimy streets peering into the gloom of lanes and doorways, listening eagerly for any sound. He moaned to himself like some baffled prowling beast[3]. He wanted to sin with another of his kind, to force another being to sin with him and to exult with her in sin. He felt some dark presence moving irresistibly upon him from the darkness, a presence subtle and murmurous as a flood filling him wholly with itself. Its murmur besieged his ears like the murmur of some multitude in sleep; its subtle streams penetrated his being. His hands clenched convulsively[4] and his teeth set together as he suffered the agony of its penetration. He stretched out his arms in the street to hold fast the frail swooning form that eluded him and incited him: and the cry that he had strangled for so long[5] in his throat issued from his lips. It broke from him like a wail of despair from a hell of sufferers and died in a wail of furious entreaty[6], a cry for an iniquitous abandonment, a cry which was but the echo of an obscene scrawl[7] which he had read on the oozing wall of a

---

① Claude Melnotte：上文提到的喜剧《里昂的贵妇》(*The Lady of Lyons*)中的男主人公　② the inarticulate cries：无法发出的叫喊　③ He moaned ... prowling beast：他像一只受了伤的野兽，四处徘徊，低声呻吟。　④ His hands clenched convulsively：他不由自主紧握拳头。　⑤ the cry ... so long：他长时间压抑的叫喊　⑥ died in a wail of furious entreaty：在一阵苦苦哀求的痛哭中消失　⑦ an obscene scrawl：下流的涂鸦

urinal.

He had wandered into a maze of narrow and dirty streets. From the foul laneways he heard bursts of hoarse riot and wrangling and the drawling of drunken singers. He walked onward, undismayed, wondering whether he had strayed into the quarter of the Jews. Women and girls dressed in long vivid gowns traversed the street from house to house. They were leisurely and perfumed. A trembling seized him and his eyes grew dim. The yellow gasflames arose before his troubled vision against the vapoury sky, burning as if before an altar. Before the doors and in the lighted halls groups were gathered arrayed as for some rite[①]. He was in another world: he had awakened from a slumber of centuries.

He stood still in the middle of the roadway, his heart clamouring against his bosom in a tumult. A young woman dressed in a long pink gown laid her hand on his arm to detain him[②] and gazed into his face. She said gaily:

— Goodnight, Willie dear!

Her room was warm and lightsome. A huge doll sat with her legs apart in the copious easychair[③] beside the bed. He tried to bid his tongue speak that he might seem at ease, watching her as she undid her gown, noting the proud conscious movements of her perfumed head.

As he stood silent in the middle of the room she came over to him and embraced him gaily and gravely. Her round arms held him firmly to her and he, seeing her face lifted to him in serious calm and feeling the warm calm rise and fall of her breast, all but burst into hysterical weeping. Tears of joy and relief shone in his delighted eyes and his lips parted though they would not speak.

She passed her tinkling hand through his hair, calling him a little rascal.

---

① gathered arrayed as for some rite：一排排地聚在一起，像正准备举行某种仪式　② detain him：拦住他　③ the copious easychair：舒适宽大的安乐椅

— Give me a kiss, she said.

His lips would not bend to kiss her. He wanted to be held firmly in her arms, to be caressed slowly, slowly, slowly. In her arms he felt that he had suddenly become strong and fearless and sure of himself. But his lips would not bend to kiss her.

With a sudden movement she bowed his head and joined her lips to his and he read the meaning of her movements in her frank uplifted eyes. It was too much for him. He closed his eyes, surrendering himself to her, body and mind, conscious of nothing in the world but the dark pressure of her softly parting lips. They pressed upon his brain as upon his lips as though they were the vehicle of a vague speech; and between them he felt an unknown and timid pressure, darker than the swoon of sin, softer than sound or odour.

CHAPTER 3

The swift December dusk had come tumbling clown-ishly[①] after its dull day and, as he stared through the dull square of the window of the schoolroom, he felt his belly crave for[②] its food. He hoped there would be stew[③] for dinner, turnips and carrots and bruised potatoes and fat mutton pieces to be ladled out in thick peppered flourfat-tened sauce[④]. Stuff it into you, his belly counselled him.

It would be a gloomy secret night. After early night-fall the yellow lamps would light up, here and there, the squalid quarter of the brothels[⑤]. He would follow a devi-ous[⑥] course up and down the streets, circling always nearer and nearer in a tremor[⑦] of fear and joy, until his feet led him suddenly round a dark corner. The whores[⑧] would be just coming out of their houses making ready for the night, yawning lazily after their sleep and settling the hairpins in their clusters of hair. He would pass by them calmly wait-ing for a sudden movement of his own will or a sudden call to his sinloving soul from their soft perfumed flesh. Yet as he prowled in quest of that call[⑨], his senses, stultified only by his desire[⑩], would note keenly all that wounded or shamed them; his eyes, a ring of porter froth[⑪] on a cloth-less table or a photograph of two soldiers standing to atten-tion or a gaudy playbill; his ears, the drawling jargon of greeting[⑫]:

---

① come tumbling clownishly: 小丑般跟跟跄跄地来了　② crave for: 渴望　③ stew: 炖过的食品　④ fat mutton ... flourfattened sauce: 舀给他浇着撒过胡椒粉的浓汁的肥羊肉　⑤ the squalid quarter of the brothels: 污秽的妓院区　⑥ devious: 弯曲的　⑦ tremor: 战栗　⑧ whores: 妓女　⑨ as he prowled in quest of that call: 当他四处逡巡寻求召唤时　⑩ stultified only by his desire: 因为他的欲望而显得愚蠢　⑪ a ring of porter froth: 一圈黑啤酒泡沫　⑫ the drawling jargon of greeting: 用拉长语调的行话喊出的问候语

— Hello, Bertie, any good in your mind?

— Is that you, pigeon?

— Number ten. Fresh Nelly is waiting on you.

— Goodnight, husband! Coming in to have a short time?

The equation on the page of his scribbler[1] began to spread out a widening tail, eyed and starred like a peacock's; and, when the eyes and stars of its indices[2] had been eliminated, began slowly to fold itself together again. The indices appearing and disappearing were eyes opening and closing; the eyes opening and closing were stars being born and being quenched[3]. The vast cycle of starry life bore his weary mind outward to its verge and inward to its centre, a distant music accompanying him outward and inward. What music? The music came nearer and he recalled the words, the words of Shelley's fragment upon the moon wandering companionless, pale for weariness. The stars began to crumble[4] and a cloud of fine stardust fell through space.

The dull light fell more faintly upon the page whereon another equation began to unfold itself slowly and to spread abroad its widening tail. It was his own soul going forth to experience, unfolding itself sin by sin, spreading abroad the balefire[5] of its burning stars and folding back upon itself, fading slowly, quenching its own lights and fires. They were quenched: and the cold darkness filled chaos.

A cold lucid[6] indifference reigned in his soul. At his first violent sin he had felt a wave of vitality pass out of him and had feared to find his body or his soul maimed[7] by the excess. Instead the vital wave had carried him on its bosom out of himself and back again when it receded: and no part of body or soul had been maimed but a dark peace had been

---

① The equation on the page of his scribbler: 他草稿本上的方程式
② indices: 指数 ③ quench: 熄灭 ④ crumble: 碎为细屑 ⑤ balefire: 邪恶的火焰 ⑥ lucid: 清冽的 ⑦ maim: 致残

established between them. The chaos in which his ardour extinguished itself was a cold indifferent knowledge of himself. He had sinned mortally not once but many times and he knew that, while he stood in danger of eternal damnation[①] for the first sin alone, by every succeeding sin he multiplied his guilt and his punishment. His days and works and thoughts could make no atonement[②] for him, the fountains of sanctifying grace[③] having ceased to refresh his soul. At most, by an alms[④] given to a beggar whose blessing he fled from, he might hope wearily to win for himself some measure of actual grace. Devotion had gone by the board. What did it avail to pray when he knew that his soul lusted after its own destruction? A certain pride, a certain awe, withheld him from offering to God even one prayer at night though he knew it was in God's power to take away his life while he slept and hurl his soul hellward ere he could beg for mercy[⑤]. His pride in his own sin, his loveless awe of God, told him that his offence was too grievous to be atoned for in whole or in part by a false homage[⑥] to the Allseeing and Allknowing.

— Well now, Ennis, I declare you have a head and so has my stick! Do you mean to say that you are not able to tell me what a surd[⑦] is?

The blundering answer[⑧] stirred the embers[⑨] of his contempt of his fellows. Towards others he felt neither shame nor fear. On Sunday mornings as he passed the churchdoor he glanced coldly at the worshippers who stood bareheaded, four deep[⑩], outside the church, morally present at the mass which they could neither see nor hear. Their dull piety and the sickly smell of the cheap hairoil with which they had anointed[⑪] their heads repelled him

---

① eternal damnation: 永久的惩罚 ② atonement: 赎罪 ③ sanctifying grace: 神圣的恩惠 ④ alms: 施舍物 ⑤ ere he could beg for mercy: 在他请求宽恕之前 ⑥ homage: 崇敬 ⑦ surd: (数学)不尽根数 ⑧ The blundering answer: 错误的答案 ⑨ embers: 余烬 ⑩ four deep: 里外四排横队 ⑪ anoint: 涂膏(尤指作为一种宗教仪式而为者)

from the altar they prayed at. He stooped to① the evil of hypocrisy with others, sceptical② of their innocence which he could cajole③ so easily.

On the wall of his bedroom hung an illuminated scroll④, the certificate of his prefecture⑤ in the college of the sodality⑥ of the Blessed Virgin Mary. On Saturday mornings when the sodality met in the chapel to recite the little office⑦ his place was a cushioned kneelingdesk at the right of the altar from which he led his wing of boys through the responses. The falsehood of his position did not pain him. If at moments he felt an impulse to rise from his post of honour and, confessing before them all his unworthiness, to leave the chapel, a glance at their faces restrained⑧ him. The imagery of the psalms of prophecy⑨ soothed his barren pride. The glories of Mary held his soul captive: spikenard and myrrh and frankincense⑩, symbolizing the preciousness of God's gifts to her soul, rich garments, symbolizing her royal lineage, her emblems, the lateflowering plant and late blossoming tree, symbolizing the agelong gradual growth of her cultus⑪ among men. When it fell to him to read the lesson towards the close of the office he read it in a veiled voice, lulling his conscience to its music.

> *Quasi cedrus exaltata sum in Libanon et quasi cupressus in monte Sion. Quasi palma exaltata sum in Gades et quasi plantatio rosae in Jericho. Quasi uliva speciosa in campis et quasi platanus exaltata sum juxta aquam in plateis. Sicut cinnamomum et balsamum aromatizans odorem dedi et quasi myrrha electa dedi*

---

① stoop to: 卑屈 ② sceptical: 怀疑的 ③ cajole: 以甜言蜜语哄骗 ④ scroll: 纸卷 ⑤ prefecture: 级长的职位(或任期) ⑥ sodality: (天主教)会社 ⑦ office: 祷告 ⑧ restrain: 阻止 ⑨ the psalms of prophecy: 赞美先知的圣歌 ⑩ spikenard and myrrh and frankincense: 甘松香油、没药和乳香 ⑪ cultus: 信徒

suavitatem odoris . ①

His sin, which had covered him from the sight of God, had led him nearer to the refuge of sinners. Her eyes seemed to regard him with mild pity; her holiness, a strange light glowing faintly upon her frail flesh, did not humiliate the sinner who approached her. If ever he was impelled to cast② sin from him and to repent the impulse that moved him was the wish to be her knight. If ever his soul, reentering her dwelling shyly after the frenzy of his body's lust had spent itself, was turned towards her whose emblem is the morning star, *bright and musical , telling of heaven and infusing peace*③ , it was when her names were murmured softly by lips whereon there still lingered foul and shameful words, the savour itself of a lewd④ kiss.

That was strange. He tried to think how it could be but the dusk, deepening in the schoolroom, covered over his thoughts. The bell rang. The master marked the sums and cuts⑤ to be done for the next lesson and went out. Heron, beside Stephen, began to hum tunelessly.

My excellent friend Bombados .

Ennis, who had gone to the yard, came back, saying:

— The boy from the house is coming up for the rector.

A tall boy behind Stephen rubbed his hands and said:

— That's game ball. We can scut the whole hour. He won't be in till after half two. Then you can ask him questions on the catechism⑥ , Dedalus.

---

① *Quasi cedrus ... suavitatem odoris*：(拉丁文)我的崇高有似黎巴嫩的雪松和锡昂山头的翠柏。我的超逸胜过杰里科的玫瑰园和约旦河畔的棕榈，田野中的一株橄榄难比我优美，我和路旁与清泉为邻的梧桐一样清高。恰像陈年桂皮和娇嫩的凤仙，我散发出芳香的气息，也像精选的没药，我散发出甜蜜的芳香。(此译文参考黄雨石译《青年艺术家的画像》第329页，人民文学出版社1986年版) ② cast：脱落 ③ *bright and ... infusing peace*：令人赏心悦目、给人带来天堂福音和无尽安抚的晨星(《圣经·启示录》第22章第16节) ④ lewd：淫荡的 ⑤ the sums and cuts：加减法算术题 ⑥ catechism：教义问答手册

Stephen, leaning back and drawing idly on his scribbler, listened to the talk about him which Heron checked from time to time by saying:

— Shut up, will you. Don't make such a bally racket[1]!

It was strange too that he found an arid pleasure in following up to the end the rigid lines of the doctrines of the church and penetrating into obscure silences only to hear and feel the more deeply his own condemnation. The sentence of saint James which says that he who offends against one commandment becomes guilty of all had seemed to him first a swollen phrase until he had begun to grope in the darkness of his own state. From the evil seed of lust all other deadly sins had sprung forth: pride in himself and contempt of others, covetousness[2] in using money for the purchase of unlawful pleasure, envy of those whose vices[3] he could not reach to and calumnious[4] murmuring against the pious, gluttonous[5] enjoyment of food, the dull glowering anger amid which he brooded upon his longing, the swamp[6] of spiritual and bodily sloth in which his whole being had sunk.

As he sat in his bench gazing calmly at the rector's shrewd harsh face his mind wound itself in and out of the curious questions proposed to it. If a man had stolen a pound in his youth and had used that pound to amass a huge fortune how much was he obliged to give back, the pound he had stolen only or the pound together with the compound interest accruing[7] upon it or all his huge fortune? If a layman in giving baptism pour the water before saying the words is the child baptized? Is baptism with a mineral water valid? How comes it that while the first beatitude[8] promises the kingdom of heaven to the poor of

---

① Don't ... bally racket: 别在这儿一个劲儿地聒噪了 ② covetousness: 贪图 ③ vices: 不道德的行为 ④ calumnious: 诬蔑的 ⑤ gluttonous: 贪吃的 ⑥ swamp: 沼地 ⑦ accrue: 自然增长 ⑧ beatitude: 福音

heart the second beatitude promises also to the meek① that they shall possess the land? Why was the sacrament of the eucharist instituted under the two species of bread and wine if Jesus Christ be present body and blood, soul and divinity, in the bread alone and in the wine alone? Does a tiny particle of the consecrated② bread contain all the body and blood of Jesus Christ or a part only of the body and blood? If the wine change into vinegar and the host crumble into corruption after they have been consecrated, is Jesus Christ still present under their species as God and as man?

— Here he is! Here he is!

A boy from his post at the window had seen the rector come from the house. All the catechisms were opened and all heads bent upon them silently. The rector entered and took his seat on the dais③. A gentle kick from the tall boy in the bench behind urged Stephen to ask a difficult question.

The rector did not ask for a catechism to hear the lesson from. He clasped his hands on the desk and said:

— The retreat④ will begin on Wednesday afternoon in honour of saint Francis Xavier whose feast day⑤ is Saturday. The retreat will go on from Wednesday to Friday. On Friday confession will be heard all the afternoon after beads⑥. If any boys have special confessors perhaps it will be better for them not to change. Mass will be on Saturday morning at nine o'clock and general communion⑦ for the whole college. Saturday will be a free day. But Saturday and Sunday being free days some boys might be inclined to think that Monday is a free day also. Beware of making that mistake. I think you, Lawless, are likely to make that mistake.

— I, sir? Why, sir?

---

① the meek：温顺的人　② consecrated：神圣的　③ dais：讲台
④ retreat：（宗教）静修　⑤ feast day：（宗教）节日　⑥ bead：数念珠而祷告
⑦ communion：圣餐仪式

A little wave of quiet mirth broke forth over the class of boys from the rector's grim smile. Stephen's heart began slowly to fold and fade with fear like a withering flower.

The rector went on gravely:

— You are all familiar with the story of the life of saint Francis Xavier, I suppose, the patron of your college①. He came of an old and illustrious Spanish family and you remember that he was one of the first followers of saint Ignatius②. They met in Paris where Francis Xavier was professor of philosophy at the university. This young and brilliant nobleman and man of letters entered heart and soul into the ideas of our glorious founder, and you know that he, at his own desire, was sent by saint Ignatius to preach to the Indians. He is called, as you know, the apostle③ of the Indies. He went from country to country in the east, from Africa to India, from India to Japan, baptizing the people. He is said to have baptized as many as ten thousand idolaters④ in one month. It is said that his right arm had grown powerless from having been raised so often over the heads of those whom he baptized. He wished then to go to China to win still more souls for God but he died of fever on the island of Sancian. A great saint, saint Francis Xavier! A great soldier of God!

The rector paused and then, shaking his clasped hands before him, went on:

— He had the faith in him that moves mountains. Ten thousand souls won for God in a single month! That is a true conqueror, true to the motto of our order: *ad majorem Dei gloriam*⑤! A saint who has great power in heaven, remember: power to intercede for us in our grief, power to obtain whatever we pray for if it be for the good of our souls, power above all to obtain for us the grace to repent if

---

① the patron of your college: 你们学校的守护神 ② Ignatius: 耶稣教会创始人 ③ apostle: 使徒 ④ idolaters: 指耶稣的崇拜者 ⑤ *ad majorem Dei gloriam*: (拉丁文)为了上帝更大的荣光, 参见前文注释。

we be in sin. A great saint, saint Francis Xavier! A great fisher of souls!

He ceased to shake his clasped hands and, resting them against his forehead, looked right and left of them keenly at his listeners out of his dark stern eyes.

In the silence their dark fire kindled the dusk into a tawny[①] glow. Stephen's heart had withered up like a flower of the desert that feels the simoom[②] coming from afar.

— *Remember only thy last things and thou shalt not sin for ever* — words taken, my dear little brothers in Christ, from the book of Ecclesiastes[③], seventh chapter, fortieth verse. In the name of the Father and of the Son and of the Holy Ghost. Amen.

Stephen sat in the front bench of the chapel. Father Arnall sat at a table to the left of the altar. He wore about his shoulders a heavy cloak; his pale face was drawn and his voice broken with rheum[④]. The figure of his old master, so strangely rearisen, brought back to Stephen's mind his life at Clongowes: the wide playgrounds, swarming with boys, the square ditch, the little cemetery off the main avenue of limes[⑤] where he had dreamed of being buried, the firelight on the wall of the infirmary where he lay sick, the sorrowful face of Brother Michael. His soul, as these memories came back to him, became again a child's soul.

— We are assembled[⑥] here today, my dear little brothers in Christ, for one brief moment far away from the busy bustle of the outer world to celebrate and to honour one of the greatest of saints, the apostle of the Indies, the patron saint also of your college, saint Francis Xavier. Year after year for much longer than any of you, my dear little boys, can remember or than I can remember the boys of this college have met in this very chapel to make their an-

---

① tawny: 黄褐色的　② simoom: 撒哈拉及阿拉伯沙漠地区所刮的干燥而带有尘沙的热风　③ Ecclesiastes: 圣经书　④ rheum: 鼻涕　⑤ the little ... of limes: 石灰路面的大道旁的小墓场　⑥ assembled: 聚集

nual retreat before the feast day of their patron saint. Time has gone on and brought with it its changes. Even in the last few years what changes can most of you not remember? Many of the boys who sat in those front benches a few years ago are perhaps now in distant lands, in the burning tropics or immersed in[1] professional duties or in seminaries or voyaging over the vast expanse of the deep or, it may be, already called by the great God to another life and to the rendering up of their stewardship[2]. And still as the years roll by, bringing with them changes for good and bad, the memory of the great saint is honoured by the boys of this college who make every year their annual retreat on the days preceding the feast day set apart by our Holy Mother the church to transmit to all the ages the name and fame of one of the greatest sons of catholic Spain.

— Now what is the meaning of this word *retreat* and why is it allowed on all hands to be a most salutary practice for all who desire to lead before God and in the eyes of men a truly christian life? A retreat, my dear boys, signifies a withdrawal for awhile from the cares of our life, the cares of this workaday world, in order to examine the state of our conscience, to reflect on the mysteries of holy religion and to understand better why we are here in this world. During these few days I intend to put before you some thoughts concerning the four last things. They are, as you know from your catechism, death, judgement, hell and heaven. We shall try to understand them fully during these few days so that we may derive from[3] the understanding of them a lasting benefit to our souls. And remember, my dear boys, that we have been sent into this world for one thing and for one thing alone: to do God's holy will and to save our immortal souls. All else is worthless. One thing alone is needful, the salvation of one's soul[4]. What doth it

---

① immersed in: 专心　② rendering up of their stewardship: 放弃了他们在世间的职责　③ derive from: 得到　④ the salvation of one's soul: 拯救自己的灵魂

profit a man to gain the whole world if he suffer the loss of his immortal soul? Ah, my dear boys, believe me there is nothing in this wretched world① that can make up for such a loss.

— I will ask you, therefore, my dear boys, to put away from your minds during these few days all worldly thoughts, whether of study or pleasure or ambition, and to give all your attention to the state of your souls. I need hardly remind you that during the days of the retreat all boys are expected to preserve a quiet and pious demeanour② and to shun all loud unseemly③ pleasure. The elder boys, of course, will see that this custom is not infringed④ and I look especially to the prefects and officers of the sodality of Our Blessed Lady and of the sodality of the holy angels to set a good example to their fellowstudents.

— Let us try, therefore, to make this retreat in honour of saint Francis with our whole heart and our whole mind. God's blessing will then be upon all your year's studies. But, above and beyond all, let this retreat be one to which you can look back in after years when maybe you are far from this college and among very different surroundings, to which you can look back with joy and thankfulness and give thanks to God for having granted you this occasion of laying the first foundation of a pious honourable zealous christian life. And if, as may so happen, there be at this moment in these benches any poor soul who has had the unutterable misfortune to lose God's holy grace and to fall into grievous sin, I fervently trust and pray that this retreat may be the turning point in the life of that soul. I pray to God through the merits of His zealous servant Francis Xavier that such a soul may be led to sincere repentance and that the holy communion on saint Francis' day of this year

---

① wretched world: 可怜的人世间　② pious demeanour: 虔诚的态度行
为　③ unseemly: 不相宜的　④ infringe: 违背

may be a lasting covenant① between God and that soul. For just and unjust, for saint and sinner alike, may this retreat be a memorable one.

— Help me, my dear little brothers in Christ. Help me by your pious attention, by your own devotion, by your outward demeanour. Banish from your minds all worldly thoughts and think only of the last things, death, judgement, hell and heaven. He who remembers these things, says Ecclesiastes, shall not sin for ever. He who remembers the last things will act and think with them always before his eyes. He will live a good life and die a good death, believing and knowing that, if he has sacrificed much in this earthly life, it will be given to him a hundredfold and a thousandfold more in the life to come, in the kingdom without end — a blessing, my dear boys, which I wish you from my heart, one and all, in the name of the Father and of the Son and of the Holy Ghost. Amen!

As he walked home with silent companions, a thick fog seemed to compass② his mind. He waited in stupor③ of mind till it should lift and reveal what it had hidden. He ate his dinner with surly④ appetite and, when the meal was over and the greasestrewn plates⑤ lay abandoned on the table, he rose and went to the window, clearing the thick scum from his mouth with his tongue and licking it from his lips. So he had sunk to the state of a beast that licks his chaps⑥ after meat. This was the end; and a faint glimmer of fear began to pierce the fog of his mind. He pressed his face against the pane of the window and gazed out into the darkening street. Forms passed this way and that through the dull light. And that was life. The letters of the name of Dublin lay heavily upon his mind, pushing one another surlily hither and thither with slow boorish⑦ insistence.

---

① covenant：承诺　② compass：围绕　③ stupor：恍惚　④ surly：粗暴的　⑤ the greasestrewn plates：满是油腻的盘子　⑥ chaps：(动物的)颚　⑦ boorish：举止粗鲁的

His soul was fattening and congealing into a gross grease①, plunging ever deeper in its dull fear into a sombre threatening dusk, while the body that was his stood, listless and dishonoured, gazing out of darkened eyes, helpless, perturbed and human for a bovine god② to stare upon.

The next day brought death and judgement, stirring his soul slowly from its listless despair. The faint glimmer of fear became a terror of spirit as the hoarse voice③ of the preacher blew death into his soul. He suffered its agony. He felt the death-chill touch the extremities and creep onward towards the heart, the film of death veiling the eyes, the bright centres of the brain extinguished one by one like lamps, the last sweat oozing upon the skin④, the powerlessness of the dying limbs, the speech thickening and wandering and failing, the heart throbbing faintly and more faintly, all but vanquished, the breath, the poor breath, the poor helpless human spirit, sobbing and sighing, gurgling and rattling in the throat⑤. No help! No help! He, he himself, his body to which he had yielded was dying. Into the grave with it! Nail it down into a wooden box, the corpse. Carry it out of the house on the shoulders of hirelings⑥. Thrust it out of men's sight into a long hole in the ground, into the grave, to rot, to feed the mass of its creeping worms and to be devoured by scuttling plumpbellied rats⑦.

And while the friends were still standing in tears by the bedside the soul of the sinner was judged. At the last moment of consciousness the whole earthly life passed before the vision of the soul and, ere it had time to reflect, the body had died and the soul stood terrified before the judgement seat. God, who had long been merciful, would

---

① congealing into a gross grease：凝结成一大团油脂　② bovine god：牛神　③ the hoarse voice：嘶哑的嗓音　④ oozing upon the skin：顺着皮肤慢慢地流下来　⑤ gurgling and rattling in the throat：在喉咙里咕咕噜噜地响　⑥ hirelings：所雇的人　⑦ scuttling plumpbellied rats：到处逃窜的大肚子老鼠

then be just. He had long been patient, pleading with the sinful soul, giving it time to repent, sparing it yet awhile. But that time had gone. Time was to sin and to enjoy, time was to scoff at[1] God and at the warnings of His holy church, time was to defy[2] His majesty, to disobey His commands, to hoodwink[3] one's fellow men, to commit sin after sin and to hide one's corruption from the sight of men. But that time was over. Now it was God's turn; and He was not to be hoodwinked or deceived. Every sin would then come forth from its lurkingplace[4], the most rebellious against the divine will and the most degrading to our poor corrupt nature, the tiniest imperfection and the most heinous atrocity[5]. What did it avail then to have been a great emperor, a great general, a marvellous inventor, the most learned of the learned? All were as one before the judgementseat of God. He would reward the good and punish the wicked. One single instant was enough for the trial of a man's soul. One single instant after the body's death, the soul had been weighed in the balance. The particular judgement was over and the soul had passed to the abode of bliss[6] or to the prison of purgatory[7] or had been hurled howling into hell.

Nor was that all. God's justice had still to be vindicated[8] before men: after the particular there still remained the general judgement. The last day had come. Doomsday was at hand. The stars of heaven were falling upon the earth like the figs cast by the figtree which the wind has shaken. The sun, the great luminary[9] of the universe, had become as sackcloth of hair. The moon was bloodred. The firmament[10] was as a scroll rolled away. The archangel Michael, the prince of the heavenly host, appeared glorious

---

① scoff at：嘲弄　② defy：不尊重　③ hoodwink：欺骗　④ lurking-place：隐藏之处　⑤ the most heinous atrocity：最残暴的行为　⑥ the abode of bliss：幸福的天国　⑦ purgatory：炼狱　⑧ vindicate：证实　⑨ luminary：天上任何的发光体　⑩ The firmament：天空

and terrible against the sky. With one foot on the sea and one foot on the land he blew from the archangelical trumpet the brazen death of time①. The three blasts② of the angel filled all the universe. Time is, time was, but time shall be no more. At the last blast the souls of universal humanity throng③ towards the valley of Jehoshaphat④, rich and poor, gentle and simple, wise and foolish, good and wicked. The soul of every human being that has ever existed, the souls of all those who shall yet be born, all the sons and daughters of Adam, all are assembled on that supreme day. And lo the supreme judge is coming! No longer the lowly Lamb of God, no longer the meek Jesus of Nazareth, no longer the Man of Sorrows, no longer the Good Shepherd, He is seen now coming upon the clouds, in great power and majesty, attended by nine choirs of angels, angels and archangels, principalities, powers and virtues, thrones and dominations, cherubim and seraphim⑤, God Omnipotent, God Everlasting. He speaks: and His voice is heard even at the farthest limits of space, even in the bottomless abyss. Supreme Judge, from His sentence there will be and can be no appeal. He calls the just to His side, bidding them enter into the kingdom, the eternity of bliss, prepared for them. The unjust He casts from Him, crying in His offended majesty: *Depart from me, ye cursed, into everlasting fire which was prepared for the devil and his angels*. O what agony then for the miserable sinners! Friend is torn apart from friend, children are torn from their parents, husbands from their wives. The poor sinner holds out his arms to those who were dear to him in this earthly world, to those whose simple piety⑥ perhaps he made a mock of⑦, to those who counselled him and tried to

---

① he blew ... of time: 用他天使长的号角吹响黄铜色的死亡的来临。
② The three blasts: 三阵号角声　③ throng: 拥挤　④ the valley of Jehoshaphat: 耶和沙法山谷, 位于耶路撒冷东部。据《圣经》, 此处是上帝审判所有国家的地方。　⑤ cherubim and seraphim: 二级天使和等级最高的天使　⑥ piety: 虔诚　⑦ made a mock of: 讥笑

lead him on the right path, to a kind brother, to a loving sister, to the mother and father who loved him so dearly. But it is too late: the just turn away from the wretched damned souls which now appear before the eyes of all in their hideous① and evil character. O you hypocrites, O you whited sepulchres②, O you who present a smooth smiling face to the world while your soul within is a foul swamp of sin, how will it fare③ with you in that terrible day?

And this day will come, shall come, must come; the day of death and the day of judgement. It is appointed unto a man to die and after death and the day of judgement. It is appointed unto a man to die and after death the judgement. Death is certain. The time and manner are uncertain, whether from long disease or from some unexpected accident; the Son of God cometh at an hour when you little expect Him. Be therefore ready every moment, seeing that you may die at any moment. Death is the end of us all. Death and judgement, brought into the world by the sin of our first parents, are the dark portals④ that close our earthly existence, the portals that open into the unknown and the unseen, portals through which every soul must pass, alone, unaided save by its good works, without friend or brother or parent or master to help it, alone and trembling. Let that thought be ever before our minds and then we cannot sin. Death, a cause of terror to the sinner, is a blessed moment for him who has walked in the right path, fulfilling the duties of his station in life, attending to his morning and evening prayers, approaching the holy sacrament frequently and performing good and merciful works. For the pious and believing catholic, for the just man, death is no cause of terror. Was it not Addison, the great English writer, who, when on his deathbed, sent for the wicked young earl⑤ of Warwick to let him see how a christian can

---

① hideous: 十分丑恶的　② whited sepulchres: 伪君子　③ fare: 进展　④ portals: 入口　⑤ earl: 伯爵

meet his end? He it is and he alone, the pious and believing christian, who can say in his heart:

O grave, where is thy victory?
O death, where is thy sting?

Every word of it was for him. Against his sin, foul① and secret, the whole wrath of God was aimed. The preacher's knife had probed deeply into his diseased conscience and he felt now that his soul was festering in sin. Yes, the preacher was right. God's turn had come. Like a beast in its lair② his soul had lain down in its own filth but the blasts of the angel's trumpet had driven him forth from the darkness of sin into the light. The words of doom cried by the angel shattered in an instant his presumptuous③ peace. The wind of the last day blew through his mind; his sins, the jewel eyed harlots④ of his imagination, fled before the hurricane, squeaking like mice in their terror and huddled⑤ under a mane of hair.

As he crossed the square, walking homeward, the light laughter of a girl reached his burning ear. The frail gay sound smote⑥ his heart more strongly than a trumpet blast, and, not daring to lift his eyes, he turned aside and gazed, as he walked, into the shadow of the tangled shrubs. Shame rose from his smitten heart and flooded his whole being. The image of Emma appeared before him and, under her eyes, the flood of shame rushed forth anew from his heart. If she knew to what his mind had subjected her or how his brutelike lust had torn and trampled upon her innocence⑦! Was that boyish love? Was that chivalry? Was that poetry? The sordid details of his orgies stank under his very nostrils⑧: the soot coated packet of pictures which he had hidden in the flue⑨ of the fireplace and in the

---

① foul：邪恶的　② lair：野兽的窝穴　③ presumptuous：自以为是的 ④harlots：(古，或辱骂语)娼妓　⑤ huddle：挤成一堆　⑥ smote：重击 ⑦ how his ... her innocence：他野兽般的欲望曾怎样撕毁和践踏她的纯真。　⑧ The sordid ... very nostrils：他那些放荡行为的可卑的细节在他的鼻子底下发出恶臭。　⑨ flue：烟道

presence of whose shameless or bashful wantonness[1] he lay for hours sinning in thought and deed; his monstrous dreams, peopled by ape like creatures and by harlots with gleaming jewel eyes; the foul long letters he had written in the joy of guilty confession and carried secretly for days and days only to throw them under cover of night among the grass in the corner of a field or beneath some hingeless[2] door or some niche in the hedges where a girl might come upon them as she walked by and read them secretly. Mad! Mad! Was it possible he had done these things? A cold sweat broke out upon his forehead as the foul memories condensed within his brain.

When the agony of shame had passed from him he tried to raise his soul from its abject[3] powerlessness. God and the Blessed Virgin were too far from him: God was too great and stern and the Blessed Virgin too pure and holy. But he imagined that he stood near Emma in a wide land and, humbly and in tears, bent and kissed the elbow of her sleeve.

In the wide land under a tender lucid evening sky, a cloud drifting westward amid a pale green sea of heaven, they stood together, children that had erred[4]. Their error had offended deeply God's majesty though it was the error of two children, but it had not offended her whose beauty *is not like earthly beauty*, *dangerous to look upon*, *but like the morning star which is its emblem*, *bright and musical*. The eyes were not offended which she turned upon them nor reproachful[5]. She placed their hands together, hand in hand, and said, speaking to their hearts:

— Take hands, Stephen and Emma. It is a beautiful evening now in heaven. You have erred but you are always my children. It is one heart that loves another heart. Take hands together, my dear children, and you will be happy

---

① wantonness: 淫荡 ② hingeless: 没有铰链的 ③ abject: 可怜的
④ children that had erred: 犯了错的孩子 ⑤ reproachful: 责备的

together and your hearts will love each other.

The chapel was flooded by the dull scarlet light that filtered through the lowered blinds①; and through the fissure between the last blind and the sash② a shaft of wan light entered like a spear and touched the embossed brasses of the candlesticks③ upon the altar that gleamed like the battle worn mail armour of angels.

Rain was falling on the chapel, on the garden, on the college. It would rain for ever, noiselessly. The water would rise inch by inch, covering the grass and shrubs, covering the trees and houses, covering the monuments and the mountain tops. All life would be choked off④, noiselessly: birds, men, elephants, pigs, children: noiselessly floating corpses amid the litter of the wreckage of the world. Forty days and forty nights the rain would fall till the waters covered the face of the earth.

It might be. Why not?

— *Hell has enlarged its soul and opened its mouth without any limits* — words taken, my dear little brothers in Christ Jesus, from the book of Isaias, fifth chapter, fourteenth verse. In the name of the Father and of the Son and of the Holy Ghost. Amen.

The preacher took a chainless watch from a pocket within his soutane and, having considered its dial⑤ for a moment in silence, placed it silently before him on the table.

He began to speak in a quiet tone.

— Adam and Eve, my dear boys, were, as you know, our first parents and you will remember that they were created by God in order that the seats in heaven left vacant by the fall of Lucifer and his rebellious angels might be filled again. Lucifer⑥, we are told, was a son of the

---

① the lowered blinds: 放下的窗帘(布质卷轴式的窗帘) ② the fissure ... the sash: 在最后一个窗帘和窗框的空隙间 ③ the embossed brasses of the candlesticks: 刻着浮雕的青铜烛台 ④ All life would be choked off: 所有的生命都会被闷死 ⑤ dial: 表盘 ⑥ Lucifer: 撒旦

morning, a radiant and mighty angel; yet he fell: he fell and there fell with him a third part of the host of heaven: he fell and was hurled with his rebellious angels into hell. What his sin was we cannot say. Theologians consider that it was the sin of pride, the sinful thought conceived in an instant: *non serviam*①: *I will not serve*. That instant was his ruin. He offended the majesty of God by the sinful thought of one instant and God cast him out of heaven into hell for ever.

— Adam and Eve were then created by God and placed in Eden, in the plain of Damascus②, that lovely garden resplendent③ with sunlight and colour, teeming with luxuriant vegetation. The fruitful earth gave them her bounty: beasts and birds were their willing servants: they knew not the ills our flesh is heir to④, disease and poverty and death: all that a great and generous God could do for them was done. But there was one condition imposed on them by God: obedience to His word. They were not to eat of the fruit of the forbidden tree.

— Alas, my dear little boys, they too fell. The devil, once a shining angel, a son of the morning, now a foul fiend⑤, came in the shape of a serpent⑥, the subtlest of all the beasts of the field. He envied them. He, the fallen great one, could not bear to think that man, a being of clay⑦, should possess the inheritance which he by his sin had forfeited⑧ for ever. He came to the woman, the weaker vessel, and poured the poison of his eloquence into her ear⑨, promising her — O, the blasphemy of that promise! — that if she and Adam ate of the forbidden fruit they would become as gods, nay as God Himself. Eve yielded to

---

① *non serviam*：(拉丁文)我不伺候了。这是撒旦堕落之前对上帝说的一句话。 ② Damascus：大马士革(叙利亚的首都) ③ resplendent：灿烂的 ④ heir to：继承 ⑤ a foul fiend：可耻的恶魔 ⑥ serpent：毒蛇 ⑦ a being of clay：粘土做的生命 ⑧ forfeit：丧失 ⑨ poured the ... her ear：将他甜言蜜语的毒汁灌入她的耳朵

the wiles① of the archtempter. She ate the apple and gave it also to Adam who had not the moral courage to resist her. The poison tongue of Satan had done its work. They fell.

— And then the voice of God was heard in that garden, calling His creature man to account: and Michael, prince of the heavenly host, with a sword of flame in his hand appeared before the guilty pair and drove them forth from Eden into the world, the world of sickness and striving, of cruelty and disappointment, of labour and hardship, to earn their bread in the sweat of their brow. But even then how merciful was God! He took pity on our poor degraded parents and promised that in the fullness of time He would send down from heaven One who would redeem them②, make them once more children of God and heirs to the kingdom of heaven: and that One, that Redeemer of fallen man, was to be God's only begotten Son, the Second Person of the Most Blessed Trinity, the Eternal Word.

— He came. He was born of a virgin pure, Mary the virgin mother. He was born in a poor cowhouse in Judea and lived as a humble carpenter for thirty years until the hour of His mission had come. And then, filled with love for men, He went forth and called to men to hear the new gospel③.

— Did they listen? Yes, they listened but would not hear. He was seized and bound like a common criminal, mocked at as a fool, set aside to give place to a public robber, scourged④ with five thousand lashes, crowned with a crown of thorns, hustled through the streets by the jewish rabble⑤ and the Roman soldiery, stripped of His garments and hanged upon a gibbet⑥ and His side was pierced with a lance⑦ and from the wounded body of Our Lord water and blood issued continually.

---

① wiles: 诡计　② redeem them: 拯救他们　③ gospel: 福音
④ scourge: 鞭打　⑤ rabble: 乱民　⑥ gibbet: 绞刑架　⑦ lance: 长矛

— Yet even then, in that hour of supreme agony, Our Merciful Redeemer had pity for mankind. Yet even there, on the hill of Calvary, He founded the holy catholic church against which, it is promised, the gates of hell shall not prevail[1]. He founded it upon the rock of ages and endowed it with His grace, with sacraments and sacrifice, and promised that if men would obey the word of His church they would still enter into eternal life but if, after all that had been done for them, they still persisted in their wickedness there remained for them an eternity of torment[2]: hell.

The preacher's voice sank. He paused, joined his palms[3] for an instant, parted them. Then he resumed:

— Now let us try for a moment to realize, as far as we can, the nature of that abode[4] of the damned which the justice of an offended God has called into existence for the eternal punishment of sinners. Hell is a strait[5] and dark and foulsmelling prison, an abode of demons[6] and lost souls, filled with fire and smoke. The straitness of this prisonhouse is expressly designed by God to punish those who refused to be bound by His laws. In earthly prisons the poor captive has at least some liberty of movement[7], were it only within the four walls of his cell or in the gloomy yard of his prison. Not so in hell. There, by reason of the great number of the damned, the prisoners are heaped together in their awful prison, the walls of which are said to be four thousand miles thick: and the damned are so utterly bound and helpless that, as a blessed saint, saint Anselm, writes in his book on similitudes, they are not even able to remove from the eye a worm that gnaws it[8]

---

① prevail against: 胜过　② an eternity of torment: 永久的折磨　③ joined his palms: 把手掌合在一起　④ abode: 住所　⑤ strait: 狭窄的通道　⑥ demons: 恶魔　⑦ some liberty of movement: 一些活动的自由　⑧ a worm that gnaws it: 咬眼睛的蛆虫

— They lie in exterior darkness. For, remember, the fire of hell gives forth no light. As, at the command of God, the fire of the Babylonian furnace lost its heat but not its light so, at the command of God, the fire of hell, while retaining the intensity of its heat, burns eternally in darkness. It is a neverending storm of darkness, dark flames and dark smoke of burning brimstone, amid which the bodies are heaped one upon another without even a glimpse of air. Of all the plagues[1] with which the land of the Pharaohs was smitten one plague alone, that of darkness, was called horrible. What name, then, shall we give to the darkness of hell which is to last for not three days alone but for all eternity?

— The horror of this strait and dark prison is increased by its awful stench[2]. All the filth of the world, all the offal and scum[3] of the world, we are told, shall run there as to a vast reeking sewer[4] when the terrible conflagration of the last day has purged the world[5]. The brimstone[6] too which burns there in such prodigious[7] quantity fills all hell with its intolerable stench; and the bodies of the damned themselves exhale such a pestilential odour[8] that as saint Bonaventure says, one of them alone would suffice to infect the whole world. The very air of this world, that pure element, becomes foul and unbreathable when it has been long enclosed. Consider then what must be the foulness of the air of hell. Imagine some foul and putrid corpse[9] that has lain rotting and decomposing[10] in the grave, a jellylike mass of liquid corruption. Imagine such a corpse a prey to flames, devoured by the fire of burning brimstone and giving off dense choking fumes of nauseous[11]

---

① plague：灾害　② stench：恶臭　③ offal and scum：垃圾和渣滓　④ reeking sewer：冒着臭气的阴沟　⑤ when the ... the world：当世界末日的大火灾将世界净化以后　⑥ brimstone：硫磺石　⑦ prodigious：庞大的　⑧ exhale such a pestilential odour：发出瘟疫般的气味　⑨ putrid corpse：腐烂的尸体　⑩ decomposing：分解　⑪ nauseous：令人作呕的

loathsome decomposition. And then imagine this sickening stench, multiplied a millionfold and a millionfold again from the millions upon millions of fetid carcasses① massed together in the reeking darkness, a huge and rotting human fungus. Imagine all this and you will have some idea of the horror of the stench of hell.

— But this stench is not, horrible though it is, the greatest physical torment to which the damned are subjected. The torment of fire is the greatest torment to which the tyrant has ever subjected his fellowcreatures. Place your finger for a moment in the flame of a candle and you will feel the pain of fire. But our earthly fire was created by God for the benefit of man, to maintain in him the spark of life and to help him in the useful arts, whereas the fire of hell is of another quality and was created by God to torture and punish the unrepentant sinner②. Our earthly fire also consumes more or less rapidly according as the object which it attacks is more or less combustible③, so that human ingenuity④ has even succeeded in inventing chemical preparations to check or frustrate its action. But the sulphurous brimstone which burns in hell is a substance which is specially designed to burn for ever and for ever with unspeakable fury. Moreover our earthly fire destroys at the same time as it burns, so that the more intense it is the shorter is its duration: but the fire of hell has this property that it preserves that which it burns and though it rages with incredible intensity it rages for ever.

— Our earthly fire again, no matter how fierce or widespread it may be, is always of a limited extent: but the lake of fire in hell is boundless, shoreless and bottomless. It is on record that the devil himself, when asked the question by a certain soldier, was obliged to confess that if a whole mountain were thrown into the burning ocean of hell it

---

① fetid carcasses：发出恶臭的尸体　② unrepentant sinner：不改悔的罪人　③ combustible：可燃的　④ ingenuity：创造力

would be burned up in an instant like a piece of wax. And this terrible fire will not afflict[1] the bodies of the damned only from without but each lost soul will be a hell unto itself, the boundless fire raging in its very vitals. O, how terrible is the lot of those wretched beings! The blood seethes and boils in the veins, the brains are boiling in the skull, the heart in the breast glowing and bursting, the bowels[2] a redhot mass of burning pulp, the tender eyes flaming like molten balls.

— And yet what I have said as to the strength and quality and boundlessness of this fire is as nothing when compared to its intensity, an intensity which it has as being the instrument chosen by divine design for the punishment of soul and body alike. It is a fire which proceeds directly from the ire of God[3], working not of its own activity but as an instrument of divine vengeance[4]. As the waters of baptism cleanse the soul with the body so do the fires of punishment torture the spirit with the flesh. Every sense of the flesh is tortured and every faculty of the soul therewith: the eyes with impenetrable utter darkness[5], the nose with noisome odours[6], the ears with yells and howls and execrations[7], the taste with foul matter, leprous corruption[8], nameless suffocating filth[9], the touch with redhot goads and spikes[10], with cruel tongues of flame. And through the several torments of the senses the immortal soul is tortured eternally in its very essence amid the leagues upon leagues of glowing fires[11] kindled in the abyss by the offended majesty of the Omnipotent God[12] and fanned into

---

① afflict: 使身体受痛苦　② bowels: 肠子　③ the ire of God: 上帝的怒火　④ as an instrument of divine vengeance: 作为神圣的报复的工具　⑤ impenetrable utter darkness: 无法穿透的绝对的黑暗　⑥ noisome odours: 有毒的恶臭　⑦ yells and howls and execrations: 叫喊、嚎叫和咒骂　⑧ leprous corruption: 麻风病人的腐肉　⑨ nameless suffocating filth: 不可名状的令人窒息的污物　⑩ redhot goads and spikes: 烧得通红的刺棒和尖铁　⑪ leagues upon leagues of glowing fires: 无边的火海。league 为长度名，在英美约为 3 哩　⑫ the Omnipotent God: 万能的上帝

everlasting and ever increasing fury by the breath of the anger of the Godhead.

— Consider finally that the torment of this infernal[①] prison is increased by the company of the damned themselves. Evil company on earth is so noxious that the plants, as if by instinct, withdraw from the company of whatsoever is deadly or hurtful to them. In hell all laws are overturned: there is no thought of family or country, of ties, of relationships. The damned howl and scream at one another, their torture and rage intensified by the presence of beings tortured and raging like themselves. All sense of humanity is forgotten. The yells of the suffering sinners fill the remotest corners of the vast abyss. The mouths of the damned are full of blasphemies against God and of hatred for their fellowsufferers and of curses against those souls which were their accomplices[②] in sin. In olden times[③] it was the custom to punish the parricide[④], the man who had raised his murderous hand against his father, by casting him into the depths of the sea in a sack in which were placed a cock, a monkey and a serpent. The intention of those lawgivers who framed such a law, which seems cruel in our times, was to punish the criminal by the company of hateful and hurtful beasts[⑤]. But what is the fury of those dumb beasts compared with the fury of execration which bursts from the parched lips[⑥] and aching throats of the damned in hell when they behold in their companions in misery those who aided and abetted[⑦] them in sin, those whose words sowed the first seeds of evil thinking and evil living[⑧] in their minds, those whose immodest suggestions[⑨] led them on to sin, those whose eyes tempted and

---

① infernal: 地狱般的 ② accomplices: 帮凶 ③ In olden times: 惜时
④ parricide: 杀父母者 ⑤ the company of hateful and hurtful beasts: 可恨而
有害的野兽的陪伴 ⑥ parched lips: 焦干的嘴唇 ⑦ abet: 教唆
⑧ sowed the ... evil living: 第一次撒下邪恶思想和邪恶生活的种子
⑨ immodest suggestions: 不正派的建议

allured them from the path of virtue. They turn upon those accomplices and upbraid them and curse them①. But they are helpless and hopeless: it is too late now for repentance.

— Last of all consider the frightful torment to those damned souls, tempters and tempted alike, of the company of the devils. These devils will afflict the damned in two ways②, by their presence and by their reproaches. We can have no idea of how horrible these devils are. Saint Catherine of Siena once saw a devil and she has written that, rather than look again for one single instant on such a frightful monster, she would prefer to walk until the end of her life along a track of red coals③. These devils, who were once beautiful angels, have become as hideous and ugly as they once were beautiful. They mock and jeer at the lost souls whom they dragged down to ruin. It is they, the foul demons, who are made in hell the voices of conscience. Why did you sin? Why did you lend an ear to the temptings of friends? Why did you turn aside from your pious practices and good works? Why did you not shun the occasions of sin? Why did you not leave that evil companion? Why did you not give up that lewd habit④, that impure habit? Why did you not listen to the counsels of your confessor⑤? Why did you not, even after you had fallen the first or the second or the third or the fourth or the hundredth time, repent of your evil ways and turn to God who only waited for your repentance to absolve you of your sins? Now the time for repentance has gone by. Time is, time was, but time shall be no more! Time was to sin in secrecy, to indulge in that sloth and pride⑥, to covet the unlawful⑦, to yield to the promptings of your lower nature⑨, to live like the

---

① upbraid them and curse them: 谴责和咒骂他们　② afflict the damned in two ways: 用两种方式折磨那些入地狱的灵魂　③ along a track of red coals: 沿着用炭火铺成的道路　④ lewd habit: 淫荡的习惯　⑤ confessor: 有权听取告解的神父　⑥ indulge in that sloth and pride: 沉溺于怠惰与骄傲中　⑦ covet the unlawful: 垂涎不合法的东西　⑨ yield to the promptings of your lower nature: 屈从于你低下的天性的驱使

beasts of the field, nay worse, than the beasts of the field for they, at least, are but brutes and have no reason to guide them: time was but time shall be no more. God spoke to you by so many voices, but you would not hear. You would not crush out① that pride and anger in your heart, you would not restore those illgotten goods②, you would not obey the precepts of your holy church nor attend to your religious duties, you would not abandon those wicked companions, you would not avoid those dangerous temptations. Such is the language of those fiendish tormentors③, words of taunting and of reproach, of hatred and of disgust. Of disgust, yes! For even they, the very devils, when they sinned, sinned by such a sin as alone was compatible with such angelical natures, a rebellion of the intellect: and they, even they, the foul devils must turn away, revolted and disgusted, from the contemplation of those unspeakable sins by which degraded man④ outrages and defiles the temple of the Holy Ghost, defiles and pollutes himself.

— O, my dear little brothers in Christ, may it never be our lot to hear that language! May it never be our lot, I say! In the last day of terrible reckoning I pray fervently to God that not a single soul of those who are in this chapel today may be found among those miserable beings whom the Great Judge shall command to depart for ever from His sight, that not one of us may ever hear ringing in his ears the awful sentence of rejection: *Depart from me, ye cursed, into everlasting fire which was prepared for the devil and his angels*!

He came down the aisle⑤ of the chapel, his legs shaking and the scalp of his head trembling as though it had been touched by ghostly fingers. He passed up the staircase

① crush out: 清除　② illgotten goods: 通过不正当手段得来的物品
③ fiendish tormentors: 魔鬼般的折磨者　④ degraded man: 堕落的人
⑤ aisle: 教堂中两排座位之间的通道

and into the corridor along the walls of which the overcoats and waterproofs hung like gibbeted malefactors①, headless and dripping and shapeless. And at every step he feared that he had already died, that his soul had been wrenched forth of the sheath of his body②, that he was plunging headlong through space.

He could not grip the floor with his feet③ and sat heavily at his desk, opening one of his books at random and poring over it④. Every word for him. It was true. God was almighty. God could call him now, call him as he sat at his desk, before he had time to be conscious of the summons. God had called him. Yes? What? Yes? His flesh shrank together as it felt the approach of the ravenous tongues of flames⑤, dried up as it felt about it the swirl of stifling air⑥. He had died. Yes. He was judged. A wave of fire swept through his body: the first. Again a wave. His brain began to glow. Another. His brain was simmering and bubbling within the cracking tenement of the skull⑦. Flames burst forth from his skull like a corolla⑧, shrieking like voices:

— Hell! Hell! Hell! Hell! Hell!

Voices spoke near him:

— On hell.

— I suppose he rubbed it into you well.

— You bet he did. He put us all into a blue funk.⑨

— That's what you fellows want: and plenty of it to make you work.

He leaned back weakly in his desk. He had not died. God had spared him still. He was still in the familiar world of the school. Mr Tate and Vincent Heron stood at the

---

① gibbeted malefactors：绞死的罪犯 ② his soul ... of his body；他的灵魂已从他的躯壳里被抓走。 ③ He could ... his feet：他站立不稳 ④ opening one ... over it：随意地翻开本书，用心研读起来。 ⑤ the ravenous tongues of flames：贪婪的火舌 ⑥ stifling air：令人窒息的空气 ⑦ the cracking tenement of the skull：正在碎裂的头颅 ⑧ corolla：花冠 ⑨ He put ... blue funk：他可真把咱们都吓得够呛 。

window, talking, jesting, gazing out at the bleak rain[1], moving their heads.

— I wish it would clear up. I had arranged to go for a spin on the bike[2] with some fellows out by Malahide. But the roads must be knee-deep.

— It might clear up, sir.

The voices that he knew so well, the common words, the quiet of the classroom when the voices paused and the silence was filled by the sound of softly browsing cattle[3] as the other boys munched their lunches tranquilly, lulled his aching soul[4].

There was still time. O Mary, refuge of sinners, intercede for him[5]! O Virgin Undefiled, save him from the gulf of death!

The English lesson began with the hearing of the history. Royal persons, favourites, intriguers, bishops, passed like mute phantoms[6] behind their veil of names. All had died: all had been judged. What did it profit a man to gain the whole world if he lost his soul? At last he had understood: and human life lay around him, a plain of peace where upon antlike men laboured in brotherhood, their dead sleeping under quiet mounds. The elbow of his companion touched him and his heart was touched: and when he spoke to answer a question of his master he heard his own voice full of the quietude of humility and contrition[7].

His soul sank back deeper into depths of contrite peace, no longer able to suffer the pain of dread, and sending forth, as he sank, a faint prayer. Ah yes, he would still be spared[8]; he would repent in his heart and be forgiven; and then those above, those in heaven, would see

---

① the bleak rain: 凄凉的雨　② go for a spin on the bike: 骑车溜一圈儿　③ the sound of softly browsing cattle: 牛群吃草的柔和的声音　④ lulled his aching soul: 安抚他痛苦的灵魂　⑤ intercede for him: 为他求求情吧　⑥ mute phantoms: 无声的幽灵　⑦ full of . . . and contrition: 充满由于谦恭和悔罪带来的平静　⑧ he would still be spared: 他还是会被饶恕的。

what he would do to make up for the past: a whole life, every hour of life. Only wait.

— All, God! All, all!

A messenger came to the door to say that confessions were being heard in the chapel. Four boys left the room; and he heard others passing down the corridor. A tremulous chill[①] blew round his heart, no stronger than a little wind, and yet, listening and suffering silently, he seemed to have laid an ear against the muscle of his own heart, feeling it close and quail, listening to the flutter of its ventricles[②].

No escape. He had to confess, to speak out in words what he had done and thought, sin after sin. How? How?

— Father, I ...

The thought slid like a cold shining rapier into his tender flesh: confession. But not there in the chapel of the college. He would confess all, every sin of deed and thought, sincerely: but not there among his school companions. Far away from there in some dark place he would murmur out his own shame; and he besought God humbly not to be offended with him if he did not dare to confess in the college chapel; and in utter abjection of spirit[③] he craved forgiveness mutely of the boyish hearts about him.

Time passed.

He sat again in the front bench of the chapel. The daylight without was already failing and, as it fell slowly through the dull red blinds, it seemed that the sun of the last day was going down and that all souls were being gathered for the judgement.

— *I am cast away from the sight of Thine eyes*[④]: words taken, my dear little brothers in Christ, from the Book of Psalms, thirtieth chapter, twenty-third verse. In

---

① A tremulous chill: 一股令人颤栗的寒意   ② the flutter of its ventricles: 心房不规则地跳动   ③ in utter abjection of spirit: 以完全卑下的心态   ④ I am ... Thine eyes: 我已从你的眼前被抛开了。

the name of the Father and of the Son and of the Holy Ghost. Amen.

The preacher began to speak in a quiet friendly tone. His face was kind and he joined gently the fingers of each hand, forming a frail cage by the union of their tips.

— This morning we endeavoured, in our reflection upon hell, to make what our holy founder calls in his book of spiritual exercises, the composition of place. We endeavoured, that is, to imagine with the senses of the mind, in our imagination, the material character of that awful place and of the physical torments which all who are in hell endure. This evening we shall consider for a few moments the nature of the spiritual torments of hell[①].

— Sin, remember, is a twofold enormity[②]. It is a base consent to the promptings of our corrupt nature to the lower instincts[③], to that which is gross and beastlike; and it is also a turning away from the counsel of our higher nature, from all that is pure and holy, from the Holy God Himself. For this reason mortal sin is punished in hell by two different forms of punishment, physical and spiritual.

— Now of all these spiritual pains by far the greatest is the pain of loss, so great, in fact, that in itself it is a torment greater than all the others. Saint Thomas, the greatest doctor of the church, the angelic doctor, as he is called, says that the worst damnation consists in this that the understanding of man is totally deprived of divine light and his affection obstinately turned away from the goodness of God[④]. God, remember, is a being infinitely good and therefore the loss of such a being must be a loss infinitely painful. In this life we have not a very clear idea of what such a loss must be but the damned in hell, for their greater torment, have a full understanding of that which they have

---

① the nature of the spiritual torments of hell: 精神在地狱中受折磨的本质　② a twofold enormity: 双重的罪行　③ It is ... lower instincts: 我们腐化的天性屈从于低下本能的驱使。　④ his affection ... of God: 他的特性顽固地背离了上帝的善意。

lost and understand that they have lost it through their own sins and have lost it for ever. At the very instant of death the bonds of the flesh are broken asunder① and the soul at once flies towards. The soul tends towards. God as towards the centre of her existence. Remember, my dear little boys, our souls long to be with God. We come from God, we live by God, we belong to God: we are His, inalienably His②. God loves with a divine love every human soul and every human soul lives in that love. How could it be otherwise? Every breath that we draw, every thought of our brain, every instant of life proceeds from God's inexhaustible goodness. And if it be pain for a mother to be parted from her child, for a man to be exiled from hearth and home, for friend to be sundered from friend, O think what pain, what anguish③, it must be for the poor soul to be spurned④ from the presence of the supremely good and loving Creator Who has called that soul into existence from nothingness and sustained it in life and loved it with an immeasurable love. This, then, to be separated for ever from its greatest good, from God, and to feel the anguish of that separation, knowing full well that it is unchangeable, this is the greatest torment which the created soul is capable of bearing, *poena damni*⑤, the pain of loss.

The second pain which will afflict the souls of the damned in hell is the pain of conscience. Just as in dead bodies worms are engendered by putrefaction⑥ so in the souls of the lost there arises a perpetual remorse⑦ from the putrefaction of sin, the sting of conscience, the worm, as Pope Innocent the Third calls it, of the triple sting⑧. The first sting inflicted by this cruel worm will be the memory of past pleasures. O what a dreadful memory will that be!

---

① the bonds ... broken asunder：灵魂和肉体的纽带被割断　② we are His, inalienably His：我们属于他(上帝)，这永远也无法改变。　③ what anguish：怎样的苦痛　④ spurn：轻蔑地拒绝　⑤ *poena damni*：(拉丁文)下地狱的人所受的惩罚　⑥ in dead ... by putrefaction：尸体会由于腐烂而生蛆　⑦ a perpetual remorse：永久的悔恨　⑧ of the triple sting：具有三重的刺

In the lake of alldevouring flame the proud king will remember the pomps of his court, the wise but wicked man his libraries and instruments of research, the lover of artistic pleasures his marbles and pictures and other art treasures, he who delighted in the pleasures of the table his gorgeous feasts①, his dishes prepared with such delicacy, his choice wines; the miser will remember his hoard of gold②, the robber his illgotten wealth, the angry and revengeful and merciless murderers their deeds of blood and violence in which they revelled③, the impure and adulterous the unspeakable and filthy pleasures in which they delighted. They will remember all this and loathe themselves and their sins. For how miserable will all those pleasures seem to the soul condemned to suffer in hellfire for ages and ages. How they will rage and fume to think that they have lost the bliss of heaven for the dross of earth④, for a few pieces of metal, for vain honours, for bodily comforts, for a tingling of the nerves⑤. They will repent indeed; and this is the second sting of the worm of conscience, a late and fruitless sorrow for sins committed. Divine justice insists that the understanding of those miserable wretches be fixed continually on the sins of which they were guilty and moreover, as saint Augustine points out, God will impart to them His own knowledge of sin so that sin will appear to them in all its hideous malice⑥ as it appears to the eyes of God Himself. They will behold their sins in all their foulness and repent but it will be too late and then they will bewail the good occasions which they neglected⑦. This is the last and deepest and most cruel sting of the worm of conscience. The conscience will say: You had time and opportunity to repent and would not. You were brought up reli-

---

① gorgeous feasts: 华丽的宴会　② hoard of gold: 储藏的黄金　③ their deeds ... they revelled: 他们从中取乐的血腥和暴力活动　④ the dross of earth: 粪土之物　⑤ a tingling of the nerves: 神经上的刺激　⑥ hideous malice: 罪恶的怨恨　⑦ bewail the ... they neglected: 为他们错过良机而感到悲哀

giously by your parents. You had the sacraments and grace and indulgences of the church to aid you. You had the minister of God to preach to you, to call you back when you had strayed, to forgive you your sins, no matter how many, how abominable①, if only you had confessed and repented. No. You would not. You flouted the ministers of holy religion, you turned your back on the confessional, you wallowed deeper and deeper in the mire of sin②. God appealed to you, threatened you, entreated you to return to Him. O, what shame, what misery! The Ruler of the universe entreated you, a creature of clay, to love Him Who made you and to keep His law. No. You would not. And now, though you were to flood all hell with your tears if you could still weep, all that sea of repentance would not gain for you what a single tear of true repentance shed during your mortal life would have gained for you. You implore now a moment of earthly life wherein to repent: in vain. That time is gone: gone for ever.

— Such is the threefold sting of conscience, the viper③ which gnaws the very heart's core of the wretches in hell so that filled with hellish fury they curse themselves for their folly and curse the evil companions who have brought them to such ruin and curse the devils who tempted them in life and now mock them and torture them in eternity and even revile and curse the Supreme Being Whose goodness and patience they scorned and slighted but Whose justice and power they cannot evade.

— The next spiritual pain to which the damned are subjected is the pain of extension④. Man, in this earthly life, though he be capable of many evils, is not capable of them all at once inasmuch as one evil corrects and counteracts another just as one poison frequently corrects another.

---

① no matter how many, how abominable: 无论罪孽有多少, 有多么可憎
② the mire of sin: 罪恶的泥沼   ③ viper: 蝰(一种毒蛇)   ④ the pain of extension: 扩展了的痛苦

In hell, on the contrary, one torment, instead of counter-acting another, lends it still greater force: and, moreover, as the internal faculties are more perfect than the external senses, so are they more capable of suffering. Just as every sense is afflicted with a fitting torment, so is every spiritual faculty[①]; the fancy with horrible images, the sensitive faculty with alternate longing and rage[②], the mind and understanding with an interior darkness more terrible even than the exterior darkness which reigns in that dreadful prison. The malice, impotent though it be[③], which possesses these demon souls is an evil of boundless extension, of limitless duration, a frightful state of wickedness which we can scarcely realize unless we bear in mind the enormity of sin and the hatred God bears to it.

— Opposed to this pain of extension and yet coexistent with it we have the pain of intensity. Hell is the centre of evils and, as you know, things are more intense at their centres than at their remotest points. There are no contraries or admixtures of any kind to temper or soften in the least the pains of hell[④]. Nay, things which are good in themselves become evil in hell. Company, elsewhere a source of comfort to the afflicted, will be there a continual torment[⑤]: knowledge, so much longed for as the chief good of the intellect, will there be hated worse than ignorance: light, so much coveted by all creatures from the lord of creation down to the humblest plant in the forest, will be loathed intensely. In this life our sorrows are either not very long or not very great because nature either overcomes them by habits or puts an end to them by sinking under their weight. But in hell the torments cannot be overcome by habit, for while they are of terrible intensity they are at

---

① Just as ... spiritual faculty: 就像每一种感官都会受到相应的折磨，精神上的官能也是这样。　② alternate longing and rage: 交替的渴望和愤怒　③ impotent though it be: 尽管本身没有什么力量　④ to temper or soften in the least the pains of hell: 至少可用来减轻或冲淡地狱的痛苦　⑤ a continual torment: 连续不断的折磨

the same time of continual variety, each pain, so to speak,
taking fire from another and reendowing that which has
enkindled it with a still fiercer flame. Nor can nature escape from these intense and various tortures by succumbing
to them① for the soul is sustained and maintained in evil so
that its suffering may be the greater. Boundless extension
of torment, incredible intensity of suffering, unceasing variety of torture — this is what the divine majesty, so outraged
by sinners, demands; this is what the holiness of heaven,
slighted and set aside for the lustful and low pleasures of
the corrupt flesh, requires, this is what the blood of the innocent Lamb of God, shed for the redemption of sinners②,
trampled upon by the vilest of the vile③, insists upon.

— Last and crowning torture④ of all the tortures of
that awful place is the eternity of hell. Eternity! O, dread
and dire⑤ word. Eternity! What mind of man can understand it? And remember, it is an eternity of pain. Even
though the pains of hell were not so terrible as they are, yet
they would become infinite, as they are destined to last for
ever. But while they are everlasting they are at the same
time, as you know, intolerably intense, unbearably exten-
sive. To bear even the sting of an insect for all eternity
would be a dreadful torment. What must it be, then, to
bear the manifold tortures⑥ of hell for ever? For ever! For
all eternity! Not for a year or for an age but for ever. Try
to imagine the awful meaning of this. You have often seen
the sand on the seashore. How fine are its tiny grains! And
how many of those tiny little grains go to make up the
small handful which a child grasps in its play. Now imagine
a mountain of that sand, a million miles high, reaching
from the earth to the farthest heavens, and a million miles
broad, extending to remotest space, and a million miles in

---

① succumbing to them：屈从于他们　② the redemption of sinners：罪
人的赎救　③ trampled upon by the vilest of the vile：遭到最卑鄙的恶人的践
踏　④ Last and crowning torture：最后和最大的折磨　⑤ dread and dire：恐
怖而可怕　⑥ manifold tortures：多样的折磨

thickness: and imagine such an enormous mass of countless particles of sand multiplied as often as there are leaves in the forest, drops of water in the mighty ocean, feathers on birds, scales on fish[①], hairs on animals, atoms in the vast expanse of the air: and imagine that at the end of every million years a little bird came to that mountain and carried away in its beak a tiny grain of that sand. How many millions upon millions of centuries would pass before that bird had carried away even a square foot[②] of that mountain, how many eons upon eons of ages[③] before it had carried away all? Yet at the end of that immense stretch of time not even one instant of eternity could be said to have ended. At the end of all those billions and trillions of years eternity would have scarcely begun. And if that mountain rose again after it had been all carried away, and if the bird came again and carried it all away again grain by grain: and if it so rose and sank as many times as there are stars in the sky, atoms in the air, drops of water in the sea, leaves on the trees, feathers upon birds, scales upon fish, hairs upon animals, at the end of all those innumerable risings and sinkings of that immeasurably vast mountain not one single instant of eternity could be said to have ended; even then, at the end of such a period, after that eon of time the mere thought of which makes our very brain reel dizzily[④], eternity would have scarcely begun.

— A holy saint (one of our own fathers I believe it was) was once vouchsafed a vision of hell[⑤]. It seemed to him that he stood in the midst of a great hall, dark and silent save for the ticking of a great clock. The ticking went on unceasingly; and it seemed to this saint that the sound of the ticking was the ceaseless repetition of the words: ever, never; ever, never. Ever to be in hell, never

---

① scales on fish: 鱼鳞　② a square foot: 一平方英尺　③ eons upon eons of ages: 亿万年(极长而无法计算的时期)　④ the mere ... reel dizzily: 稍微一想就会令我们头晕眼花　⑤ was once ... of hell: 曾被赐予机会看到地狱的景象

to be in heaven; ever to be shut off from the presence of God, never to enjoy the beatific vision①; ever to be eaten with flames, gnawed by vermin, goaded with burning spikes, never to be free from those pains; ever to have the conscience upbraid one②, the memory enrage, the mind filled with darkness and despair, never to escape; ever to curse and revile the foul demons who gloat fiendishly over the misery of their dupes③, never to behold the shining raiment of the blessed spirits④; ever to cry out of the abyss of fire to God for an instant, a single instant, of respite from such awful agony⑤, never to receive, even for an instant, God's pardon; ever to suffer, never to enjoy; ever to be damned, never to be saved; ever, never; ever, never. O, what a dreadful punishment! An eternity of endless agony, of endless bodily and spiritual torment, without one ray of hope, without one moment of cessation⑥, of agony limitless in extent, limitless in intensity, of torment infinitely lasting, infinitely varied, of torture that sustains eternally that which it eternally devours, of anguish that everlastingly preys upon the spirit while it racks the flesh⑦, an eternity, every instant of which is itself an eternity, and that eternity an eternity of woe. Such is the terrible punishment decreed for those who die in mortal sin by an almighty and a just God.

— Yes, a just God! Men, reasoning always as men, are astonished that God should mete out⑧ an everlasting and infinite punishment in the fires of hell for a single grievous sin. They reason thus because, blinded by the gross illusion of the flesh and the darkness of human understanding, they are unable to comprehend the hideous malice

---

① beatific vision: 快乐的景象　② ever to ... upbraid one: 永远受着良心的谴责　③ gloat fiendishly ... their dupes: 幸灾乐祸地看那些受他们所骗的人遭受痛苦　④ never to ... blessed spirits: 连赐福人类的神灵的一丝影儿都看不到　⑤ a single ... awful agony: 从如此可怕的痛苦中解脱一小会儿　⑥ without one moment of cessation: 没有片刻停歇　⑦ racks the flesh: 折磨肉体　⑧ mete out: 分配

of mortal sin. They reason thus because they are unable to comprehend that even venial sin[1] is of such a foul and hideous nature that even if the omnipotent Creator could end all the evil and misery in the world, the wars, the diseases, the robberies, the crimes, the deaths, the murders, on condition that He allowed a single venial sin to pass unpunished, a single venial sin, a lie, an angry look, a moment of wilful sloth, He, the great omnipotent God, could not do so because sin, be it in thought or deed, is a transgression of His law[2] and God would not be God if He did not punish the transgressor.

— A sin, an instant of rebellious pride of the intellect, made Lucifer and a third part of the cohort of angels[3] fall from their glory. A sin, an instant of folly and weakness, drove Adam and Eve out of Eden and brought death and suffering into the world. To retrieve the consequences of that sin[4] the Only Begotten Son of God[5] came down to earth, lived and suffered and died a most painful death, hanging for three hours on the cross.

— O, my dear little brethren in Christ Jesus, will we then offend that good Redeemer and provoke His anger? Will we trample again upon that torn and mangled corpse? Will we spit upon that face so full of sorrow and love? Will we too, like the cruel jews and the brutal soldiers, mock that gentle and compassionate Saviour Who trod alone for our sake the awful winepress of sorrow? Every word of sin is a wound in His tender side. Every sinful act is a thorn piercing His head. Every impure thought, deliberately yielded to, is a keen lance transfixing that sacred and loving heart[6]. No, no. It is impossible for any human being to do that which offends so deeply the divine majesty, that

---

① venial sin: 轻微的罪过　② a transgression of His law: 对他(上帝)的法规的冒犯　③ the cohort of angels: 天使群　④ To retrieve the consequences of that sin: 为了挽回这一罪恶所产生的后果　⑤ the Only Begotten Son of God: 上帝惟一的儿子　⑥ is a keen ... loving heart: 是一根锋利的长矛,能刺穿上帝神圣而仁爱的心。

which is punished by an eternity of agony, that which crucifies again the Son of God① and makes a mockery of Him.

— I pray to God that my poor words may have availed
today to confirm in holiness those who are in a state of
grace, to strengthen the wavering, to lead back to the state
of grace the poor soul that has strayed if any such be among
you. I pray to God, and do you pray with me, that we
may repent of our sins. I will ask you now, all of you, to
repeat after me the act of contrition②, kneeling here in this
humble chapel in the presence of God. He is there in the
tabernacle burning with love for mankind, ready to comfort
the afflicted. Be not afraid. No matter how many or how
foul the sins if only you repent of them they will be forgiv-
en you. Let no worldly shame hold you back. God is still
the merciful Lord Who wishes not the eternal death of the
sinner but rather that he be converted and live.

— He calls you to Him. You are His. He made you
out of nothing. He loved you as only a God can love. His
arms are open to receive you even though you have sinned
against Him. Come to Him, poor sinner, poor vain and
erring sinner. Now is the acceptable time. Now is the
hour.

The priest rose and, turning towards the altar, knelt
upon the step before the tabernacle in the fallen gloom. He
waited till all in the chapel knelt and every least noise was
still. Then, raising his head, he repeated the act of contrition, phrase by phrase, with fervour③. The boys answered
him phrase by phrase. Stephen, his tongue cleaving to his
palate④, bowed his head, praying with his heart.

  — *O my God!* —
  — *O my God!* —
  — *I am heartily sorry* —

---

① crucifies again the Son of God: 使上帝的儿子被再次钉上十字架
② the act of contrition: 忏悔的动作 ③ with fervour: 充满热情 ④ his
tongue cleaving to his palate: 舌头粘在上颚上

— *I am heartily sorry* —
— *for having offended Thee* —
— *for having offended Thee* —
— *and I detest my sins* —
— *and I detest my sins* —
— *above every other evil* —
— *above every other evil* —
— *because they displease Thee, my God* —
— *because they displease Thee, my God* —
— *Who art so deserving* —
— *Who art so deserving* —
— *of all my love* —
— *of all my love* —
— *and I firmly purpose* —
— *and I firmly purpose* —
— *by Thy holy grace* —
— *by Thy holy grace* —
— *never more to offend Thee* —
— *never more to offend Thee* —
— *and to amend my life* —
— *and to amend my life* —

He went up to his room after dinner in order to be alone with his soul: and at every step his soul seemed to sigh: at every step his soul mounted with his feet, sighing in the ascent, through a region of viscid gloom[①].

He halted on the landing before the door and then, grasping the porcelain knob[②], opened the door quickly. He waited in fear, his soul pining within him, praying silently that death might not touch his brow as he passed over the threshold, that the fiends that inhabit darkness might not be given power over him. He waited still at the threshold as at the entrance to some dark cave. Faces were there; eyes: they waited and watched.

---

① a region of viscid gloom: 潮湿、昏暗的地区　② porcelain knob: 陶瓷门把

— We knew perfectly well of course that although it was bound to come to the light① he would find considerable difficulty in endeavouring to try to induce himself to try to endeavour to ascertain the spiritual plenipotentiary② and so we knew of course perfectly well —

Murmuring faces waited and watched; murmurous voices filled the dark shell of the cave. He feared intensely in spirit and in flesh but, raising his head bravely, he strode into the room firmly. A doorway, a room, the same room, same window. He told himself calmly that those words had absolutely no sense which had seemed to rise murmurously from the dark. He told himself that it was simply his room with the door open.

He closed the door and, walking swiftly to the bed, knelt beside it and covered his face with his hands. His hands were cold and damp and his limbs ached with chill. Bodily unrest and chill and weariness beset him, routing his thoughts③. Why was he kneeling there like a child saying his evening prayers? To be alone with his soul, to examine his conscience, to meet his sins face to face, to recall their times and manners and circumstances, to weep over them. He could not weep. He could not summon them to his memory. He felt only an ache of soul and body, his whole being, memory, will, understanding, flesh, benumbed and weary④.

That was the work of devils, to scatter his thoughts and over cloud his conscience, assailing him at the gates of the cowardly and sincorrupted flesh: and, praying God timidly to forgive him his weakness, he crawled up on to the bed and, wrapping the blankets closely about him, covered his face again with his hands. He had sinned. He had sinned so deeply against heaven and before God that he was

---

① it was bound to come to the light: 总归会真相大白　② ascertain the spiritual plenipotentiary: 探知精神上的全权威力　③ routing his thoughts: 打乱了他的思想　④ benumbed and weary: 麻木而疲惫

not worthy to be called God's child.

Could it be that he, Stephen Dedalus, had done those things? His conscience sighed in answer. Yes, he had done them, secretly, filthily, time after time, and, hardened in sinful impenitence[1], he had dared to wear the mask of holiness before the tabernacle[2] itself while his soul was a living mass of corruption. How came it that God had not struck him dead? The leprous company of his sins closed about him, breathing upon him, bending over him from all sides. He strove to forget them in an act of prayer, huddling his limbs closer together and binding down his eyelids: but the senses of his soul would not be bound and, though his eyes were shut fast, he saw the places where he had sinned and, though his ears were tightly covered, he heard. He desired with all his will not to hear or see. He desired till his frame shook under the strain of his desire and until the senses of his soul closed. They closed for an instant and then opened. He saw.

A field of stiff weeds and thistles and tufted nettle-bunches[3]. Thick among the tufts of rank stiff growth lay battered canisters and clots and coils of solid excrement[4]. A faint marshlight struggled upwards from all the ordure through the bristling greygreen weeds. An evil smell, faint and foul as the light, curled upwards sluggishly out of the canisters and from the stale crusted dung.

Creatures were in the field; one, three, six: creatures were moving in the field, hither and thither. Goatish creatures with human faces[5], hornybrowed, lightly bearded and grey as india-rubber. The malice of evil glittered in their hard eyes, as they moved hither and thither, trailing their long tails behind them. A rictus of cruel malignity[6]

---

① hardened in sinful impenitence: 在罪恶的不悔悟中加强了　② taber-nacle: 圣体盘　③ A field ... nettlebunches: 一片长满硬草、蓟草和一束束荨麻的田野　④ battered canisters ... solid excrement: 瘪瘪歪歪的金属罐和一圈一圈结成块的干粪　⑤ Goatish creatures with human faces: 指希腊神话中半人半羊的淫乱之神撒特(Satyr)　⑥ A rictus of cruel malignity: 大张着的残酷而狠毒的嘴

lit up greyly their old bony faces. One was clasping about his ribs a torn flannel waistcoat①, another complained monotonously as his beard stuck in the tufted weeds. Soft language issued from their spittleless lips as they swished in slow circles round and round the field, winding hither and thither through the weeds, dragging their long tails amid the rattling canisters. They moved in slow circles, circling closer and closer to enclose, to enclose, soft language issuing from their lips, their long swishing tails besmeared with stale shite②, thrusting upwards their terrific faces . . .

Help!

He flung the blankets from him madly to free his face and neck. That was his hell. God had allowed him to see the hell reserved for his sins: stinking, bestial, malignant, a hell of lecherous goatish fiends. For him! For him!

He sprang from the bed, reeking odour pouring down his throat, clogging and revolting his entrails③. Air! The air of heaven! He stumbled towards the window, groaning and almost fainting with sickness. At the washstand a convulsion seized him within; and, clasping his cold forehead wildly, he vomited profusely in agony④.

When the fit had spent itself he walked weakly to the window and, lifting the sash, sat in a corner of the embrasure and leaned his elbow upon the sill. The rain had drawn off; and amid the moving vapours from point to point of light the city was spinning about herself a soft cocoon⑤ of yellowish haze. Heaven was still and faintly luminous and the air sweet to breathe, as in a thicket drenched with showers⑥; and amid peace and shimmering lights and quiet fragrance he made a covenant with his heart.

He prayed:

---

① a torn flannel waistcoat: 一件破旧的法兰绒背心　② their long . . . stale shite: 他们摇摆着的长尾巴上粘满干粪　③ clogging and revolting his entrails: 他的内脏纠结在一起，让他觉得恶心　④ he vomited profusely in agony: 他痛苦地呕吐了个够　⑤ soft cocoon: 柔软的茧壳　⑥ as in a thicket drenched with showers: 像在已被雨水浇透的树丛里

— He once had meant to come on earth in heavenly glory but we sinned ; and then He could not safely visit us but with a shrouded majesty and a bedimmed radiance for He was God . So He came Himself in weakness not in power and He sent thee , a creature in His stead , with a creature's comeliness and lustre suited to our state . And now thy very face and form , dear mother , speak to us of the Eternal ; not like earthly beauty , dangerous to look upon , but like the morning star which is thy emblem , bright and musical , breathing purity , telling of heaven and infusing peace . O harbinger of day[①]! O light of the pilgrim ! Lead us still as thou hast led . In the dark night , across the bleak wilderness guide us on to our Lord Jesus , guide us home .

His eyes were dimmed with tears and, looking humbly up to heaven, he wept for the innocence he had lost.

When evening had fallen he left the house and the first touch of the damp dark air and the noise of the door as it closed behind him made ache again his conscience, lulled by prayer and tears. Confess! Confess! It was not enough to lull the conscience with a tear and a prayer. He had to kneel before the minister of the Holy Ghost and tell over his hidden sins truly and repentantly. Before he heard again the footboard of the housedoor trail over the threshold as it opened to let him in, before he saw again the table in the kitchen set for supper he would have knelt and confessed. It was quite simple.

The ache of conscience ceased and he walked onward swiftly through the dark streets. There were so many flagstones[②] on the footpath of that street and so many streets in that city and so many cities in the world. Yet eternity

---

① *harbinger of day*：白昼的先驱　② flagstones：(铺路用的)石板

had no end. He was in mortal sin. Even once was a mortal sin. It could happen in an instant. But how so quickly? By seeing or by thinking of seeing. The eyes see the thing, without having wished first to see. Then in an instant it happens. But does that part of the body understand or what? The serpent, the most subtle beast of the field. It must understand when it desires in one instant and then prolongs its own desire instant after instant, sinfully. It feels and understands and desires. What a horrible thing! Who made it to be like that, a bestial part of the body able to understand bestially and desire bestially? Was that then he or an inhuman thing moved by a lower soul than his soul? His soul sickened at the thought of a torpid snaky life feeding itself out of the tender marrow of his life① and fattening upon the slime of lust. O why was that so? O why?

He cowered in the shadow of the thought, abasing himself in the awe of God Who had made all things and all men. Madness. Who could think such a thought? And, cowering in darkness and abject, he prayed mutely to his guardian angel② to drive away with his sword the demon that was whispering to his brain.

The whisper ceased and he knew then clearly that his own soul had sinned in thought and word and deed wilfully through his own body. Confess! He had to confess every sin. How could he utter in words to the priest what he had done? Must, must. Or how could he explain without dying of shame? Or how could he have done such things without shame? A madman, a loathsome madman! Confess! O he would indeed to be free and sinless again! Perhaps the priest would know. O dear God!

He walked on and on through illlit streets③, fearing to stand still for a moment lest it might seem that he held back from what awaited him, fearing to arrive at that to-

---

① a torpid ... his life：一条蛰伏在他身体里的毒蛇般的生命靠吸吮他娇嫩的骨髓维持生命　② guardian angel：守护神　③ illlit streets：灯光暗淡的街道

wards which he still turned with longing. How beautiful must be a soul in the state of grace when God looked upon it with love!

Frowsy girls sat along the curbstones before their baskets①. Their dank hair hung trailed over their brows. They were not beautiful to see as they crouched in the mire. But their souls were seen by God; and if their souls were in a state of grace they were radiant to see: and God loved them, seeing them.

A wasting breath of humiliation blew bleakly over his soul② to think of how he had fallen, to feel that those souls were dearer to God than his. The wind blew over him and passed on to the myriads and myriads of③ other souls on whom God's favour shone now more and now less, stars now brighter and now dimmer, sustained and failing④. And the glimmering souls passed away, sustained and failing, merged in a moving breath. One soul was lost; a tiny soul: his. It flickered once and went out, forgotten, lost. The end: black, cold, void waste.

Consciousness of place came ebbing back to him slowly over a vast tract of time unlit, unfelt, unlived. The squalid scene composed itself around him; the common accents, the burning gasjets in the shops⑤, odours of fish and spirits and wet sawdust, moving men and women. An old woman was about to cross the street, an oilcan in her hand. He bent down and asked her was there a chapel near.

— A chapel, sir? Yes, sir. Church Street chapel.

— Church?

She lifted the can to her other hand and directed him; and, as she held out her reeking withered right hand under its fringe of shawl, he bent lower towards her, saddened

---

① Frowsy girls ... their baskets: 邋遢的姑娘们沿路边的石头坐着,面前摆着篮子　② A wasting ... his soul: 一股令人感到衰退和羞辱的风凄凉地吹过他的灵魂　③ myriads and myriads of: 无数　④ sustained and failing: 有的将继续存在,有的正在消失　⑤ the burning gasjets in the shops: 店铺里燃烧着的煤气灯

and soothed by her voice.

— Thank you.

— You are quite welcome, sir.

The candles on the high altar had been extinguished but the fragrance of incense① still floated down the dim nave②. Bearded workmen with pious faces were guiding a canopy out through a sidedoor, the sacristan③ aiding them with quiet gestures and words. A few of the faithful still lingered praying before one of the side altars or kneeling in the benches near the confessionals. He approached timidly and knelt at the last bench in the body, thankful for the peace and silence and fragrant shadow of the church. The board on which he knelt was narrow and worn and those who knelt near him were humble followers of Jesus. Jesus too had been born in poverty and had worked in the shop of a carpenter, cutting boards and planing them, and had first spoken of the kingdom of God to poor fishermen, teaching all men to be meek and humble of heart④.

He bowed his head upon his hands, bidding his heart be meek and humble that he might be like those who knelt beside him and his prayer as acceptable as theirs. He prayed beside them but it was hard. His soul was foul with sin and he dared not ask forgiveness with the simple trust of those whom Jesus, in the mysterious ways of God, had called first to His side, the carpenters, the fishermen, poor and simple people following a lowly trade, handling and shaping the wood of trees, mending their nets with patience.

A tall figure came down the aisle and the penitents⑤ stirred; and at the last moment, glancing up swiftly, he saw a long grey beard and the brown habit of a capuchin⑥. The priest entered the box and was hidden. Two penitents

---

① the fragrance of incense：敬神的香所发出的香味 ② nave：教堂的正厅（会众所坐的部分） ③ sacristan：（天主教）教堂的司事 ④ teaching all ... of heart：教导所有的人要温和谦恭 ⑤ the penitents：悔罪的人 ⑥ the brown habit of a capuchin：托钵僧穿的棕色的服装。habit 表示宗教级别的衣着。

rose and entered the confessional at either side. The wood-en slide① was drawn back and the faint murmur of a voice troubled the silence.

His blood began to murmur in his veins, murmuring like a sinful city summoned from its sleep to hear its doom. Little flakes of fire fell and powdery ashes fell softly, a-lighting on the houses of men. They stirred, waking from sleep, troubled by the heated air.

The slide was shot back. The penitent emerged from the side of the box. The farther slide was drawn. A woman entered quietly and deftly where the first penitent had knelt. The faint murmur began again.

He could still leave the chapel. He could stand up, put one foot before the other and walk out softly and then run, run, run swiftly through the dark streets. He could still es-cape from the shame. Had it been any terrible crime but that one sin! Had it been murder! Little fiery flakes fell and touched him at all points, shameful thoughts, shameful words, shameful acts. Shame covered him wholly like fine glowing ashes falling continually. To say it in words! His soul, stifling and helpless, would cease to be② .

The slide was shot back. A penitent emerged from the farther side of the box. The near slide was drawn. A peni-tent entered where the other penitent had come out. A soft whispering noise floated in vaporous cloudlets out of the box. It was the woman: soft whispering cloudlets, soft whispering vapour, whispering and vanishing.

He beat his breast with his fist humbly, secretly under cover of the wooden armrest③ . He would be at one with others and with God. He would love his neighbour. He would love God Who had made and loved him. He would kneel and pray with others and be happy. God would look

---

① The wooden slide: 木头滑门 ② His soul, stifling and helpless, would cease to be: 他那令人窒息的无助的灵魂会因此而无法存在下去。
③ the wooden armrest: 木靠手

down on him and on them and would love them all.

It was easy to be good. God's yoke was sweet and light①. It was better never to have sinned, to have remained always a child, for God loved little children and suffered them to come to Him. It was a terrible and a sad thing to sin. But God was merciful to poor sinners who were truly sorry. How true that was! That was indeed goodness.

The slide was shot to suddenly. The penitent came out. He was next. He stood up in terror and walked blindly into the box.

At last it had come. He knelt in the silent gloom and raised his eyes to the white crucifix suspended above him. God could see that he was sorry. He would tell all his sins. His confession would be long, long. Everybody in the chapel would know then what a sinner he had been. Let them know. It was true. But God had promised to forgive him if he was sorry. He was sorry. He clasped his hands and raised them towards the white form, praying with his darkened eyes, praying with all his trembling body, swaying his head to and fro like a lost creature, praying with whimpering lips.

— Sorry! Sorry! O sorry!

The slide clicked and his heart bounded in his breast. The face of an old priest was at the grating, averted from him, leaning upon a hand②. He made the sign of the cross and prayed of the priest to bless him for he had sinned. Then, bowing his head, he repeated the *Confiteor*③ in fright. At the words *my most grievous fault*④ he ceased, breathless.

— How long is it since your last confession, my child?

— A long time, father.

---

① God's yoke was sweet and light：上帝加在人身上的轭头是甜蜜而轻柔的　② The face ... a hand：在木格子边是一张老神父的脸，并未对着他，而是靠在手上。　③ *Confiteor*：(天主教)忏悔词　④ *my most grievous fault*：我最可悲的过失

— A month, my child?

— Longer, father.

— Three months, my child?

— Longer, father.

— Six months?

— Eight months, father.

He had begun. The priest asked:

— And what do you remember since that time?

He began to confess his sins: masses missed, prayers not said, lies.

— Anything else, my child?

Sins of anger, envy of others, gluttony①, vanity, disobedience.

— Anything else, my child?

— Sloth.

— Anything else, my child?

There was no help. He murmured:

— I . . . committed sins of impurity, father.

The priest did not turn his head.

— With yourself, my child?

— And . . . with others.

— With women, my child?

— Yes, father.

— Were they married women, my child?

He did not know. His sins trickled from his lips, one by one, trickled in shameful drops from his soul, festering and oozing like a sore②, a squalid stream of vice③. The last sins oozed forth, sluggish, filthy. There was no more to tell. He bowed his head, overcome.

The priest was silent. Then he asked:

— How old are you, my child?

— Sixteen, father.

The priest passed his hand several times over his face. Then, resting his forehead against his hand, he leaned to-

---

① gluttony: 暴饮暴食　② festering and oozing like a sore: 像正在溃烂流脓的伤口　③ a squalid stream of vice: 一条肮脏罪恶的河流

wards the grating and, with eyes still averted, spoke slowly. His voice was weary and old.

— You are very young, my child, he said, and let me
implore of you to give up that sin. It is a terrible sin. It
kills the body and kills the soul. It is the cause of many
crimes and misfortunes. Give it up, my child, for God's
sake. It is dishonourable and unmanly. You cannot know
where that wretched habit will lead you or where it will
come against you. As long as you commit that sin, my poor
child, you will never be worth one farthing to God①. Pray
to our mother Mary to help you. She will help you, my
child. Pray to Our Blessed Lady when that sin comes into
your mind. I am sure you will do that, will you not? You
repent of all those sins. I am sure you do. And you will
promise God now that by His holy grace you will never offend Him any more by that wicked sin. You will make that
solemn promise to God, will you not?

— Yes, father.

The old and weary voice fell like sweet rain upon his
quaking parching heart②. How sweet and sad!

— Do so, my poor child. The devil has led you
astray③. Drive him back to hell when he tempts you to dishonour your body in that way — the foul spirit who hates
our Lord. Promise God now that you will give up that sin,
that wretched wretched sin.

Blinded by his tears and by the light of God's merciful-
ness he bent his head and heard the grave words of absolution spoken and saw the priest's hand raised above him in
token of forgiveness④.

— God bless you, my child. Pray for me.

He knelt to say his penance, praying in a corner of the
dark nave; and his prayers ascended to heaven from his pu-

---

① you will never be worth one farthing to God：你会在上帝面前变得一
文不值　② quaking parching heart：颤抖着的火烧般的心　③ The devil has
led you astray：魔鬼已将你引上了歧途。　④ in token of forgiveness：以宽
恕的手势

rified heart like perfume streaming upwards from a heart of white rose.

The muddy streets were gay. He strode homeward, conscious of an invisible grace pervading and making light his limbs. In spite of all he had done it. He had confessed and God had pardoned him. His soul was made fair and holy once more, holy and happy.

It would be beautiful to die if God so willed. It was beautiful to live if God so willed, to live in grace a life of peace and virtue and forbearance with others.

He sat by the fire in the kitchen, not daring to speak for happiness. Till that moment he had not known how beautiful and peaceful life could be. The green square of paper pinned round the lamp cast down a tender shade. On the dresser was a plate of sausages and white pudding and on the shelf there were eggs. They would be for the breakfast in the morning after the communion in the college chapel. White pudding and eggs and sausages and cups of tea. How simple and beautiful was life after all! And life lay all before him.

In a dream he fell asleep. In a dream he rose and saw that it was morning. In a waking dream he went through the quiet morning towards the college.

The boys were all there, kneeling in their places. He knelt among them, happy and shy. The altar was heaped with fragrant masses of white flowers; and in the morning light the pale flames of the candles among the white flowers were clear and silent as his own soul.

He knelt before the altar with his classmates, holding the altar cloth with them over a living rail of hands[1]. His hands were trembling and his soul trembled as he heard the priest pass with the ciborium[2] from communicant[3] to communicant.

---

① a living rail of hands: 用手组成的活的围栏　② ciborium: 圣餐盘　③ communicant: 受圣餐的人

— *Corpus Domini nostri.* [①]

Could it be? He knelt there sinless and timid; and he would hold upon his tongue the host and God would enter his purified body.

— *In vitam eternam. Amen* [②].

Another life! A life of grace and virtue and happiness! It was true. It was not a dream from which he would wake. The past was past.

— *Corpus Domini nostri.*

The ciborium had come to him.

---

① *Corpus Domini nostri*：（拉丁文）我们主的圣体。 ② *In vitam eternam. Amen*：（拉丁文）在永恒的生命之中，阿门！

CHAPTER 4

Sunday was dedicated to the mystery of the Holy Trinity, Monday to the Holy Ghost, Tuesday to the Guardian Angels, Wednesday to saint Joseph, Thursday to the Most Blessed Sacrament of the Altar①, Friday to the Suffering Jesus, Saturday to the Blessed Virgin Mary.

Every morning he hallowed himself anew② in the presence of some holy image or mystery. His day began with an heroic offering of its every moment of thought or action for the intentions of the sovereign pontiff③ and with an early mass. The raw morning air whetted his resolute piety; and often as he knelt among the few worshippers at the sidealtar, following with his interleaved prayer book④ the murmur of the priest, he glanced up for an instant towards the vested figure standing in the gloom between the two candles, which were the old and the new testaments⑤, and imagined that he was kneeling at mass in the catacombs⑥. His daily life was laid out in devotional areas. By means of ejaculations and prayers he stored up ungrudgingly for the souls in purgatory⑦ centuries of days and quarantines and years; yet the spiritual triumph which he felt in achieving with ease so many fabulous ages of canonical penances⑧ did not wholly reward his zeal of prayer, since he could never know how much temporal punishment he had remitted by way of suffrage for the agonising souls⑨; and fearful lest in the midst of the purgatorial fire, which

---

① the Most Blessed Sacrament of the Altar: 祭坛上最神圣的圣餐仪式
② hallowed himself anew: 使自己再次变得神圣　③ pontiff: (旧用法)主教
④ interleaved prayer book: 插有纸片的祈祷书　⑤ the old and the new testaments: 旧约(圣经)和新约(圣经)　⑥ catacombs: 地下墓穴　⑦ purgatory: 炼狱　⑧ canonical penances: 合乎教规的悔罪　⑨ since he ... agonising souls: 因为他永远不可能知道, 他这样为那些痛苦不堪的灵魂代作祷告, 究竟能帮助他们减轻多少肉体上的惩罚。

differed from the infernal only in that it was not everlasting, his penance might avail no more than a drop of moisture, he drove his soul daily through an increasing circle of works of supererogation①.

Every part of his day, divided by what he regarded now as the duties of his station in life, circled about its own centre of spiritual energy. His life seemed to have drawn near to eternity; every thought, word, and deed, every instance of consciousness could be made to revibrate radiantly in heaven; and at times his sense of such immediate repercussion② was so lively that he seemed to feel his soul in devotion pressing like fingers the keyboard of a great cash register③ and to see the amount of his purchase start forth immediately in heaven, not as a number but as a frail column of incense or as a slender flower.

The rosaries, too, which he said constantly — for he carried his beads loose in his trousers' pockets that he might tell them as he walked the streets — transformed themselves into coronals of flowers④ of such vague unearthly texture that they seemed to him as hueless and odourless as they were nameless. He offered up each of his three daily chaplets⑤ that his soul might grow strong in each of the three theological virtues, in faith in the Father Who had created him, in hope in the Son Who had redeemed him, and in love of the Holy Ghost Who had sanctified him⑥; and this thrice triple prayer he offered to the Three Persons⑦ through Mary in the name of her joyful and sorrowful and glorious mysteries.

On each of the seven days of the week he further prayed that one of the seven gifts of the Holy Ghost⑧

---

① supererogation：功德 ② repercussion：反响 ③ cash register：现金出纳机 ④ coronals of flowers：花环 ⑤ chaplets：祈祷时计数用的念珠 ⑥ had sanctified him：曾使他变得神圣 ⑦ this thrice … Three Persons：他向那三位圣人每日三次地进行三重的祷告。 ⑧ seven gifts of the Holy Ghost：圣灵的七种神恩，即智慧、理解、劝告、刚毅、知识、虔诚、敬畏上帝。

might descend upon his soul and drive out of it day by day the seven deadly sins① which had defiled it in the past; and he prayed for each gift on its appointed day, confident that it would descend upon him, though it seemed strange to him at times that wisdom and understanding and knowledge were so distinct in their nature that each should be prayed for apart from the others. Yet he believed that at some future stage of his spiritual progress this difficulty would be removed when his sinful soul had been raised up from its weakness and enlightened by the Third Person of the Most Blessed Trinity②. He believed this all the more, and with trepidation③, because of the divine gloom and silence wherein dwelt the unseen Paraclete④, Whose symbols were a dove and a mighty wind, to sin against Whom was a sin beyond forgiveness, the eternal, mysterious secret Being to Whom, as God, the priests offered up mass once a year, robed in the scarlet of the tongues of fire⑤.

The imagery through which the nature and kinship of the Three Persons of the Trinity were darkly shadowed forth in the books of devotion which he read — the Father contemplating from all eternity as in a mirror His Divine Perfections and thereby begetting eternally the Eternal Son and the Holy Spirit proceeding out of Father and Son from all eternity — were easier of acceptance by his mind by reason of their august incomprehensibility⑥ than was the simple fact that God had loved his soul from all eternity, for ages before he had been born into the world, for ages before the world itself had existed.

He had heard the names of the passions of love and hate pronounced solemnly on the stage and in the pulpit, had found them set forth solemnly in books and had won-

---

① seven deadly sins: 七项可遭天罚的大罪, 即骄傲、贪婪、淫欲、生气、贪食、忌妒、怠惰。 ② enlightened by ... the Most Blessed Trinity: 得到至高无上的三位一体中的圣灵的启示 ③ trepidation: 惶恐 ④ Paraclete: 圣灵 ⑤ robed in ... of fire: 穿着绘着火舌的红色外袍 ⑥ by reason of their august incomprehensibility: 由于他们那令人敬畏的神秘莫测

dered why his soul was unable to harbour them for any time[①] or to force his lips to utter their names with conviction. A brief anger had often invested him but he had never been able to make it an abiding passion and had always felt himself passing out of it as if his very body were being divested[②] with ease of some outer skin or peel. He had felt a subtle, dark and murmurous presence penetrate his being and fire him with a brief iniquitous lust[③]: it too had slipped beyond his grasp leaving his mind lucid and indifferent. This, it seemed, was the only love and that the only hate his soul would harbour.

But he could no longer disbelieve in the reality of love since God Himself had loved his individual soul with divine love from all eternity. Gradually, as his soul was enriched with spiritual knowledge, he saw the whole world forming one vast symmetrical expression of God's power and love. Life became a divine gift for every moment and sensation of which, were it even the sight of a single leaf hanging on the twig of a tree, his soul should praise and thank the Giver. The world for all its solid substance and complexity no longer existed for his soul save as a theorem[④] of divine power and love and universality. So entire and unquestionable was this sense of the divine meaning in all nature granted to his soul that he could scarcely understand why it was in any way necessary that he should continue to live. Yet that was part of the divine purpose and he dared not question its use, he above all others who had sinned so deeply and so foully against the divine purpose. Meek and abased by this consciousness of the one eternal omnipresent perfect reality his soul took up again her burden of pieties, masses and prayers and sacraments and mortifications[⑤], and only then for the first time since he had brooded on the

---

① his soul ... anytime: 他的灵魂在任何时候都无法容忍这些名字。
② divested: 脱去　③ iniquitous lust: 邪恶的淫欲　④ theorem: 表征
⑤ mortifications: 忏悔

great mystery of love did he feel within him a warm move-ment like that of some newly born life or virtue of the soul itself. The attitude of rapture in sacred art, the raised and parted hands, the parted lips and eyes as of one about to swoon[①], became for him an image of the soul in prayer, humiliated and faint before her Creator.

But he had been forewarned of the dangers of spiritual exaltation[②] and did not allow himself to desist from even the least or lowliest devotion, striving also by constant mortification to undo the sinful past rather than to achieve a saintliness fraught with[③] peril. Each of his senses was brought under a rigorous discipline. In order to mortify the sense of sight he made it his rule to walk in the street with downcast eyes, glancing neither to right nor left and never behind him. His eyes shunned every encounter with the eyes of women. From time to time also he balked[④] them by a sudden effort of the will, as by lifting them suddenly in the middle of an unfinished sentence and closing the book. To mortify his hearing he exerted no control over his voice which was then breaking, neither sang nor whistled and made no attempt to flee from noises which caused him painful nervous irritation such as the sharpening of knives on the knifeboard, the gathering of cinders on the fire-shovel and the twigging of the carpet. To mortify his smell was more difficult as he found in himself no instinctive re-pugnance[⑤] to bad odours, whether they were the odours of the outdoor world such as those of dung and tar, or the odours of his own person among which he had made many curious comparisons and experiments. He found in the end that the only odour against which his sense of smell revolted was a certain stale fishy stink like that of long standing urine; and whenever it was possible he subjected himself to this unpleasant odour. To mortify the taste he practised

---

① swoon：晕倒　② exaltation：得意　③ fraught with：充满　④ balked：故意阻止　⑤ no instinctive repugnance：没有本能的厌恶感

strict habits at table, observed to the letter all the fasts[①] of
the church and sought by distraction to divert his mind
from the savours of different foods. But it was to the mortification of touch that he brought the most assiduous ingenuity of inventiveness[②]. He never consciously changed his
position in bed, sat in the most uncomfortable positions,
suffered patiently every itch and pain, kept away from the
fire, remained on his knees all through the mass except at
the gospels, left part of his neck and face undried so that
air might sting them and, whenever he was not saying his
beads, carried his arms stiffly at his sides like a runner and
never in his pockets or clasped behind him.

He had no temptations to sin mortally. It surprised
him however to find that at the end of his course of intricate piety and selfrestraint he was so easily at the mercy of
childish and unworthy imperfections. His prayers and fasts
availed him little for the suppression of anger at hearing his
mother sneeze or at being disturbed in his devotions. It
needed an immense effort of his will to master the impulse
which urged him to give outlet to such irritation. Images of
the outbursts of trivial anger which he had often noted a-
mong his masters, their twitching mouths, closeshut lips
and flushed cheeks, recurred to his memory, discouraging
him, for all his practice of humility, by the comparison.
To merge his life in the common tide of other lives was
harder for him than any fasting or prayer, and it was his
constant failure to do this to his own satisfaction which
caused in his soul at last a sensation of spiritual dryness together with a growth of doubts and scruples[③]. His soul
traversed a period of desolation in which the sacraments
themselves seemed to have turned into dried up sources.
His confession became a channel for the escape of scrupulous and unrepented imperfections[④]. His actual reception

---

① fasts: 斋戒　② the most assiduous ingenuity of inventiveness: 最努力
的创造发明　③ scruples: 顾虑　④ scrupulous and unrepented imperfections:
使他良心不安的和未能悔改的过失

of the eucharist① did not bring him the same dissolving moments of virginal selfsurrender as did those spiritual communions made by him sometimes at the close of some visit to the Blessed Sacrament. The book which he used for these visits was an old neglected book written by saint Alphonsus Liguori, with fading characters and sere foxpapered leaves②. A faded world of fervent love and virginal responses seemed to be evoked for his soul by the reading of its pages in which the imagery of the canticles③ was interwoven with the communicant's prayers. An inaudible voice seemed to caress the soul, telling her names and glories, bidding her arise as for espousal④ and come away, bidding her look forth, a spouse, from Amana and from the mountains of the leopards; and the soul seemed to answer with the same inaudible voice, surrendering herself: *Inter ubera mea commorabitur*⑤.

This idea of surrender had a perilous attraction for his mind now that he felt his soul beset once again by the insistent voices of the flesh which began to murmur to him again during his prayers and meditations. It gave him an intense sense of power to know that he could, by a single act of consent, in a moment of thought, undo all that he had done. He seemed to feel a flood slowly advancing towards his naked feet and to be waiting for the first faint timid noiseless wavelet to touch his fevered skin. Then, almost at the instant of that touch, almost at the verge of sinful consent, he found himself standing far away from the flood upon a dry shore, saved by a sudden act of the will or a sudden ejaculation; and, seeing the silver line of the flood far away and beginning again its slow advance towards his feet, a new thrill of power and satisfaction shook his soul to know that he had not yielded nor undone all.

---

① eucharist: 圣餐　② fading characters and sere foxpapered leaves: 字迹模糊且纸张枯黄,满是褐斑　③ canticles: 赞美歌　④ espousal: 婚约　⑤ *Inter ubera mea commorabitur*: (拉丁文)让他安卧在我的两乳间

When he had eluded the flood of temptation① many times in this way he grew troubled and wondered whether the grace which he had refused to lose was not being filched② from him little by little. The clear certitude of his own immunity③ grew dim and to it succeeded a vague fear that his soul had really fallen unawares. It was with difficulty that he won back his old consciousness of his state of grace by telling himself that he had prayed to God at every temptation and that the grace which he had prayed for must have been given to him inasmuch as God was obliged to give it. The very frequency and violence of temptations showed him at last the truth of what he had heard about the trials of the saints. Frequent and violent temptations were a proof that the citadel④ of the soul had not fallen and that the devil raged to make it fall.

Often when he had confessed his doubts and scruples, some momentary inattention at prayer, a movement of trivial anger in his soul or a subtle wilfulness in speech or act, he was bidden by his confessor to name some sin of his past life before absolution⑤ was given him. He named it with humility and shame and repented of it once more. It humiliated and shamed him to think that he would never be freed from it wholly, however holily he might live or whatever virtues or perfections he might attain. A restless feeling of guilt would always be present with him: he would confess and repent and be absolved, confess and repent again and be absolved again, fruitlessly. Perhaps that first hasty confession wrung from him by the fear of hell had not been good? Perhaps, concerned only for his imminent doom, he had not had sincere sorrow for his sin? But the surest sign that his confession had been good and that he had had sincere sorrow for his sin was, he knew, the amendment of his life.

---

① eluded the flood of temptation: 避开诱惑的洪流   ② filch: 窃取
③ immunity: 免疫   ④ citadel: 堡垒   ⑤ absolution: 指天主教中的赦罪

— I have amended my life, have I not? he asked himself.

The director stood in the embrasure of the window[1], his back to the light, leaning an elbow on the brown crossblind and, as he spoke and smiled, slowly dangling and looping the cord of the other blind[2] Stephen stood before him, following for a moment with his eyes the waning of the long summer daylight above the roofs or the slow deft movements of the priestly fingers. The priest's face was in total shadow but the waning daylight from behind him touched the deeply grooved temples[3] and the curves of the skull. Stephen followed also with his ears the accents, and intervals of the priest's voice as he spoke gravely and cordially of indifferent themes, the vacation which had just ended, the colleges of the order abroad, the transference of masters. The grave and cordial voice went on easily with its tale and in the pauses Stephen felt bound to set it on again with respectful questions[4]. He knew that the tale was a prelude and his mind waited for the sequel. Ever since the message of summons had come for him from the director his mind had struggled to find the meaning of the message; and during the long restless time he had sat in the college parlour waiting for the director to come in his eyes had wandered from one sober picture to another around the walls and his mind wandered from one guess to another until the meaning of the summons had almost become clear. Then, just as he was wishing that some unforeseen cause might prevent the director from coming, he had heard the handle of the door turning and the swish of a soutane.

The director had begun to speak of the dominican and franciscan orders[5] and of the friendship between saint

---

① embrasure of the window：窗口　② the cord of the other blind：另一个窗帘的绳线　③ grooved temples：深陷的太阳穴　④ in the ... respectful questions：在停顿的间隙，斯蒂芬总感到他该提几个郑重其事的问题，以让他继续讲下去。　⑤ the dominican and franciscan orders：（天主教）多明我会和方济各会。

Thomas and saint Bonaventure. The capuchin① dress, he thought, was rather too ...

Stephen's face gave back the priest's indulgent smile and, not being anxious to give an opinion, he made a slight dubitative② movement with his lips.

— I believe, continued the director, that there is some talk now among the capuchins themselves of doing away with it and following the example of the other franciscans.

— I suppose they would retain it in the cloisters, said Stephen.

— O, certainly, said the director. For the cloister it is all right but for the street I really think it would be better to do away with it, don't you?

— It must be troublesome, I imagine.

— Of course it is, of course. Just imagine when I was in Belgium I used to see them out cycling in all kinds of weather with this thing up about their knees! It was really ridiculous. *Les jupes*, they call them in Belgium.

The vowel was so modified as to be indistinct.

— What do they call them?

— *Les jupes*③.

— O.

Stephen smiled again in answer to the smile which he could not see on the priest's shadowed face, its image or spectre④ only passing rapidly across his mind as the low discreet accent⑤ fell upon his ear. He gazed calmly before him at the waning sky, glad of the cool of the evening and of the faint yellow glow which hid the tiny flame kindling upon his cheek.

The names of articles of dress worn by women or of certain soft and delicate stuffs used in their making brought always to his mind a delicate and sinful perfume. As a boy he had imagined the reins by which horses are driven as

---

① capuchin：方济各会的僧侣　② dubitative：怀疑的　③ *Les jupes*：(拉丁文)裙子，衬裙　④ spectre：幽灵　⑤ discreet accent：谨慎的音调

slender silken bands and it shocked him to feel at Strad-
brooke the greasy leather of harness①. It had shocked him
too when he had felt for the first time beneath his tremulous fingers the brittle texture of a woman's stocking for,
retaining nothing of all he read save that which seemed to
him an echo or a prophecy of his own state, it was only
amid soft worded phrases or within rose soft stuffs that he
dared to conceive of the soul or body of a woman moving
with tender life.

But the phrase on the priest's lips was disingenuous for
he knew that a priest should not speak lightly on that
theme. The phrase had been spoken lightly with design and
he felt that his face was being searched by the eyes in the
shadow. Whatever he had heard or read of the craft of je-
suits② he had put aside frankly as not borne out by his own
experience. His masters, even when they had not attracted
him, had seemed to him always intelligent and serious
priests, athletic and high-spirited prefects. He thought of
them as men who washed their bodies briskly with cold water and wore clean cold linen. During all the years he had
lived among them in Clongowes and in Belvedere he had received only two pandies and, though these had been dealt
him in the wrong, he knew that he had often escaped punishment. During all those years he had never heard from
any of his masters a flippant③ word: it was they who had
taught him christian doctrine and urged him to live a good
life and, when he had fallen into grievous sin, it was they
who had led him back to grace. Their presence had made
him diffident④ of himself when he was a muff⑤ in Clongowes and it had made him diffident of himself also while
he had held his equivocal position in Belvedere. A constant
sense of this had remained with him up to the last year of
his school life. He had never once disobeyed or allowed tur-

---

① the greasy leather of harness: 油腻腻的皮制马具　② jesuits: (天主
教)耶稣会会员　③ flippant: 轻率的　④ diffident: 胆怯的　⑤ muff: 笨蛋

bulent companions to seduce him from his habit of quiet
obedience; and, even when he doubted some statement of a
master, he had never presumed to doubt openly. Lately
some of their judgements had sounded a little childish in his
ears and had made him feel a regret and pity as though he
were slowly passing out of an accustomed world and were
hearing its language for the last time. One day when some
boys had gathered round a priest under the shed near the
chapel, he had heard the priest say:

— I believe that Lord Macaulay[1] was a man who
probably never committed a mortal sin in his life, that is to
say, a deliberate mortal sin.

Some of the boys had then asked the priest if Victor
Hugo[2] were not the greatest French writer. The priest had
answered that Victor Hugo had never written half so well
when he had turned against the church as he had written
when he was a catholic.

— But there are many eminent French critics, said the
priest, who consider that even Victor Hugo, great as he
certainly was, had not so pure a French style as Louis
Veuillot[3].

The tiny flame which the priest's allusion had kindled
upon Stephen's cheek had sunk down again and his eyes
were still fixed calmly on the colourless sky. But an unrest-
ing doubt flew hither and thither[4] before his mind.
Masked memories passed quickly before him: he recognized
scenes and persons yet he was conscious that he had failed
to perceive some vital circumstance in them. He saw himself walking about the grounds watching the sports in Clongowes and eating slim jim out of his cricketcap. Some jesuits were walking round the cycletrack in the company of
ladies. The echoes of certain expressions used in Clongowes

---

① Lord Macaulay: Thomas Babington Macaulay (1800 – 1859), 英国历
史学家,作家和政治家 ② Victor Hugo: 维克多·雨果,法国 19 世纪著名作
家。 ③ Louis Veuillot: 法国 19 世纪天主教记者和作家 ④ hither and
thither: (旧用法)到处

sounded in remote caves of his mind.

His ears were listening to these distant echoes amid the silence of the parlour when he became aware that the priest was addressing him in a different voice.

— I sent for you today, Stephen, because I wished to speak to you on a very important subject.

— Yes, sir.

— Have you ever felt that you had a vocation①?

Stephen parted his lips to answer yes and then withheld the word suddenly. The priest waited for the answer and added:

— I mean, have you ever felt within yourself, in your soul, a desire to join the order②. Think.

— I have sometimes thought of it, said Stephen.

The priest let the blindcord③ fall to one side and, uniting his hands, leaned his chin gravely upon them, communing with himself④.

— In a college like this, he said at length, there is one boy or perhaps two or three boys whom God calls to the religious life. Such a boy is marked off from his companions by his piety, by the good example he shows to others. He is looked up to by them; he is chosen perhaps as prefect by his fellow sodalists. And you, Stephen, have been such a boy in this college, prefect of Our Blessed Lady's sodality⑤. Perhaps you are the boy in this college whom God designs to call to Himself.

A strong note of pride reinforcing the gravity of the priest's voice made Stephen's heart quicken in response.

— To receive that call, Stephen, said the priest, is the greatest honour that the Almighty God can bestow upon a man. No king or emperor on this earth has the power of the priest of God. No angel or archangel in heaven, no

---

① vocation: 使命感　② join the order: 加入教会　③ blindcord: 窗帘绳　④ communing with himself: 严肃地思索着　⑤ prefect of Our Blessed Lady's sodality: 我们圣母教会的级长

saint, not even the Blessed Virgin herself has the power of a priest of God: the power of the keys, the power to bind and to loose from sin, the power of exorcism①, the power to cast out from the creatures of God the evil spirits that have power over them, the power, the authority, to make the great God of Heaven come down upon the altar and take the form of bread and wine. What an awful power, Stephen!

A flame began to flutter again on Stephen's cheek as he heard in this proud address an echo of his own proud musings. How often had he seen himself as a priest wielding calmly and humbly the awful power of which angels and saints stood in reverence! His soul had loved to muse in secret on this desire. He had seen himself, a young and silentmannered priest, entering a confessional swiftly, ascending the altarsteps, incensing, genuflecting②, accomplishing the vague acts of the priesthood which pleased him by reason of their semblance of reality and of their distance from it. In that dim life which he had lived through in his musings he had assumed the voices and gestures which he had noted with various priests. He had bent his knee sideways like such a one, he had shaken the thurible③ only slightly like such a one, his chasuble④ had swung open like that of such another as he had turned to the altar again after having blessed the people. And above all it had pleased him to fill the second place in those dim scenes of his imagining. He shrank from the dignity of celebrant because it displeased him to imagine that all the vague pomp⑤ should end in his own person or that the ritual should assign to him so clear and final an office. He longed for the minor sacred offices, to be vested with the tunicle of subdeacon at high mass⑥, to stand aloof from the altar, forgotten by the

---

① exorcism: 驱除妖魔　② genuflecting: 曲膝跪下　③ thurible: 香炉
④ chasuble: 十字褡(神父行圣餐礼时所穿, 罩于其他衣服之外的宽松无袖长袍)　⑤ pomp: 盛大仪式　⑥ to be ... high mass: 在大弥撒中穿着副执事的法衣

people, his shoulders covered with a humeral veil①, holding the paten② within its folds, or, when the sacrifice had
been accomplished, to stand as deacon in a dalmatic③ of
cloth of gold on the step below the celebrant, his hands
joined and his face towards the people, and sing the chant
*Ite, missa est*④. If ever he had seen himself celebrant it
was as in the pictures of the mass in his child's mass-
book⑤, in a church without worshippers, save for the angel of the sacrifice, at a bare altar and served by an a-
colyte⑥ scarcely more boyish than himself. In vague sacrifi-
cial or sacramental acts alone his will seemed drawn to go
forth to encounter reality; and it was partly the absence of
an appointed rite which had always constrained him to inac-
tion whether he had allowed silence to cover his anger or
pride or had suffered only an embrace he longed to give.

He listened in reverent silence now to the priest's appeal and through the words he heard even more distinctly a
voice bidding him approach, offering him secret knowledge
and secret power. He would know then what was the sin of
Simon Magus⑦ and what the sin against the Holy Ghost for
which there was no forgiveness. He would know obscure
things, hidden from others, from those who were conceived and born children of wrath. He would know the
sins, the sinful longings and sinful thoughts and sinful
acts, of others, hearing them murmured into his ears in the
confessional under the shame of a darkened chapel by the
lips of women and of girls: but rendered immune mysteriously at his ordination by the imposition of hands his soul
would pass again uncontaminated⑧ to the white peace of
the altar. No touch of sin would linger upon the hands with

---

① humeral veil: (天主教教士的)长方形丝披肩　② paten: 圣餐盘
③ dalmatic: 主教的法衣　④ *Ite, missa est*: (拉丁文)走吧, 弥撒结束了。
⑤ massbook: 弥撒书　⑥ acolyte: (牧师等举行仪式时的)助手　⑦ Simon
Magus: 西蒙·麦加斯, 传说他是个魔法师, 曾试图用钱从圣徒那里购买将生
灵赋予信徒的权利。simony(买卖圣职罪)一词就是由他的名字而来。
⑧ uncontaminated: 未被污染的

which he would elevate and break the host; no touch of sin would linger on his lips in prayer to make him eat and drink damnation① to himself, not discerning the body of the Lord. He would hold his secret knowledge and secret power, being as sinless as the innocent; and he would be a priest for ever according to that order of Melchisedec②.

— I will offer up my mass tomorrow morning, said the director, that Almighty God may reveal to you His holy will. And let you, Stephen, make a novena③ to your holy patron saint, the first martyr④, who is very powerful with God, that God may enlighten your mind. But you must be quite sure, Stephen, that you have a vocation because it would be terrible if you found afterwards that you had none. Once a priest always a priest, remember. Your catechism tells you that the sacrament of Holy Orders is one of those which can be received only once because it imprints on the soul an indelible spiritual mark which can never be effaced. It is before you must weigh well, not after. It is a solemn question, Stephen, because on it may depend the salvation of your eternal soul. But we will pray to God together.

He held open the heavy hall door and gave his hand as if already to a companion in the spiritual life. Stephen passed out on to the wide platform above the steps and was conscious of the caress of mild evening air. Towards Findlater's church a quartet of young men were striding along with linked arms, swaying their heads and stepping to the agile melody of their leader's concertina⑤. The music passed in an instant, as the first bars of sudden music always did, over the fantastic fabrics of his mind, dissolving them painlessly and noiselessly as a sudden wave dissolves the sandbuilt turrets⑥ of children. Smiling at the trivial air

---

① damnation: 入地狱之罪　② Melchisedec: 最高神灵的祭司　③ novena: (天主教)连续九天的祈祷式　④ martyr: 殉道者　⑤ concertina: 六角手风琴　⑥ turrets: 塔楼

he raised his eyes to the priest's face and, seeing in it a
mirthless reflection of the sunken day, detached his hand
slowly which had acquiesced① faintly in that companionship.

As he descended the steps the impression which effaced his troubled selfcommunion was that of a mirthless
mask reflecting a sunken day from the threshold of the college. The shadow, then, of the life of the college passed
gravely over his consciousness. It was a grave and ordered
and passionless life that awaited him, a life without material cares. He wondered how he would pass the first night in
the novitiate② and with what dismay he would wake the
first morning in the dormitory. The troubling odour of the
long corridors of Clongowes came back to him and he heard
the discreet murmur of the burning gasflames. At once
from every part of his being unrest began to irradiate. A
feverish quickening of his pulses followed and a din of
meaningless words drove his reasoned thoughts hither and
thither confusedly. His lungs dilated③ and sank as if he
were inhaling a warm moist unsustaining air and he smelt
again the warm moist air which hung in the bath in Clongowes above the sluggish turf coloured water.

Some instinct, waking at these memories, stronger
than education or piety, quickened within him at every
near approach to that life, an instinct subtle and hostile,
and armed him against acquiescence. The chill and order of
the life repelled him. He saw himself rising in the cold of
the morning and filing down with the others to early mass
and trying vainly to struggle with his prayers against the
fainting sickness of his stomach. He saw himself sitting at
dinner with the community of a college. What, then, had
become of that deep rooted shyness of his which had made
him loth to eat or drink under a strange roof? What had
come of the pride of his spirit which had always made him

---

① acquiesced：默认 ② novitiate：修道士的见习期 ③ dilated：膨胀

conceive himself as a being apart in every order?

The Reverend Stephen Dedalus, S.J.

His name in that new life leaped into characters before his eyes and to it there followed a mental sensation of an undefined face or colour of a face. The colour faded and became strong like a changing glow of pallid① brick red. Was it the raw reddish glow he had so often seen on wintry mornings on the shaven gills of the priests? The face was eyeless and sour-favoured and devout, shot with pink tinges of suffocated anger. Was it not a mental spectre of the face of one of the jesuits whom some of the boys called Lantern Jaws② and others Foxy Campbell?

He was passing at that moment before the jesuit house in Gardiner Street, and wondered vaguely which window would be his if he ever joined the order. Then he wondered at the vagueness of his wonder, at the remoteness of his soul from what he had hitherto imagined her sanctuary, at the frail hold which so many years of order and obedience had of him when once a definite and irrevocable③ act of his threatened to end for ever, in time and in eternity, his freedom. The voice of the director urging upon him the proud claims of the church and the mystery and power of the priestly office repeated itself idly in his memory. His soul was not there to hear and greet it and he knew now that the exhortation he had listened to had already fallen into an idle formal tale. He would never swing the thurible before the tabernacle④ as priest. His destiny was to be elusive of social or religious orders. The wisdom of the priest's appeal did not touch him to the quick. He was destined to learn his own wisdom apart from others or to learn the wisdom of others himself wandering among the snares of the world.

The snares of the world were its ways of sin. He

---

① pallid: 苍白的   ② Lantern Jaws: 长下巴颏儿   ③ irrevocable: 不可改变的   ④ tabernacle: 神龛

would fall. He had not yet fallen but he would fall silently, in an instant. Not to fall was too hard, too hard; and he felt the silent lapse of his soul, as it would be at some instant to come, falling, falling but not yet fallen, still unfallen but about to fall.

He crossed the bridge over the stream of the Tolka and turned his eyes coldly for an instant towards the faded blue shrine of the Blessed Virgin which stood fowl wise on a pole in the middle of a ham shaped encampment of poor cottages. Then, bending to the left, he followed the lane which led up to his house. The faint sour stink of rotted cabbages came towards him from the kitchengardens on the rising ground above the river. He smiled to think that it was this disorder, the misrule and confusion of his father's house and the stagnation of vegetable life, which was to win the day in his soul. Then a short laugh broke from his lips as he thought of that solitary farmhand in the kitchen gardens behind their house whom they had nicknamed the man with the hat. A second laugh, taking rise from the first after a pause, broke from him involuntarily as he thought of how the man with the hat worked, considering in turn the four points of the sky and then regretfully plunging his spade[①] in the earth.

He pushed open the latchless door of the porch and passed through the naked hallway into the kitchen. A group of his brothers and sisters was sitting round the table. Tea was nearly over and only the last of the second watered tea remained in the bottoms of the small glassjars and jampots which did service for teacups. Discarded[②] crusts and lumps of sugared bread, turned brown by the tea which had been poured over them, lay scattered on the table. Little wells of tea lay here and there on the board, and a knife with a broken ivory handle was stuck through the pith[③] of a ravaged turnover[④].

---

① spade: 铁锹　② Discarded: 丢弃的　③ pith: 中心　④ turnover: 半圆形卷饼

The sad quiet grey blue glow of the dying day came through the window and the open door, covering over and allaying quietly a sudden instinct of remorse in Stephen's heart. All that had been denied them had been freely given to him, the eldest: but the quiet glow of evening showed him in their faces no sign of rancour①.

He sat near them at the table and asked where his father and mother were. One answered:

— Goneboro toboro lookboro atboro aboro houseboro.

Still another removal! A boy named Fallon in Belvedere had often asked him with a silly laugh why they moved so often. A frown of scorn② darkened quickly his forehead as he heard again the silly laugh of the questioner.

He asked:

— Why are we on the move again, if it's a fair question?

The same sister answered:

— Becauseboro theboro landboro lordboro willboro putboro usboro outboro.

The voice of his youngest brother from the farther side of the fireplace began to sing the air③ *Oft in the Stilly Night*④. One by one the others took up the air until a full choir of voices was singing. They would sing so for hours, melody after melody, glee after glee, till the last pale light died down on the horizon, till the first dark night clouds came forth and night fell. He waited for some moments, listening, before he too took up the air with them. He was listening with pain of spirit to the overtone of weariness⑤ behind their frail fresh innocent voices. Even before they set out on life's journey they seemed weary already of the way.

He heard the choir of voices in the kitchen echoed and multiplied through an endless reverberation⑥ of the choirs

---

① rancour：怨恨　② A frown of scorn：轻蔑地皱眉蹙额　③ air：曲调 ④ *Oft in the Stilly Night*：《每当夜深时分》，是托马斯·莫尔(1779－1852) 的一首诗。　⑤ the overtone of weariness：疲惫不堪的调子　⑥ reverberation：回响

of endless generations of children; and heard in all the e-
choes an echo also of the recurring note of weariness and
pain. All seemed weary of life even before entering upon it.
And he remembered that Newman had heard this note also
in the broken lines of Virgil[①], *giving utterance*, *like the*
voice of Nature herself, *to that pain and weariness yet*
hope of better things which has been the experience of her
children in every time.

He could wait no longer.

From the door of Byron's public house to the gate of
Clontarf Chapel, from the gate of Clontail Chapel to the
door of Byron's public house and then back again to the
chapel and then back again to the public house he had paced
slowly at first, planting his steps scrupulously in the spaces
of the patchwork of the footpath, then timing their fall to
the fall of verses. A full hour had passed since his father
had gone in with Dan Crosby, the tutor, to find out for
him something about the university. For a full hour he had
paced up and down, waiting: but he could wait no longer.

He set off abruptly for the Bull, walking rapidly lest
his father's shrill whistle might call him back; and in a few
moments he had rounded the curve at the police barrack[②]
and was safe.

Yes, his mother was hostile to the idea, as he had
read from her listless silence. Yet her mistrust pricked him
more keenly than his father's pride and he thought coldly
how he had watched the faith which was fading down in his
soul aging and strengthening in her eyes. A dim antago-
nism gathered force within him and darkened his mind as a
cloud against her disloyalty; and when it passed, cloud
like, leaving his mind serene and dutiful towards her again,
he was made aware dimly and without regret of a first
noiseless sundering[③] of their lives.

---

① Virgil: 维吉尔(70－19 BC), 古罗马最重要的诗人, 代表作为《伊尼
特》。 ② barrack: 营房 ③ sundering: 裂痕

The university! So he had passed beyond the challenge of the sentries who had stood as guardians of his boyhood and had sought to keep him among them that he might be subject to them and serve their ends. Pride after satisfaction uplifted him like long slow waves.① The end he had been born to serve yet did not see had led him to escape by an unseen path; and now it beckoned to him② once more and a new adventure was about to be opened to him. It seemed to him that he heard notes of fitful music leaping upwards a tone and downwards a diminished fourth, upwards a tone and downwards a major third, like triple-branching flames leaping fitfully, flame after flame, out of a midnight wood. It was an elfin③ prelude, endless and formless; and, as it grew wilder and faster, the flames leaping out of time, he seemed to hear from under the boughs and grasses wild creatures racing, their feet pattering like rain upon the leaves. Their feet passed in pattering tumult over his mind, the feet of hares and rabbits, the feet of harts and hinds④ and antelopes⑤, until he heard them no more and remembered only a proud cadence⑥ from Newman:

— *Whose feet are as the feet of harts and underneath the everlasting arms*.

The pride of that dim image brought back to his mind the dignity of the office he had refused. All through his boyhood he had mused upon that which he had so often thought to be his destiny and when the moment had come for him to obey the call he had turned aside, obeying a wayward⑦ instinct. Now time lay between: the oils of ordination would never anoint his body. He had refused. Why?

---

① Pride after ... slow waves: 获得某种满足后产生的骄傲像排排缓慢而绵延的巨浪将他高举了起来。　② beckoned to him: 招手让他过来　③ elfin: 小精灵的　④ harts and hinds: 公鹿和母鹿　⑤ antelopes: 羚羊　⑥ cadence: 节奏　⑦ wayward: 任性的

He turned seaward from the road at Dollymount and as he passed on to the thin wooden bridge he felt the planks shaking with the tramp of heavily shod feet. A squad of[①] Christian Brothers was on its way back from the Bull and had begun to pass, two by two, across the bridge. Soon the whole bridge was trembling and resounding. The uncouth[②] faces passed him two by two, stained yellow or red or livid by the sea, and as he strove to look at them with ease and indifference, a faint stain of personal shame and commiseration[③] rose to his own face. Angry with himself he tried to hide his face from their eyes by gazing down sideways into the shallow swirling water under the bridge but he still saw a reflection therein of their top heavy silk hats, and humble tape like collars and loosely hanging clerical clothes.

— Brother Hickey.

Brother Quaid.

Brother MacArdle.

Brother Keogh.

Their piety would be like their names, like their faces, like their clothes and it was idle for him to tell himself that their humble and contrite[④] hearts, it might be, paid a far richer tribute of devotion than his had ever been, a gift tenfold more acceptable than his elaborate adoration[⑤]. It was idle for him to move himself to be generous towards them, to tell himself that if he ever came to their gates, stripped of his pride, beaten and in beggar's weeds, that they would be generous towards him, loving him as themselves. Idle and embittering, finally, to argue, against his own dispassionate certitude[⑥], that the commandment of love bade us not to love our neighbour as ourselves with the same amount and intensity of love but to

---

① A squad of: 一小队　② uncouth: 粗鲁的　③ commiseration: 同情　④ contrite: 悔恨的　⑤ elaborate adoration: 矫揉造作的崇敬　⑥ certitude: 确信

love him as ourselves with the same kind of love.

He drew forth a phrase from his treasure and spoke it softly to himself:

— A day of dappled seaborne clouds①.

The phrase and the day and the scene harmonized in a chord②. Words. Was it their colours? He allowed them to glow and fade, hue after hue: sunrise gold, the russet③ and green of apple orchards, azure④ of waves, the greyfringed fleece of clouds. No, it was not their colours: it was the poise and balance of the period itself. Did he then love the rhythmic rise and fall of words better than their associations of legend and colour? Or was it that, being as weak of sight as he was shy of mind, he drew less pleasure from the reflection of the glowing sensible world through the prism⑤ of a language many coloured and richly storied than from the contemplation of an inner world of individual emotions mirrored perfectly in a lucid supple periodic prose?

He passed from the trembling bridge on to firm land again. At that instant, as it seemed to him, the air was chilled and looking askance towards the water he saw a flying squall darkening and crisping suddenly the tide. A faint click at his heart, a faint throb in his throat told him once more of how his flesh dreaded the cold infrahuman⑥ odour of the sea: yet he did not strike across the downs on his left but held straight on along the spine of rocks that pointed against the river's mouth.

A veiled sunlight lit up faintly the grey sheet of water where the river was embayed. In the distance along the course of the slowflowing Liffey⑦ slender masts flecked the sky and, more distant still, the dim fabric of the city lay prone in haze. Like a scene on some vague arras, old as

① dappled seaborne clouds: 从海上飘来的斑驳的彩云　②chord: 和弦
③ russet: 黄褐色　④ azure: 蔚蓝色　⑤ prism: 三棱镜　⑥ infrahuman:
低于人类的　⑦ Liffey: 里费河

man's weariness, the image of the seventh city of christendom① was visible to him across the timeless air, no older nor more weary nor less patient of subjection than in the days of the thingmote.

Disheartened, he raised his eyes towards the slowdrifting clouds, dappled and seaborne. They were voyaging across the deserts of the sky, a host of nomads on the march②, voyaging high over Ireland, westward bound. The Europe they had come from lay out there beyond the Irish Sea, Europe of strange tongues and valleyed and woodbegirt and citadelled③ and of entrenched and marshalled races④. He heard a confused music within him as of memories and names which he was almost conscious of but could not capture even for an instant; then the music seemed to recede; to recede, to recede, and from each receding trail of nebulous music there fell always one long-drawn calling note, piercing like a star the dusk of silence. Again! Again! Again! A voice beyond the world was calling.

— Hello, Stephanos!

— Here comes The Dedalus!

— Ao! . . . Eh, give it over, Dwyer, I'm telling you or I'll give you a stuff in the kisser for yourself⑤ . . . Ao!

— Good man, Towser! Duck him!

— Come, along Dedalus! Bous Stephanoumenos! Bous Stephaneforos!

— Duck him! Guzzle him⑥ now, Towser!

— Help! Help! . . . Ao!

He recognized their speech collectively before he distinguished their faces. The mere sight of that medley⑦ of wet nakedness chilled him to the bone. Their bodies,

---

① the seventh city of christendom: 都柏林 ② a host of nomads on the march: 一群行进中的游牧部落 ③ woodbegirt and citadelled: 林带和城堡 ④ entrenched and marshalled races: 筑有深沟高垒、严阵以待的民族 ⑤ or I'll . . . for yourself: 要不然当心我在你的臭嘴上抽一巴掌 ⑥ Guzzle him: 给他灌水 ⑦ medley: 混杂的人群

corpse white or suffused with a pallid golden light or rawly tanned by the sun, gleamed with the wet of the sea. Their diving stone, poised on its rude supports and rocking under their plunges, and the rough hewn stones of the sloping breakwater over which they scrambled in their horseplay, gleamed with cold wet lustre. The towels with which they smacked their bodies were heavy with cold seawater; and drenched with cold brine① was their matted hair.

He stood still in deference to their calls and parried their banter② with easy words. How characterless they looked: Shuley without his deep unbuttoned collar, Ennis without his scarlet belt with the snaky clasp, and Connolly without his Norfolk coat with the flapless sidepockets! It was a pain to see them and a sword like pain to see the signs of adolescence that made repellent③ their pitiable nakedness. Perhaps they had taken refuge in number and noise from the secret dread in their souls. But he, apart from them and in silence, remembered in what dread he stood of the mystery of his own body.

— Stephanos Dedalos! Bous Stephanoumenos! Bous Stephaneforos!

Their banter was not new to him and now it flattered his mild proud sovereignty. Now, as never before, his strange name seemed to him a prophecy. So timeless seemed the grey warm air, so fluid and impersonal his own mood, that all ages were as one to him. A moment before the ghost of the ancient kingdom of the Danes④ had looked forth through the vesture of the hazewrapped city⑤. Now, at the name of the fabulous artificer⑥, he seemed to hear the noise of dim waves and to see a winged form flying above the waves and slowly climbing the air. What did it

---

① brine: 盐水　② parried their banter: 避开他们的戏谑　③ repellent: 讨人嫌的　④ Danes: 丹麦人　⑤ hazewrapped city: 雾霭笼罩的城市　⑥ artificer: 这里指希腊神话传说中著名的发明家迪达勒斯。参见首页注释。

mean? Was it a quaint device opening a page of some medieval book of prophecies and symbols, a hawklike man[1] flying sunward above the sea, a prophecy of the end he had been born to serve[2] and had been following through the mists of childhood and boyhood, a symbol of the artist forging anew in his workshop out of the sluggish matter of the earth a new soaring impalpable imperishable being[3]?

His heart trembled; his breath came faster and a wild spirit passed over his limbs as though he was soaring sunward. His heart trembled in an ecstasy of fear and his soul was in flight. His soul was soaring in an air beyond the world and the body he knew was purified in a breath and delivered of incertitude and made radiant and commingled with the element of the spirit. An ecstasy of flight made radiant his eyes and wild his breath and tremulous and wild and radiant his windswept limbs.

— One! Two! ... Look out!

— O, cripes, I'm drownded!

— One! Two! Three and away!

— Me next! Me next!

— One! ... UK!

— Stephaneforos!

His throat ached with a desire to cry aloud, the cry of a hawk or eagle on high, to cry piercingly of his deliverance to the winds. This was the call of life to his soul not the dull gross voice of the world of duties and despair, not the inhuman voice that had called him to the pale service of the altar. An instant of wild flight had delivered him and the cry of triumph which his lips withheld cleft[4] his brain.

— Stephaneforos!

What were they now but cerements[5] shaken from the body of death — the fear he had walked in night and day,

---

① a hawklike man：像鹰一样的人　② a prophecy ... to serve：预言他为何而生　③ a new soaring impalpable imperishable being：一个新的、向天空飞去的、摸不到的、永不消逝的生命　④ cleft：撕裂　⑤ cerements：尸衣

the incertitude that had ringed him round, the shame that had abased him within and without — cerements, the linens of the grave?

His soul had arisen from the grave of boyhood, spurning her graveclothes①. Yes! Yes! Yes! He would create proudly out of the freedom and power of his soul, as the great artificer whose name he bore②, a living thing, new and soaring and beautiful, impalpable, imperishable.

He started up nervously from the stone block for he could no longer quench the flame in his blood. He felt his cheeks aflame and his throat throbbing with song. There was a lust of wandering in his feet that burned to set out for the ends of the earth. On! On! his heart seemed to cry. Evening would deepen above the sea, night fall upon the plains, dawn glimmer before the wanderer and show him strange fields and hills and faces. Where?

He looked northward towards Howth. The sea had fallen below the line of seawrack③ on the shallow side of the breakwater④ and already the tide was running out fast along the foreshore. Already one long oval bank of sand lay warm and dry amid the wavelets. Here and there warm isles of sand gleamed above the shallow tide, and about the isles and around the long bank and amid the shallow currents of the beach were lightclad gaydad figures, wading and delving⑤.

In a few moments he was barefoot, his stockings folded in his pockets and his canvas shoes dangling by their knotted laces over his shoulders and, picking a pointed salteaten stick out of the jetsam among the rocks⑥, he clambered down the slope of the breakwater.

---

① spurning her graveclothes: 抛掉她的尸衣。喻指斯蒂芬灵魂的重生。
② as the ... he bore: 和那个与他同名的伟大发明家一样 ③ seawrack: 失事船只 ④ breakwater: 防波堤 ⑤ amid the ... wading and delving: 在海滩的浅水中到处是穿着泳装的人，或涉水嬉戏，或潜入水中。 ⑥ picking a ... the rocks: 在乱石间的破烂物中捡起一根被海水浸过的尖头木棍儿

There was a long rivulet① in the strand and, as he waded slowly up its course, he wondered at the endless drift of seaweed. Emerald② and black and russet and olive, it moved beneath the current, swaying and turning. The water of the rivulet was dark with endless drift and mirrored the high drifting clouds. The clouds were drifting above him silently and silently the seatangle③ was drifting below him; and the grey warm air was still; and a new wild life was singing in his veins.

Where was his boyhood now? Where was the soul that had hung back from her destiny, to brood alone upon the shame of her wounds and in her house of squalor and subterfuge④ to queen it in faded cerements and in wreaths that withered at the touch? Or where was he?

He was alone. He was unheeded, happy and near to the wild heart of life. He was alone and young and wilful and wildhearted, alone amid a waste of wild air and brackish waters and the sea harvest of shells and tangle and veiled grey sunlight and gayclad lightclad figures of children and girls and voices childish and girlish in the air.

A girl stood before him in midstream, alone and still, gazing out to sea. She seemed like one whom magic had changed into the likeness of a strange and beautiful seabird. Her long slender bare legs were delicate as a crane's and pure save where an emerald trail of seaweed had fashioned itself as a sign upon the flesh. Her thighs, fuller and softhued as ivory, were bared almost to the hips where the white fringes of her drawers were like feathering of soft white down. Her slateblue skirts were kilted boldly about her waist⑤ and dovetailed behind her. Her bosom was as a bird's soft and slight, slight and soft as the breast of some darkplumaged⑥ dove. But her long fair hair was girlish:

---

① rivulet：小河　② Emerald：宝蓝色　③ seatangle：墨角藻　④ in her house of squalor and subterfuge：在她简陋的与世隔绝的房子里　⑤ Her slateblue ... her waist：她的蓝灰色的裙子大胆地卷上来，围在腰际。⑥ darkplumaged：深色羽毛的

and girlish, and touched with the wonder of mortal beauty, her face.

She was alone and still, gazing out to sea; and when she felt his presence and the worship of his eyes her eyes turned to him in quiet sufferance of his gaze, without shame or wantonness①. Long, long she suffered his gaze and then quietly withdrew her eyes from his and bent them towards the stream, gently stirring the water with her foot hither and thither. The first faint noise of gently moving water broke the silence, low and faint and whispering, faint as the bells of sleep; hither and thither; and a faint flame trembled on her cheek.

— Heavenly God! cried Stephen's soul, in an outburst of profane② joy.

He turned away from her suddenly and set off across the strand. His cheeks were aflame; his body was aglow; his limbs were trembling. On and on and on and on he strode, far out over the sands, singing wildly to the sea, crying to greet the advent③ of the life that had cried to him.

Her image had passed into his soul for ever and no word had broken the holy silence of his ecstasy. Her eyes had called him and his soul had leaped at the call. To live, to err, to fall, to triumph, to recreate life out of life! A wild angel had appeared to him, the angel of mortal youth and beauty, an envoy from the fair courts of life, to throw open before him in an instant of ecstasy the gates of all the ways of error and glory. On and on and on and on!

He halted suddenly and heard his heart in the silence. How far had he walked? What hour was it?

There was no human figure near him nor any sound borne to him over the air. But the tide was near the turn and already the day was on the wane. He turned landward

---

① without shame or wantonness: 既无羞怯之意, 也无淫荡之念
② profane: 世俗的   ③ advent: 到来

and ran towards the shore and, running up the sloping beach, reckless of the sharp shingle①, found a sandy nook amid a ring of tufted sandknolls② and lay down there that the peace and silence of the evening might still the riot of his blood.

He felt above him the vast indifferent dome and the calm processes of the heavenly bodies; and the earth beneath him, the earth that had borne him, had taken him to her breast.

He closed his eyes in the languor of sleep. His eyelids trembled as if they felt the vast cyclic movement of the earth and her watchers, trembled as if they felt the strange light of some new world. His soul was swooning③ into some new world, fantastic, dim, uncertain as under sea, traversed by cloudy shapes and beings④. A world, a glimmer or a flower? Glimmering and trembling, trembling and unfolding, a breaking light, an opening flower, it spread in endless succession to itself⑤, breaking in full crimson and unfolding and fading to palest rose, leaf by leaf and wave of light by wave of light, flooding all the heavens with its soft flushes, every flush deeper than the other.

Evening had fallen when he woke and the sand and arid grasses⑥ of his bed glowed no longer. He rose slowly and, recalling the rapture⑦ of his sleep, sighed at its joy.

He climbed to the crest of the sandhill and gazed about him. Evening had fallen. A rim of the young moon cleft the pale waste of skyline, the rim of a silver hoop embedded in grey sand; and the tide was flowing in fast to the land with a low whisper of her waves, islanding a few last figures in distant pools.

---

① shingle: 鹅卵石　② found a ... tufted sandknolls: 发现在一圈长着海草的沙丘中有一个沙窝　③ swoon: 晕厥　④ traversed by cloudy shapes and beings: 模糊的形状和生命在来回穿行　⑤ it spread ... to itself: 它在不休止地、连续地自我伸展开去　⑥ arid grasses: 干草　⑦ rapture: 销魂

CHAPTER 5

He drained his third cup of watery tea to the dregs①
and set to chewing the crusts of fried bread that were scattered near him, staring into the dark pool of the jar. The
yellow dripping had been scooped out like a boghole and the
pool under it brought back to his memory the dark turf –
coloured water of the bath in Clongowes. The box of pawn
tickets② at his elbow had just been rifled and he took up
idly one after another in his greasy fingers the blue and
white dockets③, scrawled and sanded and creased and
bearing the name of the pledger④ as Daly or MacEvoy.

1 Pair Buskins.
1 D. Coat.
3 Articles and White.
1 Man's Pants.

Then he put them aside and gazed thoughtfully at the
lid of the box, speckled with lousemarks⑤, and asked
vaguely:

— How much is the clock fast now?

His mother straightened the battered alarm clock that
was lying on its side in the middle of the mantelpiece until
its dial showed a quarter to twelve and then laid it once
more on its side.

— An hour and twenty-five minutes, she said. The
right time now is twenty past ten. The dear knows you
might try to be in time for your lectures.

— Fill out the place for me to wash, said Stephen.

— Katey, fill out the place for Stephen to wash.

— Boody, fill out the place for Stephen to wash.

---

① drain to the dregs：把……喝得一点儿不剩　② pawn tickets：当票
③ dockets：载明内容的标签　④ pledger：典当人　⑤ speckled with louse-
marks：点缀着虱子屎样的斑点

— I can't, I'm going for blue. Fill it out, you, Maggy.

When the enamelled basin① had been fitted into the well of the sink and the old washingglove flung on the side of it he allowed his mother to scrub his neck and root into the folds of his ears and into the interstices at the wings of his nose.

— Well, it's a poor case, she said, when a university student is so dirty that his mother has to wash him.

— But it gives you pleasure, said Stephen calmly.

An ear splitting whistle was heard from upstairs and his mother thrust a damp overall into his hands, saying:

— Dry yourself and hurry out for the love of goodness.

A second shrill whistle, prolonged angrily, brought one of the girls to the foot of the staircase.

— Yes, father?

— Is your lazy bitch of a brother gone out yet?

— Yes, father.

— Sure?

— Yes, father.

— Hm!

The girl came back making signs to him to be quick and go out quietly by the back. Stephen laughed and said:

— He has a curious idea of genders if he thinks a bitch is masculine.

— Ah, it's a scandalous shame for you, Stephen, said his mother, and you'll live to rue② the day you set your foot in that place. I know how it has changed you.

— Good morning, everybody, said Stephen, smiling and kissing the tips of his fingers in adieu③.

The lane behind the terrace was waterlogged and as he went down it slowly, choosing his steps and amid heaps of wet rubbish, he heard a mad nun screeching④ in the nuns'

---

① enamelled basin: 搪瓷浴盆　② rue: 后悔　③ in adieu: 再见
④ screech: 尖叫

madhouse beyond the wall.

— Jesus! O Jesus! Jesus!

He shook the sound out of his ears by an angry toss of his head and hurried on, stumbling through the mouldering offal①, his heart already bitten by an ache of loathing and bitterness. His father's whistle, his mother's mutterings, the screech of an unseen maniac② were to him now so many voices offending and threatening to humble the pride of his youth. He drove their echoes even out of his heart with an execration③; but, as he walked down the avenue and felt the grey morning light falling about him through the dripping trees and smelt the strange wild smell of the wet leaves and bark, his soul was loosed of her miseries.

The rainladen trees of the avenue evoked in him, as always, memories of the girls and women in the plays of Gerhart Hauptmann④; and the memory of their pale sorrows and the fragrance falling from the wet branches mingled in a mood of quiet joy. His morning walk across the city had begun, and he foreknew that as he passed the sloblands⑤ of Fairview he would think of the cloistral silverveined prose of Newman; that as he walked along the North Strand Road, glancing idly at the windows of the provision shops, he would recall the dark humour of Guido Cavalcanti⑥ and smile; that as he went by Baird's stonecutting works in Talbot Place the spirit of Ibsen⑦ would blow through him like a keen wind, a spirit of wayward boyish beauty; and that passing a grimy marine dealer's shop beyond the Liffey he would repeat the song by Ben Jonson⑧ which begins:

---

① stumbling through the mouldering offal：踏着腐烂的垃圾跌跌绊绊地向前走　② maniac：疯子　③ execration：诅咒　④ Gerhart Hauptmann：格哈特·霍普特曼(1862－1946)，德国剧作家、小说家及诗人。　⑤ sloblands：泥地　⑥ Guido Cavalcanti：吉多·卡瓦尔坎迪(1255－1300)，意大利诗人。　⑦ Ibsen：易卜生(1828－1906)，挪威剧作家。　⑧ Ben Jonson：本·琼森(1572－1637)，英国诗人及剧作家。

I was not wearier where I lay.

His mind, when wearied of its search for the essence of beauty amid the spectral words of Aristotle or Aquinas, turned often for its pleasure to the dainty① songs of the Elizabethans. His mind, in the vesture② of a doubting monk, stood often in shadow under the windows of that age, to hear the grave and mocking music of the lutenists③ or the frank laughter of waistcoateers④ until a laugh too low, a phrase, tarnished by time, of chambering and false honour stung his monkish pride and drove him on from his lurkingplace.

The lore⑤ which he was believed to pass his days brooding upon so that it had rapt him from the companionship of youth was only a garner of slender sentences from Aristotle's poetics and psychology and a *Synopsis Philosophiae Scholasticae ad mentem divi Thomae*⑥. His thinking was a dusk of doubt and selfmistrust, lit up at moments by the lightnings of intuition, but lightnings of so clear a splendour that in those moments the world perished about his feet as if it had been fireconsumed; and thereafter his tongue grew heavy and he met the eyes of others with unanswering eyes, for he felt that the spirit of beauty had folded him round like a mantle and that in revery at least he had been acquainted with nobility. But, when his brief pride of silence upheld him no longer he was glad to find himself still in the midst of common lives, passing on his way amid the squalor⑦ and noise and sloth of the city fearlessly and with a light heart.

Near the hoardings⑧ on the canal he met the consumptive man with the doll's face and the brimless hat coming towards him down the slope of the bridge with little

---

① dainty: 优雅的   ② vesture: 罩衣   ③ lutenists: 弹竖琴的人
④ waistcoateers: 下等妓女   ⑤ lore: 学问   ⑥ *Synopsis Philosophiae ... divi Thomae*: 拉丁文书名《圣托马斯哲学思想纲要》   ⑦ squalor: 肮脏
⑧ hoardings: 囤积物

steps, tightly buttoned into his chocolate overcoat, and holding his furled umbrella a span① or two from him like a diviningrod. It must be eleven, he thought, and peered into a dairy to see the time. The clock in the dairy told him that it was five minutes to five but, as he turned away, he heard a clock somewhere near him, but unseen, beating eleven strokes in swift precision. He laughed as he heard it for it made him think of MacCann, and he saw him a squat figure② in a shooting jacket and breeches and with a fair goatee, standing in the wind at Hopkins' corner, and heard him say:

— Dedalus, you're an antisocial being, wrapped up in yourself. I'm not. I'm a democrat: and I'll work and act for social liberty and equality among all classes and sexes in the United States of the Europe of the future.

Eleven! Then he was late for that lecture too. What day of the week was it? He stopped at a newsagent's to read the headline of a placard③. Thursday. Ten to eleven, English; eleven to twelve, French; twelve to one, physics. He fancied to himself the English lecture and felt, even at that distance, restless and helpless. He saw the heads of his classmates meekly bent as they wrote in their notebooks the points they were bidden to note, nominal definitions, essential definitions and examples or dates of birth or death, chief works, a favourable and an unfavourable criticism side by side. His own head was unbent for his thoughts wandered abroad and whether he looked around the little class of students or out of the window across the desolate gardens of the green an odour assailed him of cheerless cellardamp and decay④. Another head than his, right before him in the first benches, was poised squarely above its bending fellows like the head of a priest appealing without humility to the tabernacle⑤

---

① a span: 拇指与小指伸开时的距离, 合 9 英寸 ② squat figure: 短胖的身体 ③ placard: 布告 ④ an odour ... and decay: 一股令人沮丧的、充满地窖潮湿和腐烂气味的臭味朝他袭来 ⑤ tabernacle: 圣体盘

for the humble worshippers about him. Why was it that when he thought of Cranly he could never raise before his mind the entire image of his body but only the image of the head and face? Even now against the grey curtain of the morning he saw it before him like the phantom① of a dream, the face of a severed head or deathmask, crowned on the brows by its stiff black upright hair as by an iron crown. It was a priestlike face, priestlike in its pallor②, in the widewinged nose, in the shadowings below his eyes and along the jaws, priestlike in the lips that were long and bloodless and faintly smiling; and Stephen, remembering swiftly how he had told Cranly of all the tumults and unrest and longings in his soul, day after day and night by night, only to be answered by his friend's listening silence, would have told himself that it was the face of a guilty priest who heard confessions of those whom he had not power to absolve but that he felt again in memory the gaze of its dark womanish eyes.

Through this image he had a glimpse of a strange dark cavern③ of speculation but at once turned away from it, feeling that it was not yet the hour to enter it. But the nightshade of his friend's listlessness seemed to be diffusing in the air around him a tenuous and deadly exhalation④ and be found himself glancing from one casual word to another on his right or left in stolid⑤ wonder that they had been so silently emptied of instantaneous sense⑥ until every mean shop legend bound his mind like the words of a spell and his soul shrivelled up⑦, sighing with age as he walked on in a lane among heaps of dead language. His own consciousness of language was ebbing from his brain and trickling into the very words themselves which set to band and disband themselves in wayward rhythms:

---

① phantom：幻象　② pallor：苍白　③ cavern：大洞穴　④ a tenuous and deadly exhalation：一种稀薄的、致命的气体　⑤ stolid：神经麻木的　⑥ instantaneous sense：瞬间的感觉　⑦ shrivelled up：枯萎

The ivy whines upon the wall,
And whines and twines upon the wall,
The yellow ivy upon the wall,
Ivy, ivy up the wall.

Did any one ever hear such drivel①? Lord Almighty! Who ever heard of ivy whining on a wall? Yellow ivy; that was all right. Yellow ivory also. And what about ivory ivy?

The word now shone in his brain, clearer and brighter than any ivory sawn from the mottled tusks of elephants. *Ivory, ivoire, avorio, ebur②.* One of the first examples that he had learnt in Latin had run: *India mittit ebur③*; and he recalled the shrewd northern face of the rector who had taught him to construe the Metamorphoses of Ovid④ in a courtly English, made whimsical by the mention of porkers and potsherds and chines of bacon. He had learnt what little he knew of the laws of Latin verse from a ragged book written by a Portuguese priest.

Contrahit orator, variant in carmine vates⑤.

The crises and victories and secessions in Roman history were handed on to him in the trite words *in tanto discrimine⑥* and he had tried to peer into the social life of the city of cities through the words *implere ollam denariorum⑦* which the rector had rendered sonorously as the filling of a pot with denaries. The pages of his timeworn Horace never felt cold to the touch even when his own fingers were cold; they were human pages; and fifty years before they had been turned by the human fingers of John

---

① drivel：胡说八道   ② *Ivory, ivoire, avorio, ebur*：分别为英、法、意、拉丁文,均为象牙之意   ③ *India mittit ebur*：(拉丁文)印度出口象牙   ④ Metamorphoses of Ovid：奥维德的变形记   ⑤ *Contrahit orator, variant in carmine vates*：演说家力求简约明了,诗人却须夸张联想   ⑥ *in tanto discrimine*：(拉丁文)正当此危机之时   ⑦ *implere ollam denariorum*：(拉丁文)将这个陶罐装满银角子

Duncan Inverarity and by his brother, William Malcolm Inverarity. Yes, those were noble names on the dusky fly-leaf[①] and, even for so poor a Latinist as he, the dusky verses were as fragrant as though they had lain all those years in myrtle and lavender and vervain[②]; but yet it wounded him to think that he would never be but a shy guest at the feast of the world's culture and that the monkish learning, in terms of which he was striving to forge out an esthetic philosophy, was held no higher by the age he lived in than the subtle and curious jargons of heraldry and falconry[③].

The grey block of Trinity on his left, set heavily in the city's ignorance like a dull stone set in a cumbrous[④] ring, pulled his mind downward and while he was striving this way and that to free his feet from the fetters of the reformed conscience he came upon the droll statue of the national poet of Ireland[⑤].

He looked at it without anger; for, though sloth of the body and of the soul crept over it like unseen vermin[⑥], over the shuffling feet and up the folds of the cloak and around the servile head, it seemed humbly conscious of its indignity. It was a Firbolg in the borrowed cloak of a Milesian[⑦]; and he thought of his friend Davin, the peasant student. It was a jesting name between them, but the young peasant bore with it lightly saying:

— Go on, Stevie, I have a hard head, you tell me. Call me what you will.

The homely version of his christian name[⑧] on the lips of his friend had touched Stephen pleasantly when first heard for he was as formal in speech with others as they

---

① flyleaf: 扉页   ② they had ... and vervain: 他们这些年来一直都放在长春花、薰衣草和马鞭草中   ③ heraldry and falconry: 纹章学和驯鹰术   ④ cumbrous: 笨重的   ⑤ statue of the national poet of Ireland: 指学校西侧托马斯·穆尔(1779－1852)的塑像   ⑥ vermin: 蛆虫   ⑦ It was ... a Milesian: Firbolg 和 Milesian 都是传说中爱尔兰土著人, 前者身形矮小, 后者身形高大。   ⑧ christian name: 教名

were with him. Often, as he sat in Davin's rooms in Grantham Street, wondering at his friend's wellmade boots that flanked the wall[①] pair by pair and repeating for his friend's simple ear the verses and cadences of others which were the veils of his own longing and dejection[②], the rude Firbolg mind of his listener had drawn his mind towards it and flung it back again, drawing it by a quiet inbred courtesy of attention or by a quaint turn of old English speech or by the force of its delight in rude bodily skill — for Davin had sat at the feet of Michael Cusack[③], the Gael — repelling swiftly and suddenly by a grossness of intelligence or by a bluntness of feeling or by a dull stare of terror in the eyes, the terror of soul of a starving Irish village in which the curfew[④] was still a nightly fear.

Side by side with his memory of the deeds of prowess[⑤] of his uncle Mat Davin, the athlete, the young peasant worshipped the sorrowful legend of Ireland. The gossip of his fellow-students which strove to render the flat life of the college significant at any cost loved to think of him as a young Fenian[⑥]. His nurse had taught him Irish and shaped his rude imagination by the broken lights of Irish myth. He stood towards the myth upon which no individual mind had ever drawn out a line of beauty and to its unwieldy tales that divided themselves as they moved down the cycles in the same attitude as towards the Roman catholic religion, the attitude of a dullwitted loyal serf[⑦]. Whatsoever of thought or of feeling came to him from England or by way of English culture his mind stood armed against in obedience to a password; and of the world that lay beyond England he knew only the foreign legion of France

---

① flanked the wall: 沿墙侧摆放着　② dejection: 沮丧　③ Michael Cusack: 迈克尔·丘萨克(1847－?)是盖尔克运动协会的创始人, 曾致力于爱尔兰体育运动的复兴。　④ curfew: 宵禁　⑤ prowess: 事迹　⑥ Fenian: 芬尼亚分子。芬尼亚分子是爱尔兰革命组织的成员, 该组织于1858 年在纽约成立, 致力于建立独立的爱尔兰共和国。　⑦ a dullwitted loyal serf: 缺乏头脑的忠实的农奴

in which he spoke of serving.

Coupling this ambition with the young man's humour Stephen had often called him one of the tame geese①; and there was even a point of irritation in the name pointed against that very reluctance of speech and deed in his friend which seemed so often to stand between Stephen's mind, eager of speculation, and the hidden ways of Irish life.

One night the young peasant, his spirit stung by the violent or luxurious language in which Stephen escaped from the cold silence of intellectual revolt, had called up before Stephen's mind a strange vision. The two were walking slowly towards Davin's rooms through the dark narrow streets of the poorer jews.

— A thing happened to myself, Stevie, last autumn, coming on winter, and I never told it to a living soul and you are the first person now I ever told it to. I disremember if it was October or November. It was October because it was before I came up here to join the matriculation class②.

Stephen had turned his smiling eyes towards his friend's face, flattered by his confidence and won over to sympathy by the speaker's simple accent.

— I was away all that day from my own place over in Buttevant.

— I don't know if you know where that is — at a hurling match between the Croke's Own Boys and the Fearless Thurles and by God, Stevie, that was the hard fight. My first cousin, Fonsy Davin, was stripped to his buff that day minding cool for the Limericks but he was up with the forwards③ half the time and shouting like mad. I never will forget that day. One of the Crokes made a woeful wipe at him one time with his camann④ and I declare to God he was within an aim's ace of getting it at the side of

---

① tame geese：温顺的白鹅　② matriculation class：新生班　③ forwards：前锋　④ camann：爱尔兰棒球的球棒

the temple. Oh, honest to God, if the crook of it caught him that time he was done for①.

— I am glad he escaped, Stephen had said with a laugh, but surely that's not the strange thing that happened you?

— Well, I suppose that doesn't interest you but leastways there was such noise after the match that I missed the train home and I couldn't get any kind of a yoke to give me a lift for②, as luck would have it, there was a mass meeting that same day over in Castletownroche and all the cars in the country were there. So there was nothing for it only to stay the night or to foot it out. Well, I started to walk and on I went and it was coming on night when I got into the Ballyhoura hills, that's better than ten miles from Kilmallock and there's a long lonely road after that. You wouldn't see the sign of a christian house along the road or hear a sound. It was pitch dark③ almost. Once or twice I stopped by the way under a bush to redden my pipe and only for the dew was thick I'd have stretched out there and slept④. At last, after a bend of the road, I spied a little cottage with a light in the window. I went up and knocked at the door. A voice asked who was there and I answered I was over at the match in Buttevant and was walking back and that I'd be thankful for a glass of water. After a while a young woman opened the door and brought me out a big mug of milk⑤. She was half undressed as if she was going to bed when I knocked and she had her hair hanging and I thought by her figure and by something in the look of her eyes that she must be carrying a child. She kept me in talk a long while at the door and I thought it strange because her breast and her shoulders were bare. She asked me was I tired and would I like to stop the night there. She said she

---

① if the ... done for：如果那一棍打上了，他就算完了　② I couldn't ... lift for：我搭不上任何能带我回去的便车　③ pitch dark：漆黑　④ only for ... and slept：要不是露水太重，我都想两脚一伸就躺下来睡在那儿了。　⑤ a big mug of milk：一大杯牛奶

was all alone in the house and that her husband had gone that morning to Queenstown with his sister to see her off. And all the time she was talking, Stevie, she had her eyes fixed on my face and she stood so close to me I could hear her breathing. When I handed her back the mug at last she took my hand to draw me in over the threshold and said: *Come in and stay the night here. You've no call to be frightened. There's no one in it but ourselves* ... I didn't go in, Stevie. I thanked her and went on my way again, all in a fever①. At the first bend of the road I looked back and she was standing at the door.

The last words of Davin's story sang in his memory and the figure of the woman in the story stood forth reflected in other figures of the peasant women whom he had seen standing in the doorways at Clane as the college cars drove by, as a type of her race and of his own, a batlike soul waking to the consciousness of itself in darkness and secrecy and loneliness and, through the eyes and voice and gesture of a woman without guile②, calling the stranger to her bed.

A hand was laid on his arm and a young voice cried:

— Ah, gentleman, your own girl, sir! The first handsel③ today, gentleman. Buy that lovely bunch. Will you, gentleman?

The blue flowers which she lifted towards him and her young blue eyes seemed to him at that instant images of guilelessness, and he halted till the image had vanished and he saw only her ragged dress and damp coarse hair and hoydenish④ face.

— Do, gentleman! Don't forget your own girl, sir!

— I have no money, said Stephen.

— Buy them lovely ones, will you, sir? Only a penny.

— Did you hear what I said? asked Stephen, bending

---

① all in a fever: 浑身像发烧一样　② guile: 诡计　③ handsel: 一天的第一笔生意　④ hoydenish: 顽皮的

towards her. I told you I had no money. I tell you again now.

— Well, sure, you will some day, sir, please God, the girl answered after an instant.

— Possibly, said Stephen, but I don't think it likely.

— He left her quickly, fearing that her intimacy might turn to jibing① and wishing to be out of the way before she offered her ware to another, a tourist from England or a student of Trinity. Grafton Street, along which he walked, prolonged that moment of discouraged poverty②. In the roadway at the head of the street a slab③ was set to the memory of Wolfe Tone④ and he remembered having been present with his father at its laying. He remembered with bitterness that scene of tawdry⑤ tribute. There were four French delegates in a brake and one, a plump smiling young man, held, wedged on a stick, a card on which were printed the words: *Vive l'Irlande*⑥!

But the trees in Stephen's Green were fragrant of rain and the rainsodden earth gave its mortal odour, a faint incense rising upward through the mould from many hearts. The soul of the gallant venal⑦ city which his elders had told him of had shrunk with time to a faint mortal odour rising from the earth and he knew that in a moment when he entered the sombre college he would be conscious of a corruption other than that of Buck Egan and Burnchapel Whaley⑧.

It was too late to go upstairs to the French class. He crossed the hall and took the corridor to the left which led to the physics theatre. The corridor was dark and silent but not unwatchful. Why did he feel that it was not unwatch-

---

① jibing：嘲弄　② discouraged poverty：令人沮丧的贫穷　③ slab：石碑　④ Wolfe Tone：沃尔弗·沃恩(1763－1798)，爱尔兰革命家，曾要求法国派兵支援爱尔兰的革命运动，被英政府判处叛国罪，后自杀。　⑤ tawdry：庸俗的　⑥ *Vive l'Irlande*：(法语)爱尔兰万岁　⑦ venal：贪污的　⑧ Buck Egan and Burnchapel Whaley：18世纪晚期英国下院议员。Egan对当时英国政治十分不满，Whaley曾在联合问题上投票时受贿。

ful? Was it because he had heard that in Buck Whaley's time there was a secret staircase there? Or was the jesuit house extraterritorial and was he walking among aliens? The Ireland of Tone and of Parnell[1] seemed to have receded in space.

He opened the door of the theatre and halted in the chilly grey light that struggled through the dusty windows. A figure was crouching before the large grate and by its leanness and greyness he knew that it was the dean of studies lighting the fire. Stephen closed the door quietly and approached the fireplace.

— Good morning, sir! Can I help you?

The priest looked up quickly and said:

— One moment now, Mr Dedalus, and you will see. There is an art in lighting a fire. We have the liberal arts and we have the useful arts. This is one of the useful arts.

— I will try to learn it, said Stephen.

— Not too much coal, said the dean, working briskly at his task, that is one of the secrets.

He produced four candlebutts[2] from the sidepockets of his soutane and placed them deftly among the coals and twisted papers. Stephen watched him in silence. Kneeling thus on the flagstone to kindle the fire and busied with the disposition of his wisps of paper and candlebutts he seemed more than ever a humble server making ready the place of sacrifice in an empty temple, a levite[3] of the Lord. Like a levite's robe of plain linen the faded worn soutane draped the kneeling figure of one whom the canonicals[4] or the bellbordered ephod[5] would irk and trouble. His very body had waxed old in lowly service of the Lord — in tending the fire upon the altar, in bearing tidings secretly, in waiting upon worldlings, in striking swiftly when bidden —

---

① Parnell: 帕内尔。参见第一章注释。 ② candlebutts: 蜡烛头 ③ levite: 祭司 ④ canonicals: 教士在布道时应穿的法衣 ⑤ ephod: 高级教士所穿,有复杂刺绣的法衣。

and yet had remained ungraced by aught① of saintly or of prelatic beauty. Nay, his very soul had waxed old in that service without growing towards light and beauty or spreading abroad a sweet odour of her sanctity② — a mortified will③ no more responsive to the thrill of its obedience than was to the thrill of love or combat his aging body, spare and sinewy④, greyed with a silver — pointed down.

The dean rested back on his hunkers⑤ and watched the sticks catch. Stephen, to fill the silence, said:

— I am sure I could not light a fire.

— You are an artist, are you not, Mr Dedalus? said the dean, glancing up and blinking his pale eyes. The object of the artist is the creation of the beautiful. What the beautiful is is another question.

He rubbed his hands slowly and drily over the difficulty.

— Can you solve that question now? he asked.

— Aquinas, answered Stephen, says *pulcra sunt quae visa placent*⑥.

— This fire before us, said the dean, will be pleasing to the eye. Will it therefore be beautiful?

— In so far as it is apprehended by the sight, which I suppose means here esthetic intellection, it will be beautiful. But Aquinas also says *Bonum est in quod tendit appetitus*⑦. In so far as it satisfies the animal craving for warmth fire is a good. In hell however it is an evil.

— Quite so, said the dean, you have certainly hit the nail on the head⑧.

He rose nimbly and went towards the door, set it ajar⑨ and said:

— A draught is said to be a help in these matters.

---

① aught：任何事物　② sanctity：神圣　③ a mortified will：受克制的意志　④ sinewy：结实的　⑤ hunkers：腿臀部　⑥ *pulcra sunt quae visa placent*：(拉丁文)赏心悦目即为美　⑦ *Bonum est in quod tendit appetitus*：(拉丁文)心之所向即为善　⑧ hit the nail on the head：说到点子上了　⑨ set it ajar：让门半开着

As he came back to the hearth, limping slightly but with a brisk step, Stephen saw the silent soul of a jesuit look out at him from the pale loveless eyes. Like Ignatius he was lame but in his eyes burned no spark of Ignatius' enthusiasm. Even the legendary craft of the company[1], a craft subtler and more secret than its fabled books of secret subtle wisdom, had not fired his soul with the energy of apostleship. It seemed as if he used the shifts and lore and cunning of the world, as bidden to do, for the greater glory of God, without joy in their handling or hatred of that in them which was evil but turning them, with a firm gesture of obedience, back upon themselves; and for all this silent service it seemed as if he loved not at all the master and little, if at all, the ends he served. *Similiter atque senis baculus*[2], he was, as the founder would have had him, like a staff in an old man's hand, to be left in a corner, to be leaned on in the road at nightfall or in stress of weather, to lie with a lady's nosegay[3] on a garden seat, to be raised in menace.

The dean returned to the hearth and began to stroke his chin.

— When may we expect to have something from you on the esthetic question? he asked.

— From me! said Stephen in astonishment. I stumble on an idea once a fortnight if I am lucky.

— These questions are very profound, Mr Dedalus, said the dean. It is like looking down from the cliffs of Moher into the depths. Many go down into the depths and never come up. Only the trained diver can go down into those depths and explore them and come to the surface again.

— If you mean speculation, sir, said Stephen, I also am sure that there is no such thing as free thinking inas-

---

① company: 指耶稣门徒　② *Similiter atque senis baculus*：（拉丁文）像老年人手中的手杖　③ nosegay: 花束

much as all thinking must be bound by its own laws.

— Ha!

— For my purpose I can work on at present by the light of one or two ideas of Aristotle and Aquinas.

— I see. I quite see your point.

— I need them only for my own use and guidance until I have done something for myself by their light. If the lamp smokes or smells I shall try to trim it. If it does not give light enough I shall sell it and buy another.

— Epictetus[1] also had a lamp, said the dean, which was sold for a fancy price after his death. It was the lamp he wrote his philosophical dissertations[2] by. You know Epictetus?

— An old gentleman, said Stephen coarsely, who said that the soul is very like a bucketful of water.

— He tells us in his homely way, the dean went on, that he put an iron lamp before a statue of one of the gods and that a thief stole the lamp. What did the philosopher do? He reflected that it was in the character of a thief to steal and determined to buy an earthen lamp next day instead of the iron lamp.

A smell of molten tallow[3] came up from the dean's candlebutts and fused itself in Stephen's consciousness with the jingle of the words, bucket and lamp and lamp and bucket. The priest's voice too had a hard jingling tone. Stephen's mind halted by instinct, checked by the strange tone and the imagery and by the priest's face which seemed like an unlit lamp or a reflector hung in a false focus[4]. What lay behind it or within it? A dull torpor[5] of the soul or the dullness of the thundercloud, charged with intellection[6] and capable of the gloom of God?

---

① Epictetus：公元 2 世纪初希腊斯多葛派哲学家　② philosophical dissertations：哲学论文　③ A smell of molten tallow：熔化的蜡油味道　④ a reflector hung in a false focus：焦距错误的反光镜　⑤ torpor：麻木, 迟钝　⑥ intellection：智力活动

— I meant a different kind of lamp, sir, said Stephen.

— Undoubtedly, said the dean.

— One difficulty, said Stephen, in esthetic discussion is to know whether words are being used according to the literary tradition or according to the tradition of the marketplace. I remember a sentence of Newman's in which he says of the Blessed Virgin that she was detained[①] in the full company of the saints. The use of the word in the marketplace is quite different. *I hope I am not detaining you*[②].

— Not in the least, said the dean politely.

— No, no, said Stephen, smiling, I mean . . .

— Yes, yes; I see, said the dean quickly, I quite catch the point: *detain*.

He thrust forward his under jaw and uttered a dry short cough.

— To return to the lamp, he said, the feeding of it is also a nice problem. You must choose the pure oil and you must be careful when you pour it in not to overflow it, not to pour in more than the funnel[③] can hold.

— What funnel? asked Stephen.

— The funnel through which you pour the oil into your lamp.

— That? said Stephen. Is that called a funnel? Is it not a tundish[④]?

— What is a tundish?

— That. The . . . the funnel.

— Is that called a tundish in Ireland? asked the dean. I never heard the word in my life.

— It is called a tundish in Lower Drumcondra, said Stephen, laughing, where they speak the best English.

— A tundish, said the dean reflectively. That is a

---

① detain: 陪伴　② I hope I am not detaining you: 这句话中的 detain 是绊住的意思。斯蒂芬以此来说明这个词在市井间(marketplace)的用法，而教导主任却以为斯蒂芬是在对他表示歉意，因而有下文的误会。　③ funnel: 漏斗　④ tundish: (酿酒用)漏斗

most interesting word. I must look that word up. Upon my word I must.

His courtesy of manner rang a little false, and Stephen looked at the English convert① with the same eyes as the elder brother in the parable may have turned on the prodigal②. A humble follower in the wake of clamorous③ conversions, a poor Englishman in Ireland, he seemed to have entered on the stage of jesuit history when that strange play of intrigue and suffering and envy and struggle and indignity had been all but given through — a late comer, a tardy spirit. From what had he set out? Perhaps he had been born and bred among serious dissenters④, seeing salvation in Jesus only and abhorring the vain pomps⑤ of the establishment. Had he felt the need of an implicit faith amid the welter of sectarianism⑥ and the jargon of its turbulent schisms⑦, six principle men, peculiar people, seed and snake baptists, supralapsarian dogmatists⑧? Had he found the true church all of a sudden in winding up to the end like a reel of cotton some finespun line of reasoning upon insufflation⑨ on the imposition of hands or the procession of the Holy Ghost? Or had Lord Christ touched him and bidden him follow, like that disciple who had sat at the receipt of custom, as he sat by the door of some zincroofed chapel, yawning and telling over his church pence?

The dean repeated the word yet again.

— Tundish! Well now, that is interesting!

— The question you asked me a moment ago seems to me more interesting. What is that beauty which the artist struggles to express from lumps of earth, said Stephen coldly.

— The little word seemed to have turned a rapier⑩

---

① English convert：英格兰皈依者 ② prodigal：浪子 ③ clamorous：热闹的 ④ dissenters：离经叛道的人 ⑤ pomps：盛大仪式 ⑥ sectarianism：派别争斗 ⑦ schisms：分裂 ⑧ supralapsarian dogmatists：笃信命运先于人世论者 ⑨ insufflation：吹入 ⑩ rapier：轻剑

point of his sensitiveness against this courteous and vigilant foe①. He felt with a smart of dejection that the man to whom he was speaking was a countryman of Ben Jonson. He thought:

— The language in which we are speaking is his before it is mine. How different are the words *home*, *Christ*, *ale*②, *master*, on his lips and on mine! I cannot speak or write these words without unrest of spirit. His language, so familiar and so foreign, will always be for me an acquired speech. I have not made or accepted its words. My voice holds them at bay. My soul frets③ in the shadow of his language.

— And to distinguish between the beautiful and the sublime, the dean added, to distinguish between moral beauty and material beauty. And to inquire what kind of beauty is proper to each of the various arts. These are some interesting points we might take up.

Stephen, disheartened suddenly by the dean's firm dry tone, was silent. The dean also was silent; and through the silence a distant noise of many boots and confused voices came up the staircase.

— In pursuing these speculations, said the dean conclusively, there is, however, the danger of perishing of inanition④. First you must take your degree. Set that before you as your first aim. Then little by little, you will see your way. I mean in every sense, your way in life and in thinking. It may be uphill pedalling⑤ at first. Take Mr Moonan. He was a long time before he got to the top. But he got there.

— I may not have his talent, said Stephen quietly.

— You never know, said the dean brightly. We never can say what is in us. I most certainly should not be despondent⑥. *Per aspera ad astra*⑦.

---

① vigilant foe：警觉的敌人　② ale：麦酒　③ fret：烦恼　④ inanition：营养不足　⑤ pedalling：骑自行车　⑥ despondent：泄气的　⑦ *Per aspera ad astra*：(拉丁文)只有通过艰险之途，才能到达顶峰。

He left the hearth quickly and went towards the landing to oversee the arrival of the first arts' class.

Leaning against the fireplace Stephen heard him greet briskly and impartially every student of the class and could almost see the frank smiles of the coarser students. A desolating pity began to fall like a dew upon his easily embittered heart for this faithful servingman of the knightly Loyola, for this half – brother of the clergy, more venal① than they in speech, more steadfast of soul than they, one whom he would never call his ghostly father; and he thought how this man and his companions had earned the name of worldlings at the hands not of the unworldly only but of the worldly also for having pleaded, during all their history, at the bar of God's justice for the souls of the lax and the lukewarm and the prudent②.

The entry of the professor was signalled by a few rounds of Kentish fire from the heavy boots of those students who sat on the highest tier of the gloomy theatre under the grey cobwebbed windows. The calling of the roll began and the responses to the names were given out in all tones until the name of Peter Byrne was reached.

— Here!

A deep bass note③ in response came from the upper tier, followed by coughs of protest along the other benches.

The professor paused in his reading and called the next name:

— Cranly!

No answer.

— Mr Cranly!

A smile flew across Stephen's face as he thought of his friend's studies.

— Try Leopardstown! Said a voice from the bench behind.

---

① venal: 可以收买的　② the souls ... the prudent: 那些轻快的、缺乏热情的、谨慎的灵魂　③ A deep bass note: 低沉的音调

Stephen glanced up quickly but Moynihan's snoutish[1] face, outlined on the grey light, was impassive. A formula was given out. Amid the rustling of the notebooks Stephen turned back again and said:

— Give me some paper for God's sake.

Are you as bad as that? asked Moynihan with a broad grin.

He tore a sheet from his scribbler and passed it down, whispering:

— In case of necessity any layman or woman can do it.

The formula which he wrote obediently on the sheet of paper, the coiling and uncoiling calculations[2] of the professor, the spectrelike symbols of force and velocity[3] fascinated and jaded Stephen's mind. He had heard some say that the old professor was an atheist freemason[4]. O the grey dull day! It seemed a limbo[5] of painless patient consciousness through which souls of mathematicians might wander, projecting long slender fabrics from plane to plane of ever rarer and paler twilight, radiating swift eddies to the last verges of a universe ever vaster, farther and more impalpable.

— So we must distinguish between elliptical and ellipsoidal[6]. Perhaps some of you gentlemen may be familiar with the works of Mr W. S. Gilbert[7]. In one of his songs he speaks of the billiard[8] sharp who is condemned to play:

> *On a cloth untrue*
> *With a twisted cue*
> *And elliptical billiard balls.*

— He means a ball having the form of the ellipsoid of the principal axes of which I spoke a moment ago.

---

① snoutish：猪嘴状的　② the coiling and uncoiling calculations：那些缠绕和展开的算式　③ velocity：速度　④ an atheist freemason：持无神论的互助会会员　⑤ limbo：（宗教）地狱的边境，据说是未受洗礼的婴儿与基督诞生前的善人死后所去的地方。　⑥ elliptical and ellipsoidal：椭圆形和椭圆球体　⑦ Mr W. S. Gilber：20 世纪初英国喜剧作家　⑧ billiard：台球

Moynihan leaned down towards Stephen's ear and murmured:

— What price ellipsoidal balls! Chase me, ladies, I'm in the cavalry!

His fellowstudent's rude humour ran like a gust through the cloister① of Stephen's mind, shaking into gay life limp priestly vestments that hung upon the walls, setting them to sway and caper② in a sabbath③ of misrule. The forms of the community emerged from the gustblown vestments, the dean of studies, the portly florid bursar④ with his cap of grey hair, the president, the little priest with feathery hair who wrote devout verses, the squat peasant form⑤ of the professor of economics, the tall form of the young professor of mental science discussing on the landing a case of conscience with his class like a giraffe⑥ cropping high leafage among a herd of antelopes, the grave troubled prefect of the sodality, the plump roundheaded professor of Italian with his rogue's eyes. They came ambling and stumbling, tumbling and capering, kilting their gowns for leap frog⑦, holding one another back, shaken with deep false laughter, smacking one another behind and laughing at their rude malice, calling to one another by familiar nicknames, protesting with sudden dignity at some rough usage, whispering two and two behind their hands.

The professor had gone to the glass cases on the side wall, from a shelf of which he took down a set of coils⑧, blew away the dust from many points and, bearing it carefully to the table, held a finger on it while he proceeded with his lecture. He explained that the wires in modern coils were of a compound called platinoid⑨ lately discovered

---

① cloister: 本意为修道院或隐居地,这里指斯蒂芬心灵自守的一隅。
② caper: 雀跃 ③ sabbath: 安息日 ④ bursar: 掌管财务者 ⑤ squat peasant form: 矮墩墩的农民形象 ⑥ giraffe: 长颈鹿 ⑦ kilting their gowns for leap frog: 把长外衣提起来准备做跳蛙游戏 ⑧ coils: 线圈 ⑨ platinoid: 赛白金

by F. W. Martino[1]

He spoke clearly the initials and surname of the discoverer. Moynihan whispered from behind:

— Good old Fresh Water Martin!

— Ask him, Stephen whispered back with weary humour, if he wants a subject for electrocution[2]. He can have me.

Moynihan, seeing the professor bend over the coils, rose in his bench and, clacking noiselessly the fingers of his right hand, began to call with the voice of a slobbering urchin[3]:

— Please teacher! Please, teacher! This boy is after saying a bad word, teacher.

— Platinoid, the professor said solemnly, is preferred to German silver because it has a lower coefficient of resistance variation by changes of temperature. The platinoid wire is insulated[4] and the covering of silk that insulates it is wound on the ebonite bobbins[5] just where my finger is. If it were wound single an extra current would be induced in the coils. The bobbins are saturated in hot paraffin wax[6] ...

A sharp Ulster voice[7] said from the bench below Stephen:

— Are we likely to be asked questions on applied science?

The professor began to juggle gravely with the terms pure science and applied science. A heavybuilt student wearing gold spectacles stared with some wonder at the questioner. Moynihan murmured from behind in his natural voice:

— Isn't MacAlister a devil for his pound of flesh?

---

① F. W. Martino：马蒂诺(1863－?)，美国化学家。 ② electrocution：电刑 ③ a slobbering urchin：淌口水的顽童 ④ insulate：绝缘 ⑤ ebonite bobbin：硬橡胶的线圈架 ⑥ The bobbins ... paraffin wax：这个线圈架是用石蜡浸透过的 ⑦ Ulster voice：爱尔兰口音

Stephen looked down coldly on the oblong skull① beneath him overgrown with tangled twinecoloured hair. The voice, the accent, the mind of the questioner offended him and he allowed the offence to carry him towards wilful unkindness, bidding his mind think that the student's father would have done better had he sent his son to Belfast to study and have saved something on the train fare by so doing.

The oblong skull beneath did not turn to meet this shaft② of thought and yet the shaft came back to its bowstring③; for he saw in a moment the student's wheypale face.

— That thought is not mine, he said to himself quickly. It came from the comic Irishman in the bench behind. Patience. Can you say with certitude by whom the soul of your race was bartered④ and its elect betrayed — by the questioner or by the mocker? Patience. Remember Epictetus. It is probably in his character to ask such a question at such a moment in such a tone and to pronounce the word *science* as a monosyllable.

The droning voice of the professor continued to wind itself slowly round and round the coils it spoke of, doubling, trebling, quadrupling its somnolent⑤ energy as the coil multiplied its ohms⑥ of resistance.

Moynihan's voice called from behind in echo to a distant bell:

— Closing time, gents!

The entrance hall was crowded and loud with talk. On a table near the door were two photographs in frames and between them a long roll of paper bearing an irregular tail of signatures. MacCann went briskly to and fro among the students, talking rapidly, answering rebuffs and leading one after another to the table. In the inner hall the dean of

---

① oblong skull: 椭圆形脑袋　② shaft: 箭　③ bowstring: 弓弦
④ was bartered: 被出卖　⑤ somnolent: 催眠的　⑥ ohms: 欧姆(电阻单位)

studies stood talking to a young professor, stroking his chin gravely and nodding his head.

Stephen, checked by the crowd at the door, halted irresolutely. From under the wide falling leaf of a soft hat Cranly's dark eyes were watching him.

— Have you signed? Stephen asked.

Cranly closed his long thinlipped mouth, *communed with himself an instant*[①] *and answered*:

— *Ego habeo*[②].

— What is it for?

— *Quod*[③]?

— What is it for?

Cranly turned his pale face to Stephen and said blandly and bitterly:

— *Per pax universalis*[④].

— Stephen pointed to the Csar's photograph[⑤] and said:

— He has the face of a besotted[⑥] Christ.

The scorn and anger in his voice brought Cranly's eyes back from a calm survey of the walls of the hall.

— Are you annoyed? He asked.

— No, answered Stephen.

— Are you in bad humour?

— No.

— *Credo ut vos sanguinarius mendax estis*, *said Cranly*, *quia facies vostra monstrat ut vos in damno malo humore estis*[⑦].

Moynihan, on his way to the table, said in Stephen's ear:

— MacCann is in tiptop form. Ready to shed the last drop. Brand new world. No stimulants and votes for the

---

① communed with himself an instant: 稍稍想了想　② *Ego habeo*：(拉丁文)我已签了　③ *Quod*：(拉丁文)什么　④ *Per pax universalis*：为了普遍的和平　⑤ Csar's photograph：沙皇的照片　⑥ besotted：糊涂的　⑦ Credo … humore estis：我想你他妈的肯定在撒谎,因为你的脸色表明你已经快气炸了肺

bitches.

Stephen smiled at the manner of this confidence and, when Moynihan had passed, turned again to meet Cranly's eyes.

— Perhaps you can tell me, he said, why he pours his soul so freely into my ear. Can you?

A dull scowl[①] appeared on Cranly's forehead. He stared at the table where Moynihan had bent to write his name on the roll and then said flatly:

— A sugar[②]!

— *Quis est in malo humore*[③], *said Stephen*, *ego aut vos*[④]?

Cranly did not take up the taunt. He brooded sourly on his judgement and repeated with the same flat force:

— A flaming bloody sugar, that's what he is!

It was his epitaph[⑤] for all dead friendships and Stephen wondered whether it would ever be spoken in the same tone over his memory. The heavy lumpish phrase sank slowly out of hearing like a stone through a quagmire[⑥]. Stephen saw it sink as he had seen many another, feeling its heaviness depress his heart. Cranly's speech, unlike that of Davin, had neither rare phrases of Elizabethan English nor quaintly turned versions of Irish idioms. Its drawl was an echo of the quays[⑦] of Dublin given back by a bleak decaying seaport, its energy an echo of the sacred eloquence of Dublin given back flatly by a Wicklow pulpit[⑧].

The heavy scowl faded from Cranly's face as MacCann marched briskly towards them from the other side of the hall.

— Here you are! said MacCann cheerily.

— Here I am! said Stephen.

---

① scowl: 怒容   ② sugar: 马屁精   ③ *Quis est in malo humore*: 谁快气炸了肺   ④ *ego aut vos*: 是我还是你   ⑤ epitaph: 评语   ⑥ quagmire: 泥坑   ⑦ quays: 码头   ⑧ pulpit: 布道坛

— Late as usual. Can you not combine the progressive tendency with a respect for punctuality?

— That question is out of order, said Stephen. Next business.

His smiling eyes were fixed on a silverwrapped tablet of milk chocolate which peeped out of the propagandist's breastpocket. A little ring of listeners closed round to hear the war of wits. A lean student with olive skin and lank black hair thrust his face between the two, glancing from one to the other at each phrase and seeming to try to catch each flying phrase in his open moist mouth. Cranly took a small grey handball from his pocket and began to examine it closely, turning it over and over.

— Next business? said MacCann. Hom!

He gave a loud cough of laughter, smiled broadly and tugged twice at the strawcoloured goatee[①] which hung from his blunt chin.

— The next business is to sign the testimonial[②].

— Will you pay me anything if I sign? asked Stephen.

— I thought you were an idealist, said MacCann.

The gipsylike student looked about him and addressed the onlookers in an indistinct bleating voice.

— By hell, that's a queer notion. I consider that notion to be a mercenary[③] notion.

His voice faded into silence. No heed was paid to his words. He turned his olive face, equine[④] in expression, towards Stephen, inviting him to speak again.

MacCann began to speak with fluent energy of the Csar's rescript[⑤], of Stead[⑥], of general disarmament arbitration in cases of international disputes, of the signs of the times, of the new humanity and the new gospel of life

---

① strawcoloured goatee：稻草般颜色的山羊胡　② testimonial：证书
③ mercenary：为钱的　④ equine：似马的　⑤ rescript：官方的　⑥ Stead：
威廉·托马斯·斯特德(1849－1912)，英国著名记者，是国际和平运动的热情
支持者。

which would make it the business of the community to se-
cure as cheaply as possible the greatest possible happiness of
the greatest possible number.

The gipsy student responded to the close of the period
by crying:

— Three cheers for universal brotherhood!

— Go on, Temple, said a stout ruddy student near
him. I'll stand you a pint after. ①

— I'm a believer in universal brotherhood, said Temple, glancing about him out of his dark, oval eyes. Marx is
only a bloody cod②.

Cranly gripped his arm tightly to check his tongue,
smiling uneasily, and repeated:

— Easy, easy, easy!

Temple struggled to free his arm but continued, his
mouth flecked by a thin foam:

— Socialism was founded by an Irishman and the first
man in Europe who preached the freedom of thought was
Collins③. Two hundred years ago. He denounced
priestcraft, the philosopher of Middlesex. Three cheers for
John Anthony Collins!

A thin voice from the verge of the ring replied:

— Pip! pip!

Moynihan murmured beside Stephen's ear:

— And what about John Anthony's poor little sister:

Lottie Collins lost her drawers;
Won't you kindly lend her yours?

Stephen laughed and Moynihan, pleased with the result, murmured again:

— We'll have five bob④ eachway on John Anthony
Collins.

— I am waiting for your answer, said MacCann

---

① I'll stand you a pint after: 回头我请你喝一壶　② a bloody cod: 大傻
瓜　③ Collins: 18 世纪初的一位自然神论者　④ bob: 先令

briefly.

— The affair doesn't interest me in the least, said Stephen wearily. You know that well. Why do you make a scene about it?

— Good! said MacCann, smacking his lips. You are a reactionary, then?

— Do you think you impress me, Stephen asked, when you flourish your wooden sword?

— Metaphors! said MacCann bluntly. Come to facts.

Stephen blushed and turned aside. MacCann stood his ground and said with hostile humour:

— Minor poets, I suppose, are above such trivial questions as the question of universal peace.

Cranly raised his head and held the handball between the two students by way of a peaceoffering, saying:

— *Pax super totum sanguinarium globum* .[①]

Stephen, moving away the bystanders, jerked his shoulder angrily in the direction of the Tsar's image, saying:

— Keep your icon. If we must have a Jesus, let us have a legitimate Jesus.

— By hell, that's a good one! said the gipsy student to those about him, that's a fine expression. I like that expression immensely.

He gulped down the spittle[②] in his throat as if he were gulping down the phrase and, fumbling at the peak of his tweed cap, turned to Stephen, saying:

— Excuse me, sir, what do you mean by that expression you uttered just now?

Feeling himself jostled[③] by the students near him, he said to them:

—I am curious to know now what he meant by that expression.

—He turned again to Stephen and said in a whisper:

---

① *Pax super totum sanguinarium globum*：(拉丁文)让这整个血腥的世界和平吧。　② spittle：唾沫　③ jostled：被拥挤

—Do you believe in Jesus? I believe in man. Of course, I don't know if you believe in man. I admire you, sir. I admire the mind of man independent of all religions. Is that your opinion about the mind of Jesus?

—Go on, Temple, said the stout ruddy student, returning, as was his wont①, to his first idea, that pint is waiting for you.

— He thinks I'm an imbecile②, Temple explained to Stephen, because I'm a believer in the power of mind.

Cranly linked his arms into those of Stephen and his admirer and said:

— *Nos ad manum ballum jocabimus③*.

Stephen, in the act of being led away, caught sight of MacCann's flushed bluntfeatured face.

— My signature is of no account, he said politely. You are right to go your way. Leave me to go mine.

— Dedalus, said MacCann crisply, I believe you're a good fellow but you have yet to learn the dignity of altruism④ and the responsibility of the human individual.

A voice said:

— Intellectual crankery⑤ is better out of this movement than in it.

Stephen, recognizing the harsh tone of MacAlister's voice did not turn in the direction of the voice. Cranly pushed solemnly through the throng of students, linking Stephen and Temple like a celebrant attended by his ministers on his way to the altar.

Temple bent eagerly across Cranly's breast and said:

— Did you hear MacAlister what he said? That youth is jealous of you. Did you see that? I bet Cranly didn't see that. By hell, I saw that at once.

As they crossed the inner hall the dean of studies was

---

① wont: 习惯 ② imbecile: 白痴 ③ *Nos ad manum ballum jocabimus*: (拉丁文)我们可看不上他玩的手球游戏。 ④ altruism: 利他主义 ⑤ crankery: 怪论

in the act of escaping from the student with whom he had been conversing. He stood at the foot of the staircase, a foot on the lowest step, his threadbare soutane gathered about him for the ascent with womanish care, nodding his head often and repeating:

— Not a doubt of it, Mr Hackett! Very fine! Not a doubt of it!

In the middle of the hall the prefect of the college sodality was speaking earnestly, in a soft querulous① voice, with a boarder②. As he spoke he wrinkled a little his freckled brow and bit, between his phrases, at a tiny bone pencil.

— I hope the matricmen③ will all come. The first arts' men are pretty sure. Second arts too. We must make sure of the newcomers.

Temple bent again across Cranly, as they were passing through the doorway, and said in a swift whisper:

— Do you know that he is a married man? He was a married man before they converted him. He has a wife and children somewhere. By hell, I think that's the queerest notion I ever heard! Eh?

His whisper trailed off into sly cackling laughter. The moment they were through the doorway Cranly seized him rudely by the neck and shook him, saying:

— You flaming floundering fool!④ I'll take my dying bible there isn't a bigger bloody ape, do you know, than you in the whole flaming bloody world!

Temple wriggled in his grip, laughing still with sly content, while Cranly repeated flatly at every rude shake:

— A flaming flaring bloody idiot!

They crossed the weedy garden together. The president, wrapped in a heavy loose cloak, was coming towards them along one of the walks, reading his office⑤. At the

---

① querulous: 易怒的　② boarder: 寄宿生　③ matricmen: 新生
④ You flaming floundering fool: 你这个该死的做错事的傻瓜　⑤ reading his office: 念着他的祷文

end of the walk he halted before turning and raised his eyes. The students saluted, Temple fumbling as before at the peak of his cap. They walked forward in silence. As they neared the alley Stephen could hear the thuds of the players' hands and the wet smacks of the ball and Davin's voice crying out excitedly at each stroke.

The three students halted round the box on which Davin sat to follow the game. Temple, after a few moments, sidled across to Stephen and said:

— Excuse me, I wanted to ask you, do you believe that Jean Jacques Rousseau① was a sincere man?

Stephen laughed outright. Cranly, picking up the broken stave of a cask② from the grass at his feet, turned swiftly and said sternly:

— Temple, I declare to the living God if you say another word, do you know, to anybody on any subject I'll kill you *super spottum*③.

— He was like you, I fancy, said Stephen, an emotional man.

— Blast him, curse him! said Cranly broadly. Don't talk to him at all. Sure, you might as well be talking, do you know, to a flaming chamberpot④ as talking to Temple. Go home, Temple. For God's sake, go home.

— I don't care a damn about you, Cranly, answered Temple, moving out of reach of the uplifted stave and pointing at Stephen. He's the only man I see in this institution that has an individual mind.

— Institution! Individual! cried Cranly. Go home, blast you, for you're a hopeless bloody man.

— I'm an emotional man, said Temple. That's quite rightly expressed. And I'm proud that I'm an emotionalist.

He sidled out of the alley, smiling slyly. Cranly

---

① Jean Jacques Rousseau: 让·雅克·卢梭(1712—1778), 法国作家
② broken stave of a cask: 破木桶板 ③ *super spottum*: (拉丁文)当场
④ chamberpot: 夜壶

watched him with a blank expressionless face.

— Look at him! he said. Did you ever see such a go-by-the-wall?

His phrase was greeted by a strange laugh from a student who lounged against the wall①, his peaked cap down on his eyes. The laugh, pitched in a high key and coming from a so muscular frame, seemed like the whinny of an elephant. The student's body shook all over and, to ease his mirth, he rubbed both his hands delightedly over his groins.

— Lynch is awake, said Cranly.

Lynch, for answer, straightened himself and thrust forward his chest.

— Lynch puts out his chest, said Stephen, as a criticism of life.

Lynch smote himself sonorously on the chest② and said:

— Who has anything to say about my girth③?

Cranly took him at the word and the two began to tussle④. When their faces had flushed with the struggle they drew apart, panting. Stephen bent down towards Davin who, intent on the game, had paid no heed to the talk of the others.

— And how is my little tame goose? he asked. Did he sign, too?

David nodded and said:

— And you, Stevie?

Stephen shook his head.

— You're a terrible man, Stevie, said Davin, taking the short pipe from his mouth. Always alone.

— Now that you have signed the petition for universal peace, said Stephen, I suppose you will burn that little

---

① lounged against the wall: 懒洋洋地靠在墙上　② smote himself sonorously on the chest: 梆梆地敲打着自己的胸脯　③ girth: 腰身围长　④ tussle: 摔跤

copybook I saw in your room.

As Davin did not answer, Stephen began to quote:

— Long pace, Fianna①! Right incline, fianna! Fianna, by numbers, salute, one, two!

— That's a different question, said Davin. I'm an Irish nationalist, first and foremost. But that's you all out. You're a born sneerer, Stevie.

— When you make the next rebellion with hurley-sticks②, said Stephen, and want the indispensable informer③, tell me. I can find you a few in this college.

— I can't understand you, said Davin. One time I hear you talk against English literature. Now you talk against the Irish informers. What with your name and your ideas ... Are you Irish at all?

— Come with me now to the office of arms and I will show you the tree of my family④, said Stephen.

— Then be one of us, said Davin. Why don't you learn Irish? Why did you drop out of the league class after the first lesson?

— You know one reason why, answered Stephen.

Davin tossed his head and laughed.

— Oh, come now, he said. Is it on account of that certain young lady and Father Moran? But that's all in your own mind, Stevie. They were only talking and laughing.

Stephen paused and laid a friendly hand upon Davin's shoulder.

— Do you remember, he said, when we knew each other first? The first morning we met you asked me to show you the way to the matriculation class, putting a very strong stress on the first syllable. You remember? Then you used to address the jesuits as father, you remember? I ask myself about you: *Is he as innocent as his speech*?

— I'm a simple person, said Davin. You know that.

---

① Fianna：(盖尔语)芬尼亚分子 ② hurleystick：棒球棍 ③ indispensable informer：必不可少的告密者 ④ the tree of my family：我家的族谱

When you told me that night in Harcourt Street those things about your private life, honest to God, Stevie, I was not able to eat my dinner. I was quite bad. I was awake a long time that night. Why did you tell me those things?

— Thanks, said Stephen. You mean I am a monster.

— No, said Davin, but I wish you had not told me.

A tide began to surge[1] beneath the calm surface of Stephen's friendliness.

— This race and this country and this life produced me, he said I shall express myself as I am.

— Try to be one of us, repeated Davin. In your heart you are an Irishman but your pride is too powerful.

— My ancestors threw off their language and took another Stephen said. They allowed a handful of foreigners to subject[2] them. Do you fancy I am going to pay in my own life and person debts they made? What for?

— For our freedom, said Davin.

— No honourable and sincere man, said Stephen, has given up to you his life and his youth and his affections from the days of Tone to those of Parnell but you sold him to the enemy or failed him in need or reviled[3] him and left him for another. And you invite me to be one of you. I'd see you damned first.

— They died for their ideals, Stevie, said Davin. Our day will come yet, believe me.

Stephen, following his own thought, was silent for an instant.

— The soul is born, he said vaguely, first in those moments I told you of. It has a slow and dark birth, more mysterious than the birth of the body. When the soul of a man is born in this country there are nets flung at it to hold it back from flight. You talk to me of nationality, language, religion. I shall try to fly by those nets[4].

---

① surge：澎湃　② subject：征服　③ reviled：辱骂　④ I shall try to fly by those nets：我要冲破那些网而高飞。

Davin knocked the ashes from his pipe.

— Too deep for me, Stevie, he said. But a man's country comes first. Ireland first, Stevie. You can be a poet or a mystic after.

— Do you know what Ireland is? asked Stephen with cold violence. Ireland is the old sow that eats her farrow[①].

Davin rose from his box and went towards the players, shaking his head sadly. But in a moment his sadness left him and he was hotly disputing with Cranly and the two players who had finished their game. A match of four was arranged, Cranly insisting, however, that his ball should be used. He let it rebound twice or thrice to his hand and struck it strongly and swiftly towards the base of the alley[②], exclaiming in answer to its thud:

— Your soul!

Stephen stood with Lynch till the score began to rise. Then he plucked him by the sleeve to come away. Lynch obeyed, saying:

— Let us eke go, as Cranly has it.

Stephen smiled at this sidethrust. They passed back through the garden and out through the hall where the doddering porter[③] was pinning up a notice in the frame. At the foot of the steps they halted and Stephen took a packet of cigarettes from his pocket and offered it to his companion.

— I know you are poor, he said.

— Damn your yellow insolence[④], answered Lynch.

This second proof of Lynch's culture made Stephen smile again.

— It was a great day for European culture, he said, when you made up your mind to swear in yellow.

They lit their cigarettes and turned to the right. After

---

① Ireland is ... her farrow: 爱尔兰是一头吃掉自己的小猪崽的老母猪。② base of the alley: 球本垒 ③ doddering porter: 老态龙钟的工友 ④ Damn your yellow insolence: 让你那下流的无礼傲慢见鬼去吧。

a pause Stephen began:

— Aristotle has not defined pity and terror. I have. I say ...

Lynch halted and said bluntly:

— Stop! I won't listen! I am sick. I was out last night on a yellow drunk with Horan and Goggins.

Stephen went on:

— Pity is the feeling which arrests the mind in the presence of whatsoever is grave and constant in human sufferings and unites it with the human sufferer. Terror is the feeling which arrests the mind in the presence of whatsoever is grave and constant in human sufferings and unites it with the secret cause.

— Repeat, said Lynch.

Stephen repeated the definitions slowly.

— A girl got into a hansom① a few days ago, he went on, in London. She was on her way to meet her mother whom she had not seen for many years. At the corner of a street the shaft② of a lorry shivered the window of the hansom in the shape of a star. A long fine needle of the shivered glass pierced her heart. She died on the instant. The reporter called it a tragic death. It is not. It is remote from terror and pity according to the terms of my definitions.

— The tragic emotion, in fact, is a face looking two ways, towards terror and towards pity, both of which are phases of it. You see I use the word *arrest*. I mean that the tragic emotion is static③. Or rather the dramatic emotion is. The feelings excited by improper art are kinetic④, desire or loathing. Desire urges us to possess, to go to something; loathing urges us to abandon, to go from something. These are kinetic emotions. The arts which excite them, pornographic or didactic⑤, are therefore improper arts. The esthetic emotion (I used the general term) is therefore static. The mind is arrested and raised above de-

---

① hansom: 马车 ② shaft: 辕轩 ③ static: 静态的 ④ kinetic: 动态的 ⑤ pornographic or didactic: 色情的或说教的

sire and loathing.

— You say that art must not excite desire, said Lynch, I told you that one day I wrote my name in pencil on the backside of the Venus of Praxiteles① in the Museum. Was that not desire?

— I speak of normal natures, said Stephen. You also told me that when you were a boy in that charming carmelite school② you ate pieces of dried cowdung③.

Lynch broke again into a whinny of laughter and again rubbed both hands over his groins④ but without taking them from his pockets.

— O, I did! I did! he cried.

Stephen turned towards his companion and looked at him for a moment boldly in the eyes. Lynch, recovering from his laughter, answered his look from his humbled eyes. The long slender flattened skull beneath the long pointed cap brought before Stephen's mind the image of a hooded reptile⑤. The eyes, too, were reptilelike in glint and gaze. Yet at that instant, humbled and alert in their look, they were lit by one tiny human point, the window of a shrivelled⑥ soul, poignant and selfembittered⑦.

— As for that, Stephen said in polite parenthesis⑧, we are all animals. I also am an animal.

— You are, said Lynch.

— But we are just now in a mental world, Stephen continued. The desire and loathing excited by improper esthetic means are really unesthetic emotions not only because they are kinetic in character but also because they are not more than physical. Our flesh shrinks from what it dreads and responds to the stimulus of what it desires by a purely reflex action of the nervous system. Our eyelid closes before

---

① Praxiteles: 公元前 4 世纪雅典著名的雕刻家　② carmelite school: 加尔默罗教会学校　③ dried cowdung: 干牛粪　④ groins: 腹股沟　⑤ reptile: 眼镜蛇　⑥ shrivelled: 皱缩成一团的　⑦ poignant and selfembittered: 尖刻而又自怨自艾　⑧ parenthesis: 附加

we are aware that the fly is about to enter our eye.

— Not always, said Lynch critically.

— In the same way, said Stephen, your flesh responded to the stimulus of a naked statue, but it was, I say, simply a reflex action of the nerves. Beauty expressed by the artist cannot awaken in us an emotion which is kinetic or a sensation which is purely physical. It awakens, or ought to awaken, or induces, or ought to induce, an esthetic stasis[①], an ideal pity or an ideal terror, a stasis called forth, prolonged and at last dissolved by what I call the rhythm of beauty.

— What is that exactly? asked Lynch.

— Rhythm, said Stephen, is the first formal esthetic relation of part to part in any esthetic whole or of an esthetic whole to its part or parts or of any part to the esthetic whole of which it is a part.

— If that is rhythm, said Lynch, let me hear what you call beauty; and, please remember, though I did eat a cake of cowdung once, that I admire only beauty.

Stephen raised his cap as if in greeting. Then, blushing slightly, he laid his hand on Lynch's thick tweed sleeve[②].

—We are right, he said, and the others are wrong. To speak of these things and to try to understand their nature and, having understood it, to try slowly and humbly and constantly to express, to press out again, from the gross earth or what it brings forth, from sound and shape and colour which are the prison gates of our soul, an image of the beauty we have come to understand — that is art.

They had reached the canal bridge and, turning from their course, went on by the trees. A crude grey light[③], mirrored in the sluggish water and a smell of wet branches over their heads seemed to war against the course of

---

① stasis：静态平衡　② thick tweed sleeve：厚花呢袖子　③ A crude grey light：一道刺眼的灰色的光线

Stephen's thought.

— But you have not answered my question, said Lynch. What is art? What is the beauty it expresses?

— That was the first definition I gave you, you sleepyheaded wretch[1], said Stephen, when I began to try to think out the matter for myself. Do you remember the night? Cranly lost his temper and began to talk about Wicklow bacon.

— I remember, said Lynch. He told us about them flaming fat devils of pigs.

— Art, said Stephen, is the human disposition of sensible or intelligible matter for an esthetic end. You remember the pigs and forget that. You are a distressing pair, you and Cranly.

Lynch made a grimace[2] at the raw grey sky and said:

— If I am to listen to your esthetic philosophy give me at least another cigarette. I don't care about it. I don't even care about women. Damn you and damn everything. I want a job of five hundred a year. You can't get me one.

Stephen handed him the packet of cigarettes. Lynch took the last one that remained, saying simply:

— Proceed!

— Aquinas, said Stephen, says that is beautiful the apprehension of which pleases.

Lynch nodded.

— I remember that, he said, *Pulcra sunt quae visa placent*[3].

— He uses the word visa, said Stephen, to cover esthetic apprehensions of all kinds, whether through sight or hearing or through any other avenue of apprehension. This word, though it is vague, is clear enough to keep away good and evil which excite desire and loathing. It means

---

① you sleepyheaded wretch: 你这个昏头昏脑的臭小子。　② Lynch made a grimace: 做了个鬼脸　③ *Pulcra sunt quae visa placent*: (拉丁文)赏心悦目即为美

certainly a stasis and not a kinesis. How about the true? It produces also a stasis of the mind. You would not write your name in pencil across the hypotenuse of a rightangled triangle[①].

— No, said Lynch, give me the hypotenuse of the Venus of Praxiteles.

— Static therefore, said Stephen. Plato[②], I believe, said that beauty is the splendour of truth. I don't think that it has a meaning but the true and the beautiful are akin. Truth is beheld by the intellect which is appeased by the most satisfying relations of the intelligible; beauty is beheld by the imagination which is appeased by the most satisfying relations of the sensible. The first step in the direction of truth is to understand the frame and scope of the intellect itself, to comprehend the act itself of intellection. Aristotle's entire system of philosophy rests upon his book of psychology and that, I think, rests on his statement that the same attribute cannot at the same time and in the same connexion belong to and not belong to the same subject. The first step in the direction of beauty is to understand the frame and scope of the imagination, to comprehend the act itself of esthetic apprehension. Is that clear?

— But what is beauty? asked Lynch impatiently. Out with another definition. Something we see and like! Is that the best you and Aquinas can do?

— Let us take woman, said Stephen.

— Let us take her! said Lynch fervently.

— The Greek, the Turk, the Chinese, the Copt[③], the Hottentot[④], said Stephen, all admire a different type of female beauty. That seems to be a maze out of which we cannot escape. I see however, two ways out. One is this hypothesis[⑤]: that every physical quality admired by men in women is in direct connection with the manifold functions[⑥]

---

① hypotenuse of a rightangled triangle: 直角三角形的斜边　② Plato: 柏拉图(427－347 BC),希腊哲学家。　③ the Copt: 一种埃及土人　④ the Hottentot: 西南非的一个少数民族　⑤ hypothesis: 假设　⑥ manifold functions: 多方面的功能

of women for the propagation① of the species. It may be
so. The world, it seems, is drearier than even you,
Lynch, imagined. For my part I dislike that way out. It
leads to eugenics② rather than to esthetic. It leads you out
of the maze into a new gaudy③ lectureroom where Mac-
Cann, with one hand on *The Origin of Species*④ and the
other hand on the new testament, tells you that you admired the great flanks of Venus because you felt that she
would bear you burly⑤ offspring and admired her great
breasts because you felt that she would give good milk to
her children and yours.

— Then MacCann is a sulphuryellow⑥ liar, said
Lynch energetically.

— There remains another way out, said Stephen,
laughing.

— To wit? said Lynch.

— This hypothesis, Stephen began.

A long dray laden with old iron⑦ came round the corner of Sir Patrick Dun's hospital covering the end of
Stephen's speech with the harsh roar of jangled and rattling
metal. Lynch closed his ears and gave out oath after oath⑧
till the dray had passed. Then he turned on his heel rudely.
Stephen turned also and waited for a few moments till his
companion's illhumour had had its vent⑨.

— This hypothesis, Stephen repeated, is the other
way out: that, though the same object may not seem beautiful to all people, all people who admire a beautiful object
find in it certain relations which satisfy and coincide with
the stages themselves of all esthetic apprehension. These
relations of the sensible, visible to you through one form

---

① propagation：繁殖　② eugenics：优生学　③ gaudy：装饰花哨的
④ The Origin of Species：《物种起源》,达尔文(1809－1882)著。　⑤ burly：
强壮的　⑥ sulphuryellow：下流的　⑦ A long dray laden with old iron：一辆
装满破铜烂铁的长平板车　⑧ gave out oath after oath：不停地咒骂着
⑨ had its vent：发泄出来

and to me through another, must be therefore the necessary qualities of beauty. Now, we can return to our old friend saint Thomas for another pennyworth of wisdom①.

Lynch laughed.

— It amuses me vastly, he said, to hear you quoting him time after time like a jolly round friar. Are you laughing in your sleeve?②

— MacAlister, answered Stephen, would call my esthetic theory applied Aquinas. So far as this side of esthetic philosophy extends, Aquinas will carry me all along the line. When we come to the phenomena of artistic conception, artistic gestation③, and artistic reproduction I require a new terminology④ and a new personal experience.

— Of course, said Lynch, after all Aquinas, in spite of his intellect, was exactly a good round friar. But you will tell me about the new personal experience and new terminology some other day. Hurry up and finish the first part.

— Who knows? said Stephen, smiling. Perhaps Aquinas would understand me better than you. He was a poet himself. He wrote a hymn for Maundy Thursday. It begins with the words *Pange lingua gloriosi*⑤. They say it is the highest glory of the hymnal. It is an intricate and soothing hymn⑥. I like it; but there is no hymn that can be put beside that mournful and majestic processional song⑦, the *Vexilla Regis*⑧ of Venantius Fortunatus.

Lynch began to sing softly and solemnly in a deep bass voice:

Impleta sunt quae concinit
David fideli carmine

---

① pennyworth of wisdom: 几分钱的智慧　② Are you laughing in your sleeve: 你在偷偷暗笑吗?　③ artistic gestation: 艺术的孕育　④ terminology: 术语　⑤ *Pange lingua gloriosi*: (拉丁文)唱吧, 我光荣的舌啊。　⑥ soothing hymn: 给人以安慰的赞美诗　⑦ mournful and majestic processional song: 悲哀而庄严的列队行进歌　⑧ *Vexilla Regis*: (拉丁文)国王行进的旗帜

Dicendo nationibus
*Regnavit a ligno Deus.*①

— That's great! he said, well pleased. Great music!

They turned into Lower Mount Street. A few steps from the corner a fat young man, wearing a silk neckcloth, saluted them and stopped.

— Did you hear the results of the exams? he asked. Griffin was plucked②. Halpin and O'Flynn are through the home civil. Moonan got fifth place in the Indian. O'Shaughnessy got fourteenth. The Irish fellows in Clarke's gave them a feed last night③. They all ate curry.

His pallid bloated face expressed benevolent malice and, as he had advanced through his tidings of success, his small fatencircled eyes vanished out of sight and his weak wheezing voice out of hearing.

In reply to a question of Stephen's his eyes and his voice came forth again from their lurkingplaces④.

— Yes, MacCullagh and I, he said. He's taking pure mathematics and I'm taking constitutional history. There are twenty subjects. I'm taking botany⑤ too. You know I'm a member of the field club.

He drew back from the other two in a stately fashion and placed a plump woollengloved hand on his breast from which muttered wheezing laughter at once broke forth.

— Bring us a few turnips and onions⑥ the next time you go out, said Stephen drily, to make a stew.

The fat student laughed indulgently and said:

— We are all highly respectable people in the field club. Last Saturday we went out to Glenmalure, seven of us.

— With women, Donovan? said Lynch.

---

① *Impleta sunt ... a ligno Deus*：(拉丁文)大卫所言都已成真/真实而古老的预言之歌/在十字架上的上帝/仍统治着一切　② plucked：考试不及格　③ gave them a feed last night：昨晚请他们大吃了一顿　④ lurkingplaces：隐匿之处　⑤ botany：植物学　⑥ turnips and onions：萝卜和洋葱

Donovan again laid his hand on his chest and said:

— Our end is the acquisition of knowledge[1].

Then he said quickly:

— I hear you are writing some essays about esthetics.

Stephen made a vague gesture of denial.

— Goethe[2] and Lessing[3], said Donovan, have written a lot on that subject, the classical school and the romantic school and all that. *The Laocoon* interested me very much when I read it. Of course it is idealistic, German, ultraprofound[4].

Neither of the others spoke. Donovan took leave of them urbanely[5].

— I must go, he said softly and benevolently, I have a strong suspicion, amounting almost to a conviction, that my sister intended to make pancakes today for the dinner of the Donovan family.

— Goodbye, Stephen said in his wake. Don't forget the turnips for me and my mate.

Lynch gazed after him his lip curling in slow scorn till his face resembled a devil's mask:

— To think that that yellow pancakeeating excrement[6] can get a good job, he said at length, and I have to smoke cheap cigarettes!

They turned their faces towards Merrion Square and went on for a little in silence.

— To finish what I was saying about beauty, said Stephen, the most satisfying relations of the sensible must therefore correspond to the necessary phases of artistic apprehension. Find these and you find the qualities of universal beauty. Aquinas says: *ad pulcritudinem tria requiruntur, integritas, consonantia, claritas*. I translate it so:

---

① Our end ... of knowledge: 我们的目的是获取知识。　② Goethe: 歌德(1749－1832), 德国伟大的诗人、小说家和思想家。　③ Lessing: 来辛 (1729－1781), 德国文艺批评家和剧作家, 下文出现的《拉奥孔》(*The Laocoon*)为来辛所著。　④ ultraprofound: 极深奥的　⑤ urbanely: 有礼貌的 ⑥ excrement: 粪便

Three things are needed for beauty, wholeness, harmony, and radiance. Do these correspond to the phases of apprehension? Are you following?

— Of course, I am, said Lynch. If you think I have an excrementitious intelligence run after Donovan and ask him to listen to you.

Stephen pointed to a basket which a butcher's boy had slung inverted on his head.

— Look at that basket, he said.

— I see it, said Lynch.

— In order to see that basket, said Stephen, your mind first of all separates the basket from the rest of the visible universe which is not the basket. The first phase of apprehension is a bounding line drawn about the object to be apprehended. An esthetic image is presented to us either in space or in time. What is audible is presented in time, what is visible is presented in space. But, temporal or spatial①, the esthetic image is first luminously apprehended as selfbounded and selfcontained upon the immeasurable background of space or time which is not it. You apprehended it as *one* thing. You see it as one whole. You apprehend its wholeness. That is *integritas*②.

— Bull's eye③! said Lynch, laughing. Go on.

— Then, said Stephen, you pass from point to point, led by its formal lines; you apprehend it as balanced part against part within its limits; you feel the rhythm of its structure. In other words the synthesis④ of immediate perception is followed by the analysis of apprehension. Having first felt that it is *one* thing you feel now that it is a *thing*. You apprehend it as complex, multiple, divisible, separable, made up of its parts, the result of its parts and their sum, harmonious. That is *consonantia*⑤.

---

① temporal or spatial: 时间的或空间的　② integritas: 完整　③ Bull's eye: 一语中的　④ synthesis: 综合　⑤ consonantia: 和谐

— Bull's eye again! said Lynch wittily. Tell me now what is *claritas*[①] and you win the cigar.

— The connotation of the word, Stephen said, is rather vague. Aquinas uses a term which seems to be inexact. It baffled me for a long time. It would lead you to believe that he had in mind symbolism or idealism, the supreme quality of beauty being a light from some other world, the idea of which the matter is but the shadow, the reality of which it is but the symbol. I thought he might mean that *claritas* is the artistic discovery and representation of the divine purpose in anything or a force of generalization which would make the esthetic image a universal one, make it outshine its proper conditions[②]. But that is literary talk. I understand it so. When you have apprehended that basket as one thing and have then analysed it according to its form and apprehended it as a thing you make the only synthesis which is logically and esthetically permissible. You see that it is that thing which it is and no other thing. The radiance of which he speaks in the scholastic *quidditas*, the *whatness* of a thing. This supreme quality is felt by the artist when the esthetic image is first conceived in his imagination. The mind in that mysterious instant Shelley likened beautifully to a fading coal[③]. The instant wherein that supreme quality of beauty, the clear radiance of the esthetic image, is apprehended luminously by the mind which has been arrested by its wholeness and fascinated by its harmony is the luminous silent stasis of esthetic pleasure, a spiritual state very like to that cardiac[④] condition which the Italian physiologist Luigi Galvani, using a phrase almost as beautiful as Shelley's, called the enchantment of the heart[⑤].

Stephen paused and, though his companion did not

---

① claritas: 光彩   ② make it outshine its proper conditions: 使它散发出超越它自身条件的光辉   ③ likened beautifully to a fading coal: 美妙地把它比做即将熄灭的炉火   ④ cardiac: 心的   ⑤ enchantment of the heart: 心醉

speak, felt that his words had called up around them a thoughtenchanted silence.

— What I have said, he began again, refers to beauty in the wider sense of the word, in the sense which the word has in the literary tradition. In the marketplace it has another sense. When we speak of beauty in the second sense of the term our judgement is influenced in the first place by the art itself and by the form of that art. The image, it is clear, must be set between the mind or senses of the artist himself and the mind or senses of others. If you bear this in memory you will see that art necessarily divides itself into three forms progressing from one to the next. These forms are: the lyrical form, the form wherein the artist presents his image in immediate relation to himself; the epical form①, the form wherein he presents his image in mediate relation to himself and to others; the dramatic form, the form wherein he presents his image in immediate relation to others.

— That you told me a few nights ago, said Lynch, and we began the famous discussion.

— I have a book at home, said Stephen, in which I have written down questions which are more amusing than yours were. In finding the answers to them I found the theory of esthetic which I am trying to explain. Here are some questions I set myself: *Is a chair finely made tragic or comic? Is the portrait of Mona Lisa② good if I desire to see it? Is the bust of Sir Philip Crampton lyrical, epical or dramatic? Can excrement or a child or a louse be a work of art? If not, why not?*

— Why not, indeed? said Lynch, laughing.

— *If a man hacking③ in fury at a block of wood,* Stephen continued, *make there an image of a cow, is that image a work of art? If not, why not?*

— That's a lovely one, said Lynch, laughing again. That has the true scholastic stink.

---

① epical form: 史诗的形式　② Mona Lisa: 蒙娜·丽莎,欧洲文艺复兴时期著名的美术家达·芬奇的画作。　③ hack: 砍

— Lessing, said Stephen, should not have taken a group of statues to write of. The art, being inferior, does not present the forms I spoke of distinguished clearly one from another. Even in literature, the highest and most spiritual art, the forms are often confused. The lyrical form is in fact the simplest verbal vesture of an instant of emotion, a rhythmical cry such as ages ago cheered on the man who pulled at the oar① or dragged stones up a slope. He who utters it is more conscious of the instant of emotion than of himself as feeling emotion. The simplest epical form is seen emerging out of lyrical literature when the artist prolongs and broods upon② himself as the centre of an epical event and this form progresses till the centre of emotional gravity is equidistant③ from the artist himself and from others. The narrative is no longer purely personal. The personality of the artist passes into the narration itself, flowing round and round the persons and the action like a vital sea. This progress you will see easily in that old English ballad *Turpin Hero*④ which begins in the first person and ends in the third person. The dramatic form is reached when the vitality which has flowed and eddied round each person fills every person with such vital force that he or she assumes a proper and intangible⑤ esthetic life. The personality of the artist, at first a cry or a cadence or a mood and then a fluid and lambent⑥ narrative, finally refines itself out of existence, impersonalizes itself, so to speak. The esthetic image in the dramatic form is life purified in and re-projected from the human imagination. The mystery of esthetic, like that of material creation, is accomplished. The artist, like the God of creation, remains within or behind or beyond or above his handiwork, invisible, refined out of existence, indifferent, paring his fingernails.

---

① pulled at the oar: 摇桨　② broods upon: 反复思索　③ equidistant: 距离相等　④ ballad *Turpin Hero*: 民谣《特平英雄》，特平是传说中 18 世纪英国的著名大盗。　⑤ intangible: 无形的　⑥ lambent: 巧妙的

— Trying to refine them also out of existence, said Lynch.

A fine rain began to fall from the high veiled sky and they turned into the duke's lawn, to reach the national library before the shower came.

— What do you mean, Lynch asked surlily[1], by prating about[2] beauty and the imagination in this miserable Godforsaken island[3]? No wonder the artist retired within or behind his handiwork after having perpetrated this country.

The rain fell faster. When they passed through the passage beside the royal Irish academy they found many students sheltering under the arcade[4] of the library. Cranly, leaning against a pillar, was picking his teeth with a sharpened match, listening to some companions. Some girls stood near the entrance door. Lynch whispered to Stephen:

— Your beloved is here.

Stephen took his place silently on the step below the group of students, heedless of the rain which fell fast, turning his eyes towards her from time to time. She too stood silently among her companions. She has no priest to flirt with, he thought with conscious bitterness, remembering how he had seen her last. Lynch was right. His mind, emptied of theory and courage, lapsed back into a listless peace[5].

He heard the students talking among themselves. They spoke of two friends who had passed the final medical examination, of the chances of getting places on ocean liners, of poor and rich practices[6].

— That's all a bubble. An Irish country practice is better.

---

① surlily：阴郁地　② prate about：空谈　③ this miserable Godforsaken island：这个被上帝抛弃的岛国　④ arcade：有拱顶的走道　⑤ lapsed back into a listless peace：坠落到一种无精打采的平静中　⑥ of the chances ... rich practices：谈到在远洋客轮上找工作的机会和行医挣多少钱的问题

— Hynes was two years in Liverpool and he says the same. A frightful hole he said it was. Nothing but midwifery cases.

— Do you mean to say it is better to have a job here in the country than in a rich city like that? I know a fellow.

— Hynes has no brains. He got through by stewing, pure stewing.

— Don't mind him. There's plenty of money to be made in a big commercial city.

— Depends on the practice.

— *Ego credo ut vita pauperum est simpliciter atrox, simpliciter sanguinarius atrox, in Liverpoolio.* ①

Their voices reached his ears as if from a distance in interrupted pulsation②. She was preparing to go away with her companions.

The quick light shower had drawn off, tarrying in clusters of diamonds among the shrubs of the quadrangle where an exhalation③ was breathed forth by the blackened earth. Their trim boots prattled as they stood on the steps of the colonnade④, talking quietly and gaily, glancing at the clouds, holding their umbrellas at cunning angles against the few last raindrops, closing them again, holding their skirts demurely⑤.

And if he had judged her harshly? If her life were a simple rosary of hours, her life simple and strange as a bird's life, gay in the morning, restless all day, tired at sundown? Her heart simple and wilful as a bird's heart?

Towards dawn he awoke. O what sweet music! His soul was all dewy wet. Over his limbs in sleep pale cool waves of light had passed. He lay still, as if his soul lay amid cool waters, conscious of faint sweet music. His mind

---

① *Ego credo ... in Liverpoolio*：(拉丁文)我相信在利物浦，穷人的日子简直太可怕了，可怕得就是他妈的没法过。 ② pulsation：跳动 ③ exhalation：气味 ④ colonnade：柱廊 ⑤ demurely：一本正经地

was waking slowly to a tremulous morning knowledge, a morning inspiration. A spirit filled him, pure as the purest water, sweet as dew, moving as music. But how faintly it was inbreathed, how passionlessly, as if the seraphim[1] themselves were breathing upon him! His soul was waking slowly, fearing to awake wholly. It was that windless hour of dawn when madness wakes and strange plants open to the light and the moth flies forth silently.

An enchantment of the heart! The night had been enchanted. In a dream or vision he had known the ecstasy of seraphic life. Was it an instant of enchantment only or long hours and days and years and ages?

The instant of inspiration seemed now to be reflected from all sides at once from a multitude of cloudy circumstances of what had happened or of what might have happened. The instant flashed forth like a point of light and now from cloud on cloud of vague circumstance confused form was veiling softly its afterglow[2]. O! In the virgin womb of the imagination the word was made flesh. Gabriel[3] the seraph had come to the virgin's chamber. An afterglow deepened within his spirit. whence the white flame had passed, deepening to a rose and ardent light. That rose and ardent light was her strange wilful heart, strange that no man had known or would know, wilful from before the beginning of the world: and lured by that ardent roselike glow the choirs of the seraphim were falling from heaven.

Are you not weary of ardent[4] ways,
Lure of the fallen seraphim?
Tell no more of enchanted[5] days.

The verses passed from his mind to his lips and, mur-

---

① seraphim：六翼天使(等级最高的天使) ② confused form was veiling softly its afterglow：混乱的形式正轻柔地盖住它的余光 ③ Gabriel：加布里埃尔，《圣经》中，他是向人间宣布贞女玛丽亚是耶稣的母亲的天使。 ④ ardent：热情的 ⑤ enchanted：令人陶醉的

muring them over, he felt the rhythmic movement of a villanelle[1] pass through them. The roselike glow sent forth
its rays of rhyme; ways, days, blaze, praise, raise. Its
rays burned up the world, consumed the hearts of men and
angels: the rays from the rose that was her wilful heart.

> *Your eyes have set man's heart ablaze*
> *And you have had your will of him.*
> *Are you not weary of ardent ways?*

And then? The rhythm died away, ceased, began a-
gain to move and beat. And then? Smoke, incense ascending from the altar of the world[2].

> *Above the flame the smoke of praise*
> *Goes up from ocean rim to rim[3]*
> *Tell no more of enchanted days.*

Smoke went up from the whole earth, from the
vapoury oceans, smoke of her praise. The earth was like a
swinging swaying censer[4], a ball of incense, an ellipsoidal
fall. The rhythm died out at once; the cry of his heart was
broken. His lips began to murmur the first verses over and
over; then went on stumbling through half verses, stammering and baffled[5]; then stopped. The heart's cry was
broken.

The veiled windless hour had passed and behind the
panes[6] of the naked window the morning light was gathering. A bell beat faintly very far away. A bird twittered;
two birds, three. The bell and the bird ceased; and the
dull white light spread itself east and west, covering the
world, covering the roselight in his heart.

Fearing to lose all, he raised himself suddenly on his

---

① villanelle: 一种十九行二韵的诗体　② the altar of the world: 世间的
祭坛　③ rim to rim: 一圈圈地　④ The earth ... swaying censer: 地球像一
个不断旋转着的、冒着烟的香炉。　⑤ stammering and baffled: 结结巴巴,
念不下去了　⑥ panes: 窗格玻璃

elbow to look for paper and pencil. There was neither on the table; only the soup plate he had eaten the rice from for supper and the candlestick with its tendrils of tallow① and its paper socket, singed by the last flame. He stretched his arm wearily towards the foot of the bed, groping with his hand in the pockets of the coat that hung there. His fingers found a pencil and then a cigarette packet②. He lay back and tearing open the packet, placed the last cigarette on the windowledge and began to write out the stanzas of the villanelle in small neat letters on the rough cardboard surface.

Having written them out he lay back on the lumpy pillow③, murmuring them again. The lumps of knotted flock④ under his head reminded him of the lumps of knotted horsehair in the sofa of her parlour on which he used to sit, smiling or serious, asking himself why he had come, displeased with her and with himself, confounded by the print of the Sacred Heart above the untenanted⑤ sideboard. He saw her approach him in a lull of the talk and beg him to sing one of his curious songs. Then he saw himself sitting at the old piano, striking chords⑥ softly from its speckled keys and singing, amid the talk which had risen again in the room, to her who leaned beside the mantelpiece a dainty song of the Elizabethans⑦, a sad and sweet loth to depart, the victory chant of Agincourt⑧, the happy air of Greensleeves⑨. While he sang and she listened, or feigned to listen, his heart was at rest but when the quaint old songs had ended and he heard again the voices in the room he remembered his own sarcasm: the house where young

---

① the candlestick with its tendrils of tallow: 满是蜡泪的烛台　② a cigarette packet: 香烟盒　③ lumpy pillow: 硌人的枕头　④ The lumps of knotted flock: 结成团的棉絮　⑤ untenanted: 光秃秃的　⑥ chords: 和音　⑦ a dainty song of the Elizabethans: 一支伊丽莎白时代的优雅的歌　⑧ the victory chant of Agincourt: 歌颂阿金库尔胜利的歌。此歌用以纪念亨利五世于 1415 年在此大败法军的一战。　⑨ the happy air of Greensleeves: 一支欢快的有关绿袖姑娘的歌。绿袖姑娘是思恋中的姑娘的代称,曾流行于英国民歌中。

men are called by their christian names a little too soon.

At certain instants her eyes seemed about to trust him but he had waited in vain. She passed now dancing lightly across his memory as she had been that night at the carnival ball①, her white dress a little lifted, a white spray nodding in her hair. She danced lightly in the round. She was dancing towards him and, as she came, her eyes were a little averted and a faint glow was on her cheek. At the pause in the chain of hands her hand had lain in his an instant, a soft merchandise②.

— You are a great stranger now.

— Yes. I was born to be a monk.

— I am afraid you are a heretic.

— Are you much afraid?

For answer she had danced away from him along the chain of hands, dancing lightly and discreetly, giving herself to none. The white spray nodded to her dancing and when she was in shadow the glow was deeper on her cheek.

A monk! His own image started forth a profaner③ of the cloister, a heretic franciscan, willing and willing not to serve, spinning like Gherardino da Borgo San Donnino④, a lithe web of sophistry⑤ and whispering in her ear.

No, it was not his image. It was like the image of the young priest in whose company he had seen her last, looking at him out of dove's eyes, toying with the pages of her Irish phrasebook.

— Yes, yes, the ladies are coming round to us. I can see it every day. The ladies are with us. The best helpers the language has.

— And the church, Father Moran?

— The church too. Coming round too. The work is

---

① the carnival ball: 狂欢节舞会 ② a soft merchandise: 一件轻柔的商品 ③ profaner: 破坏者 ④ Gherardino da Borgo San Donnino: 13 世纪意大利僧侣和神学家 ⑤ a lithe web of sophistry: 一张充满诡谲的柔软的蛛网

going ahead there too. Don't fret① about the church.

Bah! he had done well to leave the room in disdain②. He had done well not to salute her on the steps of the library! He had done well to leave her to flirt with her priest, to toy with a church which was the scullerymaid of christendom③.

Rude brutal anger routed the last lingering instant of ecstasy from his soul. It broke up violently her fair image and flung the fragments on all sides. On all sides distorted reflections of her image started from his memory: the flower girl in the ragged dress with damp coarse hair and a hoyden's face who had called herself his own girl and begged his handsel, the kitchengirl in the next house who sang over the clatter of her plates with the drawl of a country singer④ the first bars of *By Killarney's Lakes and Fells*, a girl who had laughed gaily to see him stumble when the iron grating in the footpath near Cork Hill had caught the broken sole of his shoe, a girl he had glanced at, attracted by her small ripe mouth as she passed out of Jacob's biscuit factory, who had cried to him over her shoulder:

— Do you like what you see of me, straight hair and curly eyebrows?

And yet he felt that, however he might revile⑤ and mock her image, his anger was also a form of homage⑥. He had left the classroom in disdain that was not wholly sincere, feeling that perhaps the secret of her race lay behind those dark eyes upon which her long lashes flung a quick shadow. He had told himself bitterly as he walked through the streets that she was a figure of the womanhood of her country, a batlike soul waking to the consciousness

---

① fret：发愁　② leave the room in disdain：不屑地离开了房间　③ the scullerymaid of christendom：基督教世界的下等厨娘　④ the drawl of a country singer：农村歌者拉长的音调　⑤ revile：辱骂　⑥ homage：敬意

of itself in darkness and secrecy and loneliness, tarrying awhile[1], loveless and sinless, with her mild lover and leaving him to whisper of innocent transgressions in the latticed ear of a priest[2]. His anger against her found vent in coarse railing at her paramour,[3] whose name and voice and features offended his baffled pride: a priested peasant, with a brother a policeman in Dublin and a brother a potboy in Moycullen. To him she would unveil her soul's shy nakedness, to one who was but schooled in the discharging of[4] a formal rite rather than to him, a priest of the eternal imagination, transmuting the daily bread of experience into the radiant body of everliving life.

The radiant image of the eucharist united again in an instant his bitter and despairing thoughts, their cries arising unbroken in a hymn of thanksgiving.

> *Our broken cries and mournful lays*
> *Rise in one eucharistic[5] hymn*
> *Are you not weary of ardent ways?*
>
> *While sacrificing hands upraise*
> *The chalice[6] flowing to the brim.*
> *Tell no more of enchanted days.*

He spoke the verses aloud from the first lines till the music and rhythm suffused his mind, turning it to quiet indulgence; then copied them painfully to feel them the better by seeing them; then lay back on his bolster[7].

The full morning light had come. No sound was to be heard: but he knew that all around him life was about to awaken in common noises, hoarse voices, sleepy prayers. Shrinking from that life he turned towards the wall, making a cowl of the blanket[8] and staring at the great

---

① tarrying awhile: 逗留一会儿 ② the latticed ear of a priest: 躲在格子后面的神父的耳朵 ③ His anger ... her paramour: 只有粗鲁地痛骂上她的情人一顿,他对她的愤怒才可得以稍稍缓解。 ④ in the discharging of: 履行 ⑤ eucharistic: 圣餐的 ⑥ chalice: 圣餐杯 ⑦ bolster: 垫枕 ⑧ making a cowl of the blanket: 用毯子罩住头

overblown scarlet flowers of the tattered wallpaper. He tried to warm his perishing joy in their scarlet glow, imagining a roseway from where he lay upwards to heaven all strewn with scarlet flowers. Weary! Weary! He too was weary of ardent ways.

A gradual warmth, a languorous weariness passed over him, descending along his spine from his closely cowled head. He felt it descend and, seeing himself as he lay, smiled. Soon he would sleep.

He had written verses for her again after ten years. Ten years before she had worn her shawl cowlwise about her head[1], sending sprays of her warm breath into the night air, tapping her foot upon the glassy road. It was the last tram; the lank brown horses knew it and shook their bells to the clear night in admonition[2]. The conductor talked with the driver, both nodding often in the green light of the lamp. They stood on the steps of the tram, he on the upper, she on the lower. She came up to his step many times between their phrases and went down again and once or twice remained beside him forgetting to go down and then went down. Let be! Let be!

Ten years from that wisdom of children to his folly. If he sent her the verses? They would be read out at breakfast amid the tapping of eggshells. Folly indeed! The brothers would laugh and try to wrest the page from each other with their strong hard fingers. The suave[3] priest, her uncle, seated in his armchair, would hold the page at arm's length, read it smiling and approve of the literary form.

No, no: that was folly. Even if he sent her the verses she would not show them to others. No, no; she could not.

He began to feel that he had wronged her.[4] A sense

---

① she had ... her head: 她曾把她的披肩像帽子一样罩在头上。
② admonition: 告戒 ③ suave: 温和的 ④ He began to ... wronged her: 他开始感到冤枉了她。

of her innocence moved him almost to pity her, an innocence he had never understood till he had come to the
knowledge of it through sin, an innocence which she too
had not understood while she was innocent or before the
strange humiliation of her nature had first come upon her.
Then first her soul had begun to live as his soul had when
he had first sinned: and a tender compassion[1] filled his
heart as he remembered her frail pallor and her eyes, humbled and saddened by the dark shame of womanhood.

While his soul had passed from ecstasy to languor[2]
where had she been? Might it be, in the mysterious ways
of spiritual life, that her soul at those same moments had
been conscious of his homage? It might be.

A glow of desire kindled again his soul and fired and
fulfilled all his body. Conscious of his desire she was waking from odorous[3] sleep, the temptress of his villanelle.
Her eyes, dark and with a look of languor, were opening to
his eyes. Her nakedness yielded to him, radiant, warm,
odorous and lavishlimbed, enfolded him like a shining
cloud, enfolded him like water with a liquid life; and like a
cloud of vapour or like waters circumfluent in space[4] the
liquid letters of speech, symbols of the element of mystery,
flowed forth over his brain.

> Are you not weary of ardent ways,
> Lure of the fallen seraphim?
> Tell no more of enchanted days.
>
> Your eyes have set man's heart ablaze
> And you have had your will of him.
> Are you not weary of ardent ways?
>
> Above the flame the smoke of praise
> Goes up from ocean rim to rim.
> Tell no more of enchanted days.

---

① compassion: 怜悯之情 ② languor: 消沉 ③ odorous: 香的
④ like waters circumfluent in space: 像在空中周游流动的清水

Our broken cries and mournful lays
Rise in one eucharistic hymn.
Are you not weary of ardent ways?

While sacrificing hands upraise
The chalice flowing to the brim.
Tell no more of enchanted days.

And still you hold our longing gaze
With languorous① look and lavish limb!
Are you not weary of ardent ways?
Tell no more of enchanted days.

What birds were they? He stood on the steps of the library to look at them, leaning wearily on his ashplant②. They flew round and round the jutting shoulder of a house in Molesworth Street. The air of the late March evening made clear their flight, their dark quivering bodies flying clearly against the sky as against a limphung cloth of smoky tenuous blue③.

He watched their flight; bird after bird: a dark flash, a swerve, flash again, a dart aside, a curve, a flutter of wings. He tried to count them before all their darting quivering bodies passed: six, ten, eleven: and wondered were they odd or even④ in number. Twelve, thirteen: for two came wheeling down from the upper sky. They were flying high and low but ever round and round in straight and curving lines and ever flying from left to right, circling about a temple of air⑤.

He listened to the cries: like the squeak of mice behind the wainscot⑥: a shrill twofold note. But the notes were long and shrill and whirring, unlike the cry of vermin, falling a third or a fourth and trilled as the flying beaks

---

① languorous: 无精打采的　② ashplant: 白蜡树　③ as against ... tenuous blue: 仿佛衬着一块软软悬挂着的薄如轻烟的幕布　④ odd or even: 单数还是双数　⑤ circling about a temple of air: 围着一座空中庙宇盘旋　⑥ like the ... the wainscot: 就像躲在护墙板后面的老鼠发出的尖叫

clove the air. Their cry was shrill and clear and fine and falling like threads of silken light unwound from whirring spools[①].

The inhuman clamour[②] soothed his ears in which his mother's sobs and reproaches murmured insistently and the dark frail quivering bodies wheeling and fluttering and swerving round an airy temple of the tenuous sky soothed his eyes which still saw the image of his mother's face.

Why was he gazing upwards from the steps of the porch, hearing their shrill twofold cry, watching their flight? For an augury[③] of good or evil? A phrase of Cornelius Agrippa[④] flew through his mind and then there flew hither and thither shapeless thoughts from Swedenborg on the correspondence of birds to things of the intellect and of how the creatures of the air have their knowledge and know their times and seasons because they, unlike man, are in the order of their life and have not perverted that order by reason.

And for ages men had gazed upward as he was gazing at birds in flight. The colonnade above him made him think vaguely of an ancient temple and the ashplant on which he leaned wearily of the curved stick of an augur. A sense of fear of the unknown moved in the heart of his weariness, a fear of symbols and portents[⑤], of the hawklike man whose name he bore soaring out of his captivity on osierwoven wings[⑥], of Thoth[⑦], the god of writers, writing with a reed upon a tablet and bearing on his narrow ibis[⑧] head the cusped[⑨] moon.

---

① whirring spools: 发出嗡嗡声的线轴　② clamour: 鸣叫声　③ augury: 占卜术,此处指古希腊、罗马时开始使用的一种鸟占术,鸟儿和他们的各种飞翔情况被看做是某种事情发生的前兆。　④ Cornelius Agrippa: Cornelius Agrippa(1486—1535),德国一名宣扬炼金术和魔术的术士。　⑤ a fear of symbols and portents: 对各种象征和符号的恐惧　⑥ osierwoven wings: 这里还应是指用蜡翼作翅膀,飞出牢笼的迪达勒斯,但此处"用柳条编织的翅膀"无从考据。　⑦ Thoth: 埃及神话中司智慧和魔法的神,他被画做人身鸟头的形象。　⑧ ibis: 朱鹭　⑨ cusped: 尖尖的

He smiled as he thought of the god's image for it made him think of a bottle – nosed judge in a wig, putting commas into a document which he held at arm's length and he knew that he would not have remembered the god's name but that it was like an Irish oath. It was folly. But was it for this folly that he was about to leave for ever the house of prayer and prudence into which he had been born and the order of life out of which he had come?

They came back with shrill cries over the jutting shoulder of the house, flying darkly against the fading air. What birds were they? He thought that they must be swallows who had come back from the south. Then he was to go away for they were birds ever going and coming, building ever an unlasting home under the eaves of men's houses and ever leaving the homes they had built to wander.

> *Bend down your faces, Oona and Aleel.*
> *I gaze upon them as the swallow gazes*
> *Upon the nest under the eave before*
> *He wander the loud waters* [①].

A soft liquid joy like the noise of many waters flowed over his memory and he felt in his heart the soft peace of silent spaces of fading tenuous sky above the waters, of oceanic silence, of swallows flying through the seadusk over the flowing waters.

A soft liquid joy flowed through the words where the soft long vowels hurtled noiselessly and fell away, lapping and flowing back and ever shaking the white bells of their waves in mute chime and mute peal, and soft low swooning cry [②]; and he felt that the augury he had sought in the wheeling darting birds and in the pale space of sky above him had come forth from his heart like a bird from a turret, quietly and swiftly.

---

① *Bend down . . . loud waters*：叶芝诗剧《卡斯琳公爵夫人》中卡斯琳临终时所唱之曲　② mute chime . . . swooning cry：无声的韵律，无声的狂喊，以及柔和而低沉的令人昏厥的痛哭。

Symbol of departure or of loneliness? The verses crooned[①] in the ear of his memory composed slowly before his remembering eyes the scene of the hall on the night of the opening of the national theatre. He was alone at the side of the balcony, looking out of jaded eyes at the culture of Dublin in the stalls[②] and at the tawdry[③] scenecloths and human dolls framed by the garish[④] lamps of the stage. A burly policeman sweated behind him and seemed at every moment about to act. The catcalls and hisses and mocking cries ran in rude gusts round the hall from his scattered fellowstudents.

— A libel on Ireland!
— Made in Germany!
— Blasphemy!
— We never sold our faith!
— No Irish woman ever did it!
— We want no amateur atheists[⑤].
— We want no budding buddhists[⑥].

A sudden swift hiss fell from the windows above him and he knew that the electric lamps had been switched on in the reader's room. He turned into the pillared hall, now calmly lit, went up the staircase and passed in through the clicking turnstile[⑦].

Cranly was sitting over near the dictionaries. A thick book, opened at the frontispiece, lay before him on the wooden rest. He leaned back in his chair, inclining his ear like that of a confessor to the face of the medical student who was reading to him a problem from the chess page of a journal. Stephen sat down at his right and the priest at the other side of the table closed his copy of *The Tablet* with an angry snap and stood up.

Cranly gazed after him blandly[⑧] and vaguely. The

---

① crooned: 低吟 ② stalls: 书摊 ③ tawdry: 花哨的 ④ garish: 装饰得俗不可耐的 ⑤ amateur atheists: 业余的无神论者 ⑥ buddhists: 佛教徒 ⑦ clicking turnstile: 嘎嘎作响的转门 ⑧ blandly: 温和地

medical student went on in a softer voice:

— Pawn to king's fourth.

— We had better go, Dixon, said Stephen in warning. He has gone to complain.

Dixon folded the journal and rose with dignity[1], saying:

— Our men retired in good order.

— With guns and cattle, added Stephen, pointing to the titlepage of Cranly's book on which was printed *Diseases of the Ox*[2].

As they passed through a lane of the tables Stephen said:

— Cranly, I want to speak to you.

Cranly did not answer or turn. He laid his book on the counter and passed out, his wellshod feet sounding flatly on the floor. On the staircase he paused and gazing absently at Dixon[3] repeated:

— Pawn to king's bloody fourth.

— Put it that way if you like, Dixon said.

He had a quiet toneless voice and urbane manners and on a finger of his plump clean hand he displayed at moments a signet ring[4].

As they crossed the hall a man of dwarfish stature came towards them. Under the dome of his tiny hat his unshaven face began to smile with pleasure and he was heard to murmur.

The eyes were melancholy as those of a monkey.

— Good evening, gentlemen, said the stubblegrown monkeyish face[5].

— Warm weather for March, said Cranly. They have the windows open upstairs.

Dixon smiled and turned his ring. The blackish, mon-

---

① rose with dignity：威严地站起来　② *Diseases of the Ox*：《牛病大全》　③ gazing absently at Dixon：心不在焉地盯着狄克逊　④ signet ring：图章戒指　⑤ the stubblegrown monkeyish face：那张布满胡子茬儿的猴子般的脸

key-puckered face pursed its human mouth with gentle pleasure: and its voice purred:

— Delightful weather for March. Simply delightful.

— There are two nice young ladies upstairs, captain, tired of waiting, Dixon said.

Cranly smiled and said kindly:

— The captain has only one love: sir Walter Scott. Isn't that so, captain?

— What are you reading now, captain? Dixon asked. *The Bride of Lammermoor*①?

— I love old Scott, the flexible lips said, I think he writes something lovely. There is no writer can touch sir Walter Scott②.

He moved a thin shrunken brown hand gently in the air in time to his praise and his thin quick eyelids beat often over his sad eyes.

Sadder to Stephen's ear was his speech: a genteel accent③, low and moist, marred by errors: and listening to it he wondered was the story true and was the thin blood that flowed in his shrunken frame noble and come of an incestuous love④?

The park trees were heavy with rain; and rain fell still and ever in the lake, lying grey like a shield⑤. A game of swans flew there and the water and the shore beneath were fouled with their green white slime. They embraced softly, impelled by the grey rainy light, the wet silent trees, the shieldlike witnessing lake, the swans. They embraced without joy or passion, his arm about his sister's neck. A grey woollen cloak was wrapped athwart her⑥ from her shoulder to her waist: and her fair head was bent in willing shame. He had loose red-brown hair and tender shapely

---

① *The Bride of Lammermoor*：《拉默尔穆尔》的新娘　② sir Walter Scott：瓦尔特·司各特爵士（1771—1832），苏格兰小说家和诗人。　③ a genteel accent：一口绅士腔调　④ incestuous love：乱伦的爱情　⑤ shield：盾牌　⑥ wrapped athwart her：斜着包裹着她

strong freckled hands. Face. There was no face seen. The brother's face was bent upon her fair rainfragrant hair. The hand freckled and strong and shapely and caressing was Davin's hand.

He frowned angrily upon his thought and on the shrivelled mannikin① who had called it forth. His father's gibes② at the Bantry gang leaped out of his memory. He held them at a distance and brooded uneasily on his own thought again. Why were they not Cranly's hands? Had Davin's simplicity and innocence stung him more secretly?

He walked on across the hall with Dixon, leaving Cranly to take leave elaborately of the dwarf.

Under the colonnade Temple was standing in the midst of a little group of students. One of them cried:

— Dixon, come over till you hear. Temple is in grand form.

Temple turned on him his dark gipsy eyes.

— You're a hypocrite, O'Keeffe, he said, and Dixon is a smiler. By hell, I think that's a good literary expression.

He laughed slily, looking in Stephen's face, repeating:

— By hell, I'm delighted with that name. A smiler.

A stout student who stood below them on the steps said:

— Come back to the mistress, Temple. We want to hear about that.

— He had, faith, Temple said. And he was a married man too. And all the priests used to be dining there. By hell, I think they all had a touch.

— We shall call it riding a hack to spare the hunter, said Dixon.

— Tell us, Temple, O'Keeffe said, how many quarts of porter have you in you③?

---

① shrivelled mannikin：干瘦的矮个子　② gibes：嘲笑　③ how many ... in you：你肚子里盛着多少夸脱黑啤酒

— All your intellectual soul is in that phrase, O'Keeffe, said Temple with open scorn.

He moved with a shambling gait[1] round the group and spoke to Stephen.

— Did you know that the Forsters are the kings of Belgium? he asked.

Cranly came out through the door of the entrance hall, his hat thrust back on the nape[2] of his neck and picking his teeth with care.

— And here's the wiseacre[3], said Temple. Do you know that about the Forsters?

He paused for an answer. Cranly dislodged a figseed[4] from his teeth on the point of his rude toothpick and gazed at it intently

— The Forster family, Temple said, is descended from Baldwin the First, king of Flanders. He was called the Forester. Forester and Forster are the same name. A descendant of Baldwin the First, captain Francis Forster, settled in Ireland and married the daughter of the last chieftain[5] of Clanbrassil. Then there are the Blake Forsters. That's a different branch.

— From Baldhead, king of Flanders, Cranly repeated, rooting again deliberately at his gleaming uncovered teeth.

— Where did you pick up all that history? O'Keeffe asked.

— I know all the history of your family too, Temple said, turning to Stephen. Do you know what Giraldus Cambrensis says about your family?

— Is he descended from Baldwin too? asked a tall consumptive student with dark eyes.

— Baldhead, Cranly repeated, sucking at a crevice in his teeth.

---

① shambling gait：蹒跚的步态　② nape：后颈　③ wiseacre：自作聪明的人　④ figseed：无花果籽　⑤ chieftain：酋长

— *Pernobilis et pervetusta familia*,[①] Temple said to Stephen.

The stout student who stood below them on the steps farted briefly. Dixon turned towards him saying in a soft voice:

— Did an angel speak?

Cranly turned also and said vehemently[②] but without anger:

— Goggins, you're the flamingest dirty devil I ever met, do you know.

— I had it on my mind to say that, Goggins answered firmly. It did no one any harm, did it?

— We hope, Dixon said suavely[③], that it was not of the kind known to science as a *paulo post futurum*[④].

— Didn't I tell you he was a smiler? said Temple, turning right and left. Didn't I give him that name?

— You did. We're not deaf, said the tall consumptive.

Cranly still frowned at the stout student below him. Then, with a snort of disgust, he shoved him violently down the steps.

— Go away from here, he said rudely. Go away, you stinkpot. And you are a stinkpot[⑤].

Goggins skipped down on to the gravel and at once returned to his place with good humour. Temple turned back to Stephen and asked:

— Do you believe in the law of heredity?

— Are you drunk or what are you or what are you trying to say? asked Cranly, facing round on him with an expression of wonder.

— The most profound sentence ever written, Temple said with enthusiasm, is the sentence at the end of the zoology[⑥]. Reproduction is the beginning of death.

---

① *Pernobilis et pervetusta familia*：(拉丁文)来自于一个显赫的贵族家庭　② vehemently：激烈地　③ suavely：温和地　④ *paulo post futurum*：(拉丁文)有待证实　⑤ stinkpot：盛臭物的容器　⑥ zoology：动物学

He touched Stephen timidly at the elbow and said eagerly:

— Do you feel how profound that is because you are a poet? Cranly pointed his long forefinger.

— Look at him! he said with scorn to the others. Look at Ireland's hope!

They laughed at his words and gesture. Temple turned on him bravely, saying:

— Cranly, you're always sneering at me. I can see that. But I am as good as you any day. Do you know what I think about you now as compared with myself?

— My dear man, said Cranly urbanely, you are incapable, do you know, absolutely incapable of thinking.

— But do you know, Temple went on, what I think of you and of myself compared together?

— Out with it, Temple! the stout student cried from the steps. Get it out in bits! [1]

Temple turned right and left, making sudden feeble gestures as he spoke.

— I'm a ballocks, he said, shaking his head in despair. I am. And I know I am. And I admit it that I am.

Dixon patted him lightly on the shoulder and said mildly:

— And it does you every credit [2], Temple.

— But he, Temple said, pointing to Cranly, he is a ballocks too like me. Only he doesn't know it. And that's the only difference I see.

A burst of laughter covered his words. But he turned again to Stephen and said with a sudden eagerness:

— That word is a most interesting word. That's the only English dual number. Did you know?

— Is it? Stephen said vaguely.

He was watching Cranly's firmfeatured suffering face,

---

① Get it out in bits: 一点儿一点儿地说出来　② it does you every credit: 这个称呼真是适合你。

lit up now by a smile of false patience. The gross name had passed over it like foul water poured over an old stone image, patient of injuries: and, as he watched him, he saw him raise his hat in salute and uncover the black hair that stood up stiffly from his forehead like an iron crown[①].

She passed out from the porch of the library and bowed across Stephen in reply to Cranly's greeting. He also? Was there not a slight flush on Cranly's cheek? Or had it come forth at Temple's words? The light had waned. He could not see.

Did that explain his friend's listless silence, his harsh comments, the sudden intrusions of rude speech with which he had shattered so often Stephen's ardent wayward confessions? Stephen had forgiven freely for he had found this rudeness also in himself towards himself. And he remembered an evening when he had dismounted from a borrowed creaking bicycle to pray to God in a wood near Malahide. He had lifted up his arms and spoken in ecstasy to the sombre nave of the trees[②], knowing that he stood on holy ground and in a holy hour. And when two constabularymen[③] had come into sight round a bend in the gloomy road he had broken off his prayer to whistle loudly an air from the last pantomime[④].

He began to beat the frayed end[⑤] of his ashplant against the base of a pillar. Had Cranly not heard him? Yet he could wait. The talk about him ceased for a moment: and a soft hiss fell again from a window above. But no other sound was in the air and the swallows whose flight he had followed with idle eyes were sleeping.

She had passed through the dusk. And therefore the air was silent save for one soft hiss that fell. And therefore

---

① stood stiffly ... iron crown：从前额硬硬地直竖上去，好似一顶铁制王冠　② the sombre nave of the trees：阴森的树林深处　③ constabularymen：警察　④ the last pantomime：最新的滑稽剧　⑤ the frayed end：带杈儿的一端

the tongues about him had ceased their babble. Darkness was falling.

Darkness falls from the air.

A trembling joy, lambent① as a faint light, played like a fairy host around him. But why? Her passage through the darkening air or the verse with its black vowels and its opening sound, rich and lutelike②?

He walked away slowly towards the deeper shadows at the end of the colonnade, beating the stone softly with his stick to hide his revery③ from the students whom he had left: and allowed his mind to summon back to itself the age of Dowland and Byrd and Nash④.

Eyes, opening from the darkness of desire, eyes that dimmed the breaking east. What was their languid grace but the softness of chambering? And what was their shimmer but the shimmer⑤ of the scum⑥ that mantled the cesspool⑦ of the court of a slobbering Stuart. And he tasted in the language of memory ambered wines⑧, dying fallings of sweet airs, the proud pavan⑨, and saw with the eyes of memory kind gentlewomen in Covent Garden wooing from their balconies with sucking mouths and the poxfouled wenches⑩ of the taverns and young wives that, gaily yielding to their ravishers⑪, clipped and clipped again.

The images he had summoned gave him no pleasure. They were secret and inflaming but her image was not entangled by them. That was not the way to think of her. It was not even the way in which he thought of her. Could his mind then not trust itself? Old phrases, sweet only with

---

① lambent: 闪烁的　② lutelike: 如笛声般　③ revery: 梦想　④ Dowland and Byrd and Nash: 三人均为英国伊丽莎白时期的音乐家或作家　⑤ shimmer: 闪烁　⑥ scum: 浮渣　⑦ cesspool: 粪坑　⑧ ambered wines: 琥珀色的酒　⑨ proud pavan: 骄傲的宫廷舞　⑩ wenches: 妓女　⑪ ravishers: 强奸者

a disinterred① sweetness like the figseeds Cranly rooted out of his gleaming teeth.

It was not thought nor vision though he knew vaguely that her figure was passing homeward through the city. Vaguely first and then more sharply he smelt her body. A conscious unrest seethed② in his blood. Yes, it was her body he smelt: a wild and languid③ smell: the tepid limbs④ over which his music had flowed desirously and the secret soft linen upon which her flesh distilled odour and a dew.

A louse crawled over the nape of his neck and, putting his thumb and forefinger deftly beneath his loose collar, he caught it. He rolled its body, tender yet brittle as a grain of rice, between thumb and finger for an instant before he let it fall from him and wondered would it live or die. There came to his mind a curious phrase from Cornelius a Lapide which said that the lice born of human sweat were not created by God with the other animals on the sixth day. But the tickling of the skin of his neck made his mind raw and red. The life of his body, illclad, illfed, louseeaten, made him close his eyelids in a sudden spasm of despair⑤: and in the darkness he saw the brittle bright bodies of lice falling from the air and turning often as they fell. Yes; and it was not darkness that fell from the air. It was brightness.

Brightness falls from the air.

He had not even remembered rightly Nash's line. All the images it had awakened were false. His mind bred vermin. His thoughts were lice born of the sweat of sloth⑥.

He came back quickly along the colonnade towards the group of students. Well then, let her go and be damned to

---

① disinterred: 被挖掘出的　② seethed: 沸腾　③ languid: 倦怠的
④ tepid limbs: 温热的肢体　⑤ a sudden spasm of despair: 一阵绝望的情绪
⑥ lice born of the sweat of sloth: 从懒惰的汗水中产生出来的虱子

her! She could love some clean athlete who washed himself every morning to the waist and had black hair on his chest. Let her.

Cranly had taken another dried fig from the supply in his pocket and was eating it slowly and noisily. Temple sat on the pediment① of a pillar, leaning back, his cap pulled down on his sleepy eyes. A squat young man came out of the porch, a leather portfolio② tucked under his armpit. He marched towards the group, striking the flags③ with the heels of his boots and with the ferrule of his heavy umbrella. Then, raising the umbrella in salute, he said to all:

— Good evening, sirs.

He struck the flags again and tittered while his head trembled with a slight nervous movement. The tall consumptive student and Dixon and O'Keeffe were speaking in Irish and did not answer him. Then, turning to Cranly, he said:

— Good evening, particularly to you.

He moved the umbrella in indication and tittered again. Cranly, who was still chewing the fig, answered with loud movements of his jaws.

— Good? Yes. It is a good evening.

The squat student looked at him seriously and shook his umbrella gently and reprovingly④.

— I can see, he said, that you are about to make obvious remarks.

— Um, Cranly answered, holding out what remained of the halfchewed fig and jerking it towards the squat student's mouth in sign that he should eat.

The squat student did not eat it but, indulging his special humour, said gravely, still tittering and prodding his phrase with his umbrella:

— Do you intend that . . .

---

① pediment：三角墙　② portfolio：公事包　③ flags：石板路　④ reprovingly：责备地

He broke off, pointed bluntly① to the munched② pulp of the fig and said loudly:

— I allude to that.

— Um, Cranly said as before.

— Do you intend that now, the squat student said, as *ipso facto*③ or, let us say, as so to speak?

Dixon turned aside from his group, saying:

— Goggins was waiting for you, Glynn. He has gone round to the Adelphi to look for you and Moynihan. What have you there? he asked, tapping the portfolio under Glynn's arm.

— Examination papers, Glynn answered. I give them monthly examinations to see that they are profiting by my tuition.

He also tapped the portfolio and coughed gently and smiled.

— Tuition! said Cranly rudely. I suppose you mean the barefooted children that are taught by a bloody ape like you. God help them!

He bit off the rest of the fig and flung away the butt④.

— I suffer little children to come unto me, Glynn said amiably.

— A bloody ape, Cranly repeated with emphasis, and a blasphemous bloody ape!

Temple stood up and, pushing past Cranly, addressed Glynn:

— The phrase you said now, he said, is from the new testament about suffer the children to come to me.

— Go to sleep again, Temple, said O'Keeffe.

— Very well, then, Temple continued, still addressing Glynn, and if Jesus suffered the children to come why does the church send them all to hell if they die unbaptized?

---

① bluntly: 直截了当地　② munched: 嚼过了的　③ *ipso facto*: (拉丁文) 以事实而论　④ flung away the butt: 丢掉果蒂

Why is that?

— Were you baptized yourself, Temple? the consumptive student asked.

— But why are they sent to hell if Jesus said they were all to come? Temple said, his eyes searching Glynn's eyes.

Glynn coughed and said gently, holding back with difficulty the nervous titter in his voice and moving his umbrella at every word:

— And, as you remark, if it is thus I ask emphatically whence comes① this thusness.

— Because the church is cruel like all old sinners, Temple said.

— Are you quite orthodox② on that point, Temple? Dixon said suavely.

— Saint Augustine says that about unbaptized children going to hell, Temple answered, because he was a cruel old sinner too.

— I bow to you, Dixon said, but I had the impression that limbo existed for such cases.

— Don't argue with him, Dixon, Cranly said brutally. Don't talk to him or look at him. Lead him home with a sugan③ the way you'd lead a bleating goat④.

— Limbo! Temple cried. That's a fine invention too. Like hell.

— But with the unpleasantness left out, Dixon said.

He turned smiling to the others and said:

— I think I am voicing the opinions of all present in saying so much.

— You are, Glynn said in a firm tone. On that point Ireland is united.

He struck the ferrule of his umbrella on the stone floor of the colonnade.

— Hell, Temple said. I can respect that invention of

---

① whence comes: 从何处来　② orthodox: 正统的　③ sugan: 草绳
④ a bleating goat: 咩咩叫的山羊

the grey spouse of Satan. Hell is Roman, like the walls of the Romans, strong and ugly. But what is limbo?

— Put him back into the perambulator①, Cranly, O'Keeffe called out.

Cranly made a swift step towards Temple, halted, stamping his foot, crying as if to a fowl:

— Hoosh!

Temple moved away nimbly②.

— Do you know what limbo is? he cried. Do you know what we call a notion like that in Roscommon?

— Hoosh! Blast you③! Cranly cried, clapping his hands.

— Neither my arse nor my elbow! Temple cried out scornfully. And that's what I call limbo.

— Give us that stick here, Cranly said.

He snatched the ashplant roughly from Stephen's hand and sprang down the steps: but Temple, hearing him move in pursuit, fled through the dusk like a wild creature, nimble and fleetfooted. Cranly's heavy boots were heard loudly charging across the quadrangle and then returning heavily, foiled and spurning the gravel at each step④.

His step was angry and with an angry abrupt gesture he thrust the stick back into Stephen's hand. Stephen felt that his anger had another cause but, feigning patience⑤, touched his arm slightly and said quietly:

— Cranly, I told you I wanted to speak to you. Come away.

Cranly looked at him for a few moments and asked:

— Now?

— Yes, now, Stephen said. We can't speak here. Come away.

They crossed the quadrangle together without speak-

---

① perambulator：婴儿车　② nimbly：敏捷地　③ Blast you：该死的
④ foiled and spurning the gravel at each step：每跑一步都把脚下的石子踢得
乱飞　⑤ feigning patience：装出有耐性的样子

ing. The bird call from *Sigfried* ① whistled softly followed
them from the steps of the porch. Cranly turned: and
Dixon, who had whistled, called out:

— Where are you fellows off to? What about that
game, Cranly?

They parleyed in shouts② across the still air about a
game of billiards to be played in the Adelphi hotel. Stephen
walked on alone and out into the quiet of Kildare Street.
Opposite Maple's hotel he stood to wait, patient again.
The name of the hotel, a colourless quiet polished wood,
and its colourless quiet front stung him like a glance of polite disdain. He stared angrily back at the softly lit drawing
room of the hotel in which he imagined the sleek lives of
the patricians③ of Ireland housed in calm. They thought of
army commissions and land agents: peasants greeted them
along the roads in the country: they knew the names of
certain French dishes and gave orders to jarvies④ in high-
pitched provincial voices which pierced through their
skintight accents.

How could he hit their conscience or how cast his
shadow over the imaginations of their daughters, before
their squires⑤ begat upon them, that they might breed a
race less ignoble⑥ than their own? And under the deepened
dusk he felt the thoughts and desires of the race to which
he belonged flitting like bats. Across the dark country
bogs⑦. A woman had waited in the doorway as Davin had
passed by at night and, offering him a cup of milk, had all
but wooed⑧ him to her bed; for Davin had the mild eyes of
one who could be secret. But him no woman's eyes had
wooed.

His arm was taken in a strong grip and Cranly's voice

---

① *Sigfried*：德国作曲家理查德·瓦格纳（1813—1883）的作品
② parleyed in shouts：大声叫喊着商量 ③ the sleek lives of the patricians：
显贵们豪华的生活 ④ jarvies：马车夫 ⑤ squires：乡绅 ⑥ ignoble：卑
鄙的 ⑦ bogs：沼泽 ⑧ wooed：诱劝

said:

— Let us eke go.

They walked southward in silence. Then Cranly said:

— That blithering idiot①, Temple! I swear to Moses, do you know, that I'll be the death of that fellow one time.

But his voice was no longer angry and Stephen wondered was he thinking of her greeting to him under the porch.

They turned to the left and walked on as before. When they had gone on so for some time Stephen said:

— Cranly, I had an unpleasant quarrel this evening.

— With your people? Cranly asked.

— With my mother.

— About religion?

— Yes, Stephen answered.

After a pause Cranly asked:

— What age is your mother?

— Not old, Stephen said. She wishes me to make my easter duty②.

— And will you?

— I will not, Stephen said.

— Why not? Cranly said.

— I will not serve, answered Stephen.

— That remark was made before, Cranly said calmly.

— It is made behind now, said Stephen hotly.

Cranly pressed Stephen's arm, saying:

— Go easy, my dear man. You're an excitable bloody man, do you know.

He laughed nervously as he spoke and, looking up into Stephen's face with moved and friendly eyes, said:

— Do you know that you are an excitable man?

— I daresay I am, said Stephen, laughing also.

Their minds, lately estranged, seemed suddenly to

---

① blithering idiot: 头号傻瓜 ② She wishes … easter duty: 她希望我在复活节时去向上帝履行我的职责。

have been drawn closer, one to the other.

— Do you believe in the eucharist? Cranly asked.

— I do not, Stephen said.

— Do you disbelieve then?

— I neither believe in it nor disbelieve in it, Stephen answered.

— Many persons have doubts, even religious persons, yet they overcome them or put them aside, Cranly said. Are your doubts on that point too strong?

— I do not wish to overcome them, Stephen answered.

Cranly, embarrassed for a moment, took another fig from his pocket and was about to eat it when Stephen said:

— Don't, please. You cannot discuss this question with your mouth full of chewed fig.

Cranly examined the fig by the light of a lamp under which he halted. Then he smelt it with both nostrils①, bit a tiny piece, spat it out and threw the fig rudely into the gutter②. Addressing it as it lay, he said:

— Depart from me, ye cursed, into everlasting fire!

Taking Stephen's arms, he went on again and said:

— Do you not fear that those words may be spoken to you on the day of judgement?

— What is offered me on the other hand? Stephen asked. An eternity of bliss③ in the company of the dean of studies?

— Remember, Cranly said, that he would be glorified.

— Ay, Stephen said somewhat bitterly, bright, agile, impassible④ and, above all, subtle.

— It is a curious thing, do you know, Cranly said dispassionately⑤, how your mind is supersaturated with⑥ the religion in which you say you disbelieve. Did you believe in

---

① nostrils: 鼻孔 ② gutter: 阴沟 ③ An eternity of bliss: 永恒的幸福 ④ impassible: 无动于衷的 ⑤ dispassionately: 不带任何感情的 ⑥ super-saturated with: 塞满

it when you were at school? I bet you did.

— I did, Stephen answered.

— And were you happier then? Cranly asked softly. Happier than you are now, for instance?

— Often happy, Stephen said, and often unhappy. I was someone else then.

— How someone else? What do you mean by that statement?

— I mean, said Stephen, that I was not myself as I am now, as I had to become.

— Not as you are now, not as you had to become, Cranly repeated. Let me ask you a question. Do you love your mother?

Stephen shook his head slowly.

— I don't know what your words mean, he said simply.

— Have you never loved anyone? Cranly asked.

— Do you mean women?

— I am not speaking of that, Cranly said in a colder tone. I ask you if you ever felt love towards anyone or anything.

Stephen walked on beside his friend, staring gloomily at the footpath.

— I tried to love God, he said at length. It seems now I failed. It is very difficult. I tried to unite my will with the will of God instant by instant. In that I did not always fail. I could perhaps do that still . . .

Cranly cut him short by asking:

— Has your mother had a happy life?

— How do I know? Stephen said.

— How many children had she?

— Nine or ten, Stephen answered. Some died.

— Was your father . . . Cranly interrupted himself for an instant; and then said: I don't want to pry into① your family affairs. But was your father what is called well – to

---

① pry into: 打听

– do? I mean when you were growing up?

— Yes, Stephen said.

— What was he? Cranly asked after a pause.

Stephen began to enumerate glibly① his father's attributes.

— A medical student, an oarsman②, a tenor③, an amateur actor, a shouting politician, a small landlord, a small investor, a drinker, a good fellow, a storyteller, somebody's secretary, something in a distillery④, a tax – gatherer, a bankrupt and at present a praiser of his own past.

Cranly laughed, tightening his grip on Stephen's arm, and said:

— The distillery is damn good.

— Is there anything else you want to know? Stephen asked.

— Are you in good circumstances at present?

— Do I look it? Stephen asked bluntly.

— So then, Cranly went on musingly, you were born in the lap of luxury.

He used the phrase broadly and loudly as he often used technical expressions, as if he wished his hearer to understand that they were used by him without conviction⑤.

— Your mother must have gone through a good deal of suffering, he said then. Would you not try to save her from suffering more even if ... or would you?

— If I could, Stephen said. That would cost me very little.

— Then do so, Cranly said. Do as she wishes you to do. What is it for you? You disbelieve in it. It is a form: nothing else. And you will set her mind at rest.

He ceased and, as Stephen did not reply, remained silent. Then, as if giving utterance to the process of his

---

① enumerate glibly: 流利地列举　② an oarsman: 划桨能手　③ a tenor: 男高音　④ distillery: 造酒厂　⑤ conviction: 确信

own thought, he said:

— Whatever else is unsure in this stinking dunghill① of a world a mother's love is not. Your mother brings you into the world, carries you first in her body. What do we know about what she feels? But whatever she feels, it, at least, must be real. It must be. What are our ideas or ambitions? Play. Ideas! Why, that bloody bleating goat Temple has ideas. MacCann has ideas too. Every jackass② going the roads thinks he has ideas.

Stephen, who had been listening to the unspoken speech behind the words, said with assumed carelessness:

— Pascal, if I remember rightly, would not suffer his mother to kiss him as he feared the contact of her sex.

— Pascal was a pig, said Cranly.

— Aloysius Gonzaga, I think, was of the same mind, Stephen said.

— And he was another pig then, said Cranly.

— The church calls him a saint, Stephen objected.

— I don't care a flaming damn what anyone calls him, Cranly said rudely and flatly. I call him a pig.

Stephen, preparing the words neatly in his mind, continued:

— Jesus, too, seems to have treated his mother with scant courtesy in public but Suarez, a jesuit theologian and Spanish gentleman, has apologized for him.

— Did the idea ever occur to you, Cranly asked, that Jesus was not what he pretended to be?

— The first person to whom that idea occurred, Stephen answered, was Jesus himself.

— I mean, Cranly said, hardening in his speech, did the idea ever occur to you that he was himself a conscious hypocrite, what he called the jews of his time, a whited sepulchre③? Or, to put it more plainly, that he was a

---

① stinking dunghill: 臭烘烘的粪堆 ② jackass: 笨蛋 ③ a whited sepulchre: 伪君子

blackguard①?

— That idea never occurred to me, Stephen answered. But I am curious to know are you trying to make a convert of me or a pervert② of yourself?

He turned towards his friend's face and saw there a raw smile which some force of will strove to make finely significant.

Cranly asked suddenly in a plain sensible tone:

— Tell me the truth. Were you at all shocked by what I said?

— Somewhat, Stephen said.

— And why were you shocked, Cranly pressed on in the same tone, if you feel sure that our religion is false and that Jesus was not the son of God?

— I am not at all sure of it, Stephen said. He is more like a son of God than a son of Mary.

— And is that why you will not communicate, Cranly asked, because you are not sure of that too, because you feel that the host too may be the body and blood of the son of God and not a wafer③ of bread? And because you fear that it may be?

— Yes, Stephen said quietly. I feel that and I also fear it.

— I see, Cranly said.

Stephen, struck by his tone of closure, reopened the discussion at once by saying:

— I fear many things: dogs, horses, firearms, the sea, thunder – storms, machinery, the country roads at night.

— But why do you fear a bit of bread?

— I imagine, Stephen said, that there is a malevolent reality behind those things I say I fear.

— Do you fear then, Cranly asked, that the God of the Roman catholics would strike you dead and damn you if

---

① blackguard: 恶棍 ② pervert: 堕落 ③ wafer: (宗教)圣饼

you made a sacrilegious① communion?

— The God of the Roman catholics could do that now, Stephen said. I fear more than that the chemical action which would be set up in my soul by a false homage to a symbol behind which are massed twenty centuries of authority and veneration②.

— Would you, Cranly asked, in extreme danger, commit that particular sacrilege? For instance, if you lived in the penal③ days?

— I cannot answer for the past, Stephen replied. Possibly not.

— Then, said Cranly, you do not intend to become a protestant?

— I said that I had lost the faith, Stephen answered, but not that I had lost selfrespect. What kind of liberation would that be to forsake④ an absurdity which is logical and coherent and to embrace one which is illogical and incoherent?

They had walked on towards the township of Pembroke and now, as they went on slowly along the avenues, the trees and the scattered lights in the villas soothed their minds. The air of wealth and repose diffused about them seemed to comfort their neediness. Behind a hedge of laurel⑤ a light glimmered in the window of a kitchen and the voice of a servant was heard singing as she sharpened knives. She sang, in short broken bars⑥, *Rosie O'Grady*.

Cranly stopped to listen, saying:

— *Mulier cantat*⑦.

The soft beauty of the Latin word touched with an enchanting touch the dark of the evening, with a touch fainter and more persuading than the touch of music or of a

---

① sacrilegious: 亵渎神灵的 ② veneration: 崇拜 ③ penal: 受罚的 ④ forsake: 抛弃 ⑤ laurel: 桂花树 ⑥ bars: (音乐)小节 ⑦ *Mulier cantat*: (拉丁文)一个女人在唱歌

woman's hand. The strife of their minds was quelled①. The figure of a woman as she appears in the liturgy② of the church passed silently through the darkness: a white − robed figure, small and slender as a boy and with a falling girdle③. Her voice, frail and high as a boy's, was heard intoning from a distant choir the first words of a woman which pierce the gloom and clamour of the first chanting of the passion:

— *Et tu cum Jesu Galilaeo eras*. ④

And all hearts were touched and turned to her voice, shining like a young star, shining clearer as the voice intoned the proparoxytone⑤ and more faintly as the cadence died.

The singing ceased. They went on together, Cranly repeating in strongly stressed rhythm the end of the refrain:

And when we are married,
O, how happy we'll be
For I love sweet Rosie O'Grady
And Rosie O'Grady loves me.

— There's real poetry for you, he said. There's real love.

He glanced sideways at Stephen with a strange smile and said:

— Do you consider that poetry? Or do you know what the words mean?

— I want to see Rosie first, said Stephen.

— She's easy to find, Cranly said.

His hat had come down on his forehead. He shoved it back and in the shadow of the trees Stephen saw his pale face, framed by the dark, and his large dark eyes. Yes.

---

① quelled：平静下来　② liturgy：礼拜仪式　③ girdle：腰带　④ *Et tu cum Jesu Galilaeo eras*：(拉丁文)你和加利利的上帝同在。　⑤ intoned the proparoxytone：和着先重后轻的节奏

His face was handsome and his body was strong and hard. He had spoken of a mother's love. He felt then the sufferings of women, the weaknesses of their bodies and souls: and would shield them with a strong and resolute arm and bow his mind to them.

Away then: it is time to go. A voice spoke softly to Stephen's lonely heart, bidding him go and telling him that his friendship was coming to an end. Yes; he would go. He could not strive against another. He knew his part.

— Probably I shall go away, he said.

— Where? Cranly asked.

— Where I can, Stephen said.

— Yes, Cranly said. It might be difficult for you to live here now. But is it that makes you go?

— I have to go, Stephen answered.

— Because, Cranly continued, you need not look upon yourself as driven away if you do not wish to go or as a heretic or an outlaw. There are many good believers who think as you do. Would that surprise you? The church is not the stone building nor even the clergy and their dog-mas①. It is the whole mass of those born into it. I don't know what you wish to do in life. Is it what you told me the night we were standing outside Harcourt Street station?

— Yes, Stephen said, smiling in spite of himself at Cranly's way of remembering thoughts in connexion with places. The night you spent half an hour wrangling② with Doherty about the shortest way from Sallygap to Larras.

— Pothead! Cranly said with calm contempt. What does he know about the way from Sallygap to Larras? Or what does he know about anything for that matter? And the big slobbering washing pot head of him!

He broke out into a loud long laugh.

Well? Stephen said. Do you remember the rest?

— What you said, is it? Cranly asked. Yes, I remem-

---

① dogmas: 教义 ② wrangle: 争吵

ber it. To discover the mode of life or of art whereby your spirit could express itself in unfettered freedom①.

Stephen raised his hat in acknowledgement.

— Freedom! Cranly repeated. But you are not free enough yet to commit a sacrilege. Tell me, would you rob?

— I would beg first, Stephen said.

— And if you got nothing, would you rob?

— You wish me to say, Stephen answered, that the rights of property are provisional and that in certain circumstances it is not unlawful to rob. Everyone would act in that belief. So I will not make you that answer. Apply to the jesuit theologian Juan Mariana de Talavera②, who will also explain to you in what circumstances you may lawfully kill your king and whether you had better hand him his poison in a goblet③ or smear④ it for him upon his robe or his saddlebow⑤. Ask me rather would I suffer others to rob me or, if they did, would I call down upon them what I believe is called the chastisement⑥ of the secular arm?

— And would you?

— I think, Stephen said, it would pain me as much to do so as to be robbed.

— I see, Cranly said.

He produced his match and began to clean the crevice between two teeth. Then he said carelessly:

— Tell me, for example, would you deflower a virgin?

— Excuse me, Stephen said politely, is that not the ambition of most young gentlemen?

— What then is your point of view? Cranly asked.

His last phrase, soursmelling as the smoke of charcoal and disheartening, excited Stephen's brain, over which its fumes seemed to brood.

---

① unfettered freedom: 不受任何约束的自由　② Juan Mariana de Talavera: 德塔拉贝拉(1536—1623)，西班牙历史学家和政治哲学家。
③ goblet: 酒杯　④ smear: 涂　⑤ saddlebow: 马鞍的前穹　⑥ chastisement: 严惩

— Look here, Cranly, he said. You have asked me what I would do and what I would not do. I will tell you what I will do and what I will not do. I will not serve that in which I no longer believe whether it call itself my home, my fatherland, or my church: and I will try to express myself in some mode of life or art as freely as I can and as wholly as I can, using for my defence the only arms I allow myself to use — silence, exile, and cunning.

Cranly seized his arm and steered him round so as to lead him back towards Leeson Park. He laughed almost slily① and pressed Stephen's arm with an elder's affection.

— Cunning indeed! he said. Is it you? You poor poet, you!

— And you made me confess to you, Stephen said, thrilled by his touch, as I have confessed to you so many other things, have I not?

— Yes, my child, Cranly said, still gaily.

— You made me confess the fears that I have. But I will tell you also what I do not fear. I do not fear to be alone or to be spurned② for another or to leave whatever I have to leave. And I am not afraid to make a mistake, even a great mistake, a lifelong mistake and perhaps as long as eternity too.

Cranly, now grave again, slowed his pace and said:

— Alone, quite alone. You have no fear of that. And you know what that word means? Not only to be separate from all others but to have not even one friend.

— I will take the risk, said Stephen.

— And not to have any one person, Cranly said, who would be more than a friend, more even than the noblest and truest friend a man ever had.

His words seemed to have struck some deep chord in his own nature. Had he spoken of himself, of himself as he was or wished to be? Stephen watched his face for some

---

① slily: 狡猾地 ② be spurned: 被轻蔑地拒绝

moments in silence. A cold sadness was there. He had spoken of himself, of his own loneliness which he feared.

— Of whom are you speaking? Stephen asked at length. Cranly did not answer.

20 *March* : Long talk with Cranly on the subject of my revolt.

He had his grand manner on. I supple and suave①. Attacked me on the score of love for one's mother. Tried to imagine his mother: cannot. Told me once, in a moment of thoughtlessness, his father was sixty-one when he was born. Can see him. Strong farmer type. Pepper and salt② suit. Square feet. Unkempt grizzled beard③. Probably attends coursingmatches④. Pays his dues regularly but not plentifully to Father Dwyer of Larras. Sometimes talks to girls after nightfall. But his mother? Very young or very old? Hardly the first. If so, Cranly would not have spoken as he did. Old then. Probably, and neglected. Hence Cranly's despair of soul: the child of exhausted loins.

21 *March* : morning: Thought this in bed last night but was too lazy and free to add to it. Free, yes. The exhausted loins are those of Elizabeth and Zachary⑤. Then he is the precursor⑥. Item: he eats chiefly belly bacon and dried figs. Read locusts and wild honey. Also, when thinking of him, saw always a stern severed head or death. mask as if outlined on a grey curtain or veronica⑦. Decollation⑧ they call it in the fold⑨. Puzzled for the moment by saint John at the Latin gate. What do I see? A decollated precursor trying to pick the lock⑩.

21 *March*, *night* : Free. Soulfree and fancyfree. Let the dead bury the dead. Ay. And let the dead marry the

---

① supple and suave: 顺从而温和　② Pepper and salt: (布料)黑白点子混合而呈灰色的　③ Unkempt grizzled beard: 蓬乱的灰色胡子　④ coursingmatches: 田径赛　⑤ Elizabeth and Zachary: 据《圣经》,上帝使这对年老的夫妇生下了儿子。　⑥ precursor: 先驱者　⑦ veronica: 幕幔　⑧ Decollation: 杀头　⑨ fold: (具有共同信仰的)信徒　⑩ pick the lock: 撬锁

dead.

22 *March*: In company with Lynch followed a sizable hospital nurse. Lynch's idea. Dislike it. Two lean hungry greyhounds walking after a heifer①.

23 *March*: Have not seen her since that night. Unwell? Sits at the fire perhaps with mamma's shawl on her shoulders. But not peevish②. A nice bowl of gruel③? Won't you now?

24 *March*: Began with a discussion with my mother. Subject: B.V.M.④ Handicapped by my sex and youth. To escape held up relations between Jesus and Papa against those between Mary and her son. Said religion was not a lying-in hospital. Mother indulgent⑤. Said I have a queer mind and have read too much. Not true. Have read little and understood less. Then she said I would come back to faith because I had a restless mind. This means to leave church by backdoor of sin and reenter through the skylight of repentance⑥. Cannot repent. Told her so and asked for sixpence. Got threepence.

Then went to college. Other wrangle with little roundhead rogue'seye Ghezzi. This time about Bruno⑦ the Nolan. Began in Italian and ended in pidgin English⑧. He said Bruno was a terrible heretic. I said he was terribly burned. He agreed to this with some sorrow. Then gave me recipe for what he calls *risotto alla bergamasca*⑨. When he pronounces a soft o he protrudes his full carnal lips as if he kissed the vowel. Has he? And could he repent? Yes, he could: and cry two round rogue's tears, one from each eye.

Crossing Stephen's, that is, my green, remembered that his countrymen and not mine had invented what Cran-

---

① heifer: 小母牛   ② peevish: 闹别扭的   ③ gruel: 粥   ④ B.V.M.: Blessed Virgin Mary   ⑤ indulgent: 宽容的   ⑥ repentance: 悔罪 ⑦ Bruno: 布鲁诺(1548—1600),意大利著名哲学家。   ⑧ pidgin English: 不纯粹的英语   ⑨ *risotto alla bergamasca*: (拉丁文)柏加莫风味的米饭

ly the other night called our religion. A quartet of them, soldiers of the ninety seventh infantry regiment, sat at the foot of the cross① and tossed up dice② for the overcoat of the crucified.

Went to library. Tried to read three reviews. Useless. She is not out yet. Am I alarmed? About what? That she will never be out again.

Blake wrote:

> *I wonder if William Bond will die*
> *For assuredly he is very ill.*

Alas, poor William!

I was once at a diorama③ in Rotunda. At the end were pictures of big nobs④. Among them William Ewart Gladstone, just then dead. Orchestra played *O, Willie, we have missed you*.

A race of clodhoppers⑤!

25 *March, morning*: A troubled night of dreams. Want to get them off my chest.

A long curving gallery. From the floor ascend pillars of dark vapours. It is peopled by the images of fabulous kings, set in stone. Their hands are folded upon their knees in token of weariness and their eyes are darkened for the errors of men go up before them for ever as dark vapours.

Strange figures advance as from a cave. They are not as tall as men. One does not seem to stand quite apart from another. Their faces are phosphorescent⑥, with darker streaks. They peer at me and their eyes seem to ask me something. They do not speak.

30 *March*: This evening Cranly was in the porch of

---

① sat at the foot of the cross: 坐在十字架脚下　② dice: 骰子　③ diorama: 透明画　④ nobs: (俚)有钱人　⑤ clodhoppers: 乡下佬　⑥ phosphorescent: 发磷光的

the library, proposing a problem to Dixon and her brother. A mother let her child fall into the Nile①. Still harping on the mother. A crocodile seized the child. Mother asked it back. Crocodile said all right if she told him what he was going to do with the child, eat it or not eat It.

This mentality②, Lepidus would say, is indeed bred out of your mud by the operation of your sun.

And mine? Is it not too? Then into Nilemud with it!

1 *April*: Disapprove of this last phrase.

2 *April*: Saw her drinking tea and eating cakes in Johnston's, Mooney and O'Brien's. Rather, lynxeyed③ Lynch saw her as we passed. He tells me Cranly was invited there by brother. Did he bring his crocodile? Is he the shining light now? Well, I discovered him. I protest I did. Shining quietly behind a bushel④ of Wicklow bran⑤.

3 *April*: Met Davin at the cigar shop opposite Findlater's church. He was in a black sweater and had a hurleystick. Asked me was it true I was going away and why. Told him the shortest way to Tara was *via* Holyhead. Just then my father came up. Introduction. Father, polite and observant. Asked Davin if he might offer him some refreshment⑥. Davin could not, was going to a meeting. When we came away father told me he had a good honest eye. Asked why I did not join a rowingclub. I pretended to think it over. Told me then how he broke Pennyfeather's heart. Wants me to read law. Says I was cut out for that. More mud, more crocodiles.

5 *April*: Wild spring. Scudding clouds⑦. O life! Dark stream of swirling bogwater⑧ on which appletrees have cast down their delicate flowers. Eyes of girls among the leaves. Girls demure and romping. All fair or auburn⑨: no

---

① Nile: 尼罗河 ② mentality: 思维方式 ③ lynxeyed: 目光锐利的 ④ bushel: 计量谷物的容量单位。英语中有一句成语: hide one's light under a bushel 是不露锋芒的意思, 这里是借用其意。 ⑤ bran: 麸糠 ⑥ refreshment: 茶点、便餐 ⑦ Scudding clouds: 疾驰而过的云彩 ⑧ bogwater: 泥塘 ⑨ auburn: 金棕色的

dark ones. They blush better. Houp-la!

6 *April*: Certainly she remembers the past. Lynch says all women do. Then she remembers the time of her childhood — and mine if I was ever a child. The past is consumed in the present and the present is living only because it brings forth the future. Statues of women, if Lynch be right, should always be fully draped①, one hand of the woman feeling regretfully her own hinder parts.

6 *April*, *later*: Michael Robartes remembers forgotten beauty and, when his arms wrap her round, he presses in his arms the loveliness which has long faded from the world. Not this. Not at all. I desire to press in my arms the loveliness which has not yet come into the world.

10 *April*: Faintly, under the heavy night, through the silence of the city which has turned from dreams to dreamless sleep as a weary lover whom no caresses move, the sound of hoofs upon the road. Not so faintly now as they come near the bridge: and in a moment, as they pass the darkened windows, the silence is cloven② by alarm as by an arrow. They are heard now far away, hoofs that shine amid the heavy night as gems③, hurrying beyond the sleeping fields to what journey's end — what heart? — bearing what tidings?

11 *April*: Read what I wrote last night. Vague words for a vague emotion. Would she like it? I think so. Then I should have to like it also.

13 *April*: That tundish has been on my mind for a long time. I looked it up and find it English and good old blunt English too. Damn the dean of studies and his funnel! What did he come here for to teach us his own language or to learn it from us? Damn him one way or the other!

14 *April*: John Alphonsus Mulrennan has just returned from the west of Ireland. European and Asiatic pa-

---

① drape: 披盖 ② cloven: 劈开的 ③ gems: 宝石

pers please copy①. He told us he met an old man there in a mountain cabin. Old man had red eyes and short pipe. Old man spoke Irish. Mulrennan spoke Irish. Then old man and Mulrennan spoke English. Mulrennan spoke to him about universe and stars. Old man sat, listened, smoked, spat. Then said:

— Ah, there must be terrible queer creatures at the latter and of the world.

I fear him. I fear his red rimmed horny② eyes. It is with him I must struggle all through this night till day come, till he or I lie dead, gripping him by the sinewy throat③ till ... Till what? Till he yield to me? No. I mean him no harm.

15 *April*: Met her today pointblank④ in Grafton Street. The crowd brought us together. We both stopped. She asked me why I never came, said she had heard all sorts of stories about me. This was only to gain time. Asked me, was I writing poems? About whom? I asked her. This confused her more and I felt sorry and mean. Turned off that valve⑤ at once and opened the spiritual — heroic refrigerating apparatus, invented and patented in all countries by Dante Alighieri. Talked rapidly of myself and my plans. In the midst of it unluckily I made a sudden gesture of a revolutionary nature. I must have looked like a fellow throwing a handful of peas into the air. People began to look at us. She shook hands a moment after and, in going away, said she hoped I would do what I said.

Now I call that friendly, don't you?

Yes, I liked her today. A little or much? Don't know. I liked her and it seems a new feeling to me. Then, in that case, all the rest, all that I thought I thought and all that I felt I felt, all the rest before now, in fact ... O, give it

---

① European and Asiatic papers please copy: 欧洲和亚洲的报纸请刊登这条消息吧。Asiatic = Asian, 现一般都用 Asian, Asiatic 带有贬义。
② horny: 发硬的   ③ gripping him by the sinewy throat: 抓住他结实的喉咙
④ pointblank: 近距离地   ⑤ valve: 阀门

up, old chap! Sleep it off!

16 *April* : Away! Away!

The spell of arms and voices: the white arms of roads, their promise of close embraces and the black arms of tall ships that stand against the moon, their tale of distant nations. They are held out to say: We are alone come. Come. And the voices say with them: We are your kinsmen. And the air is thick with their company as they call to me, their kinsman, making ready to go, shaking the wings of their exultant① and terrible youth.

26 *April* : Mother is putting my new secondhand clothes in order. She prays now, she says, that I may learn in my own life and away from home and friends what the heart is and what it feels. Amen. So be it. Welcome, O life! I go to encounter for the millionth time the reality of experience and to forge in the smithy of my soul the uncreated conscience of my race②.

27 *April* : Old father, old artificer, stand me now and ever in good stead.

Dublin 1904

Trieste 1914

---

① exultant: 狂喜的 ② to forge ... my race: 在我心灵的工场里铸造出我的民族还未被创造出的良心。